SPECIALIZED
Communications
Techniques
for the
Radio Amateur

Published by

THE AMERICAN RADIO RELAY LEAGUE, INC.

Newington, Connecticut

CONTENTS

Chapter 1 — **Communications Techniques** 7

Beginning of radio; special techniques; specialists; the era of specialization.

Chapter 2 — **Amateur Television** 10

Practical ideas for the ATV enthusiast; ATV reception; antennas and transmission lines; transmitters; video modulation; fm sound subcarrier; cameras; ATV horizons; ATV with the Motorola T44 uhf transmitter; a tuner for ATV reception; a sync generator for interlaced scanning; a character generator for ATV.

Chapter 3 — **Slow-Scan Television** 44

History; transmission; flying-spot scanner system; a vidicon system; the WA3BTK camera; the K3BWW camera; the W7FEN camera; the W9NTP camera; camera operation; reception of SSTV; reception with conventional TV sets; the basic SSTV system; solid-state SSTV monitors; electrostatic vs. magnetic deflection; adapting an oscilloscope for SSTV monitoring; storage tubes, electrical and mechanical characteristics.

Chapter 4 — **Facsimile** 78

FAX transmission; receiving FAX; conversion of Telefax transceivers to amateur service; reception of weather-satellite facsimile signals; cathode-ray-tube display unit for satellite weather pictures; weather satellite picture reception with Telefax receivers.

Chapter 5 — **Radioteletype** **99**

Teleprinter equipment and hardware; transmitting RTTY; audio frequency-shift keying; receiving radioteletype; high-performance RTTY filters; the Mainline TT/L-2 fsk demodulator; the Mainline ST-4 RTTY demodulator; RTTY indicator systems; checking RTTY shifts; station control, assembly of equipment, operating procedures; handling traffic by radioteletype; fun with tape.

Chapter 6 — **Space Communication** **170**

Oscar satellites; equipment required for satellite communication via Amsat-Oscar C; circularly polarized crossed yagi antennas; a turnstile reflector array; range measurements with Oscar; satellite-locating aids; instant Oscar 6 locator; a satellite timing mechanism; earth-moon-earth (EME) communications; EME scheduling; almanacs and tables; libration fading of EME signals; EME operating techniques.

Chapter 7 — **Advanced Techniques** **196**

Laser fundamentals; laser communications; digital communications; pulse-code modulation; time-division multiplexing; speech-recognition circuits.

Appendix **207**

U.S. American Standard Code for Information Interchange (ASCII); satellite orbital data.

Communications Techniques

In the beginning of radio, application of the concepts fathered by such great men as Marconi, Hertz, and a host of others who were at least their equals, was indeed the employment of specialized techniques. The radio amateur has been known from the beginning as an experimenter, innovator, and achiever of difficult self-imposed assignments in electronics and communications. His contributions to the art were often a result of laboring at some task with an unregimented thought process. There were no specific rules at the dawning of amateur radio which would restrict his imaginative powers or the methods with which he toiled to solve a problem related to his equipment performance. Each day brought a new and exciting challenge to him, for stretching his signal coverage a few miles (or feet) was his purpose in being. The specialized technique of the day was communication by means of Morse code, wireless fashion. The first radio amateurs found that technique as exciting as the modern-day amateur views communicating via slow-scan TV, moon-bounce, or RTTY. One might say that today's amateur is playing the same game that his predecessors did: the players are different, and the tools are more sophisticated, but that's all.

The goal of increasing the signal-coverage range in amateur communications required more than pure imagination. Few achievers were possessors of formal educations related to their scientific endeavors. The radio concept was simply too new to support a meaningful curriculum in an institution of higher learning. Thus, each contributor to the art worked with the tools of intuition, trial-and-error experience, and knowledge gained from

his fellows. Selfless dedication, long hours in the laboratory/workshop, and a flaming curiosity about the specialized technique of the day drove the experimenter onward to an improvement of the art, which was passed along to the next group of amateurs.

Many of today's amateurs are motivated to strive for scientific achievement. Their work is refined and enjoys greater rapidity of completion because a formal education in electronics can be obtained by those who seek that level of learning. However, many of those to whom we owe recognition for their achievements are not men with

—EACH A POTENTIAL SPECIALIST—

degrees; they are plumbers, farmers, physicians, clergymen, office workers and others of the same general nonprofessional ilk. The latter are usually driven by a desire for knowledge of their amateur radio pastime. They are not satisfied merely to purchase a set of electronic gadgets (produced by some manufacturer) for the sole purpose of com-

An early day a-m phone transmitter (1930). In its time, voice operation was considered a specialized communications technique. Digital modulation may some day be the specialized phone technique — a great advance forward from the original voice-mode concept.

municating with other amateurs. They want to know *how* the system operates, how to repair it when it fails. . . and more importantly, how to improve the performance and effectiveness of the mode made possible by the equipment. Specialized communications techniques appeal to these stalwart fellows, and it is this group for whom this book is written. Furthermore, it is this class of curious, enterprising amateur experimenters which will contribute something to the improvement of the state of the art in specialized communications techniques. Many of them will be looked upon in the years to come as architects of the improved techniques being enjoyed by the next generation of communicators and designers.

What is a Specialized Technique?

One may argue that any interest which is a departure from routine amateur radio practices is a special pursuit or technique. The QRP enthusiast feels that his attention is being focused on a special technique. One who is interested solely in digital circuitry might have a similar outlook. The 160-meter man may be so dedicated to his study of medium-frequency work and propagation in that section of our spectrum that he considers his subject a specialized technique. If a book were to be written about every unique facet of amateur radio circuit development and application, it would

probably lead to the preparation of an encyclopedia rather than a mere book. The scope of this publication will be confined to only those subjects that require special knowledge and equipment which is not attendant to a typical ham station. Among the themes to be treated here are ATV (fast scan), SSTV (slow-scan TV), RTTY (radioteletype), FAX (facsimile), EME (earth-moon-earth, or moonbounce), and other subjects apart from the more common ssb and cw operating modes.

Amateurs have always exhibited an outstanding ability to improve upon existing techniques and available components. Here HB9RF and his XYL are seen at work with his moonbounce antenna. It was expanded to a diameter of 16 feet from the smaller dimension it possessed as a commercial product.

Are You a Specialist?

If you are a vhf/uhf enthusiast who has designed and built his own equipment and antennas, you are probably a specialist. Many years ago, operation in the vhf/uhf part of the spectrum was a specialized technique. Though the techniques required above 50 MHz are quite different in many ways from those used in the hf region, they are well-established practices today. However, much of the specialization covered in this book takes place in the vhf region and higher. The amateur who is experienced and capable in work above 50 MHz will become a specialist when he converts and communicates with the aid of a surplus FAX machine; when he builds his first moonbounce station and hears the echo from that station returning to earth; when he transmits video signals and receives them from other ATV or SSTV enthusiasts. Though he may be communicating by means of factory-built equipment intended solely for amateur use, he is not necessarily a specialist; he is merely *utilizing* a specialized technique. It will be the *specialists* who improve and refine the capabilities of the specialized techniques which are covered in this book.

Most of the material contained in these pages was written by amateur specialists. The circuits which accompany the equipment descriptions were developed by those contributors to the art. Their achievements were often the result of many hours of hard work and experimentation with components that were *made* to do the job, though not necessarily the most ideal parts for the application. Their ability to innovate and achieve has set them apart from their commercial bretheren. In many instances they were able to achieve their goals with considerable dispatch because they were not hindered by the restrictions in thinking and technique imposed upon their industrial counterparts – those who were forced to follow established developmental procedures, and observe rigid MIL

Specs (military specifications) in the design of the apparatus. Thus, we are the beneficiaries of specialists who developed and worked with specialized techniques.

This Era of Specialization

Generally speaking, the radio amateur who designed and built his own equipment in bygone days was a general practitioner, as was also true of the commercial equipment designer or serviceman. The technology explosion which followed the introduction of the transistor by Shockley, Brattain, and Bardeen at Bell Labs in 1948 brought with it the day of specialization. From that fountainhead has come a number of "springoffs" in specialty work – ICs, FETs, COSMOS devices, Zener diodes, varactors, LEDs, liquid-crystal displays, and many more. The foregoing have made it possible for amateurs to work with and perfect many new techniques for use in specialized communications modes. The complexity of each modern subject has made obsolete the concept of general practice in our line of endeavor. Each experimentally minded radio amateur must now be a specialist in some phase of communications electronics if he is to excel and make a contribution to his art. The pages of *QST* offer mute testimony to this fact, as one achievement after another is documented. The fallout from these significant steps forward is gleaned by the operating class of amateurs, and in many instances by the commercial interests who have the capability to mass produce and sell at a price which is highly competitive to that which an amateur would pay for the parts to build a similar unit.

Specialization is the challenge that has been a long-standing inspiration to radio amateurs, and many of them become licensed merely to permit legal operation of the circuits they develop. New frontiers lie ahead for future generations of amateurs. Much of what has been achieved to date will serve as the nucleus for future development of

Some amateur radio designs become quite sophisticated, depending upon the skills of the constructors. It is interesting to note that many amateurs who are involved in specialized-techniques work are not engineers. They come from practically every walk of life.

some specialized technique. It is hoped that this book will serve to inspire all amateurs to learn more about their pastime, and to contribute their skills and imaginations to the refinement of existing specialized techniques. In the process of improving the present special communication modes, new techniques will surely result, and these will be passed on to the enterprising amateurs who succeed us.

Amateur Television

Amateurs have worked with television since the earliest scanning-disk days. Television was treated five times in *QST* in 1928. Electronic television was described by and for amateurs as early as 1937, almost 20 years before the advent of commercial TV. By 1950 substantial numbers of amateurs were using the 420-MHz band for ATV, again leading commercial uhf TV by several years. Slow-scan TV, using bandwidths narrow enough for our hf bands, opened up the possibility of long-distance TV communication in the late 1950s. SSTV techniques discussed elsewhere in this book supplemented but by no means displaced wide-band television as an amateur communications medium.*

High cost, bulkiness, and technical complexity of television equipment generally remained limiting factors in ATV interest, until recent developments in video pickup devices triggered a boom in use of TV for surveillance as well as communications purposes. The modern TV camera — compact, simple to use, economical to operate, and relatively inexpensive as well — was perhaps, more than any other factor, the key that opened up television as a practical communications medium for the average amateur.

Added impetus came from availability of large numbers of uhf fm transceivers on the surplus market. With certain of these "bargain" rigs, cameras developed for closed-circuit television, antennas of moderate gain, and slightly modified home-TV receivers, amateurs can now transmit and receive television pictures of "broadcast quality," for an overall cost somewhat less than that of a good hf-band ssb transceiver. Judicious shopping and time spent in construction of one's own gear can bring the overall cost of ATV down to quite low levels. The following pages help to point the way.

PRACTICAL IDEAS FOR THE ATV ENTHUSIAST

Amateur television is an experimenter's paradise, and anyone working in this field soon learns or develops techniques that are helpful to others. In this section are described tricks of the trade that may speed the ATV newcomer on his way to achieving maximum coverage and sharp, snow-free pictures. Most of this information is from Tom O'Hara, W6ORG, long active in Southern California ATV circles.

Amateur television, using commercial video standards, should not be confused with slow-scan TV now popular on the hf bands. Both have their uses, but methods and results are very different. Slow-scan takes time — about 8 seconds per frame — whereas the TV we'll be discussing in this chapter is essentially instantaneous. Slow-scan is also limited in definition, but it has the marked advantage of being a narrow-band system, so it is permitted in our hf bands. What will hereinafter be called ATV is inherently a wide-band mode, so it is restricted to use above 420 MHz. (The U.S. 420-MHz band is 109 times the width of the slow-scan segment of the 14-MHz band!) ATV picture detail can be excellent — potentially at least equal to the best commercial TV.

You may like one or the other, or both. If worldwide DX using all-commercial equipment interests you, slow-scan can add a new dimension to an already exciting DX medium. If you like building gear or revamping surplus equipment, and you think that televising a parade, or watching a friend's home movies on your TV screen might be fun, uhf ATV may be your field. It need not be expensive. Good ATV signals have been put on the air for a total investment under $200, and little more technical involvement is entailed than in getting on 2-meter fm with an old Motorola police rig. You may end up using ATV to brag about your 20-meter DX, as WB6MEU appears to be doing in one of the photographs.

ATV DX may not be great in miles or countries, but consistent coverage with pictures of usable quality can be quite good. When tropospheric conditions are favorable, you may be swapping reports (visually, of course) over paths like the mountainous one between Los Angeles and San Diego. Several hundred miles up and down the Atlantic Seaboard, or 1000 or so across the Gulf,

*Complete bibliographies of both fast-scan and slow-scan television treatment in *QST* are available from ARRL Headquarters, Newington, CT 06111. Send stamped self-addressed business-size envelope.

ATV need not be all test patterns and tweaking. Here WB6MEU focuses on some choice DX QSLs from stations worked on the hf bands.

between Florida and Texas, is well within the bounds of possibility. A reliable rule-of-thumb for average propagation is that a distance you can cover satisfactorily with 5 watts on 2-meter a-m or fm will give good pictures with 15 watts and a good antenna in ATV work.

A Few Preliminaries

The block diagram of a complete ATV station is shown in Fig. 1. Most ATV beginners use equipment along the lines detailed here — inexpensive to buy and relatively easy to adapt to ATV needs. Once you're on the air you can refine and expand as time, talents, and resources allow. A desirable first step is to locate a fellow ham who is already on ATV or about ready to go on. Two stations working together is much better than one person working alone. Your friend can "talk your picture in" on another frequency, while you adjust for picture quality. Monitoring your own signal can be misleading, because of almost certain overloading of your receiver. Your picture may look fine on your own set, but have low contrast at distant points.

An agreed-on voice calling frequency in a well-used band is helpful in building ATV interest and activity. (Video transmissions are made on a higher frequency band.) In Southern California, 146.91 MHz is almost universally monitored for ATV purposes. The 146.52-MHz fm simplex channel is also popular. In many areas local fm repeater channels are useful in initiating ATV tests and QSOs.

Some standard for video carrier frequency is important. Most people find it hard to believe, but the 420-MHz band is filling up fast. The range from 442 to 450 is loaded with fm in many areas; 435 to 438 is satellite territory. The 431- to 433-MHz range is used for narrow-band modes, in DX and local communication, with moonbounce becoming ever more widely used. Californians have settled on 427.0 MHz for the video carrier, and 431.5 MHz for the fm-sound subcarrier.

Even though the sidebands in a good ATV system extend out to plus-or-minus 6 MHz, sync-buzz interference is troublesome out to only about 2 MHz on either side, as the instantaneous video power at any one frequency beyond that point is negligible. Crystal control should be employed, so that the transmitter frequency will not drift into other portions of the band. The modulated-oscillator approach, long used in getting started in ATV work, is no longer acceptable on this account.

ATV RECEPTION

Amateur TV of the fast-scan (uhf) variety uses the same video standards as commercial TV, so the simplest way to receive it is to modify the uhf tuner in a conventional home TV receiver, to tune the 420-MHz amateur band. Rather than borrow the family TV set, it may be better to buy an inexpensive set, new or of recent manufacture. Some of the best are small Japanese models made after 1970, which usually have low-noise hot-carrier diode mixers. Before you dig into the set, get a service manual, a Sams Fotofact sheet, or at least a circuit diagram, if you can. Almost any TV receiver is usable, and conversion is not difficult.

A tunable converter ahead of a TV set having no uhf coverage will do, though such old sets may not have very good definition by now, and early uhf converters are generally low on sensitivity. Tunable converters are preferred over the crystal-controlled variety, for several reasons. ATV is normally a-m, with two sidebands, rather than the carrier-and-one-sideband of commercial TV. For the clearest picture it is helpful to be able to tune off to one side or the other of the ATV carrier, depending on the shape of the receiver i-f pass-band, and local occupancy of the lower vhf TV channels. (A strong local vhf TV signal may ride through the uhf converter, or be picked up by the receiver circuits directly.) Crystal-controlled con-

Fig. 1 — Block diagram of a complete ATV station. The beginner may go on the air minus one or more of the station components shown. Where frequencies are given they are channels commonly used in Southern California, and not necessarily applicable in other localities. The 146-MHz channels are used primarily for calling purposes. Local 2-meter repeater frequencies may be used briefly for this purpose, as well.

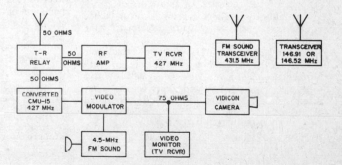

verters made for amateur narrow-band communication, mainly around 432 MHz, may have high-Q circuitry that restricts the receiving bandwidth to less than needed for high-resolution video. Adequate bandwidth is important in assuring really clear, crisp picture reception.

External uhf converters, such as those made by Blonder-Tongue and Archer, can be padded down easily. Practically all older uhf front ends in TV receivers are in converter form, designed to work into one of the lower vhf channels. Newer sets have provision for working directly into the receiver i-f system. Modification of a Sickles uhf converter, found in many home TV sets having uhf coverage, is described elsewhere in this chapter. Procedure is likely to be more or less the same, regardless of tuner make or design.

The simplest way to get the tuning range down into the 420-MHz band is to add capacitance across the tuned circuits of the uhf converter. This may be desirable, as it will leave the receiver still capable of tuning the low end of the uhf TV range, and restoration of the original tuning range is fairly easy. Smoother tuning and much better reception will result from removing plates from each section of the variable capacitor and adding adjustable padder capacitors. Leave one stator and one rotor plate in each capacitor section, the rotor plate left to be that having radial slits for adjustment of tracking.

If the tuning capacitor is left intact, add trimmers of about 1-3 pF in range. If plates are removed for band spreading, about 9-pF maximum capacitance will be needed in the padders. In either case, the first alignment step is to locate the ATV frequency by adjusting the oscillator padder. Then peak the other sections for maximum signal, as in any receiver alignment. A signal generator is helpful, though not absolutely necessary.

In some converters the L/C ratio may get too low to sustain oscillation. If this happens, cut the oscillator line and insert a loop or turn of No. 20 wire, about 3/16 inch in diameter. When the additional needed inductance is found, a similar change can be made in the other lines, to maintain tracking.

In lieu of a signal generator, the signal from a nearby ATV station can be used for alignment. If you have the other's cooperation, start with a strong signal and progress to a weaker one as circuits are adjusted. The third harmonic of a 2-meter rig can be used, but be sure that you have tuned in the desired frequency, not a spurious product of the oscillator or multiplier stages. A reliable indication of any improvement can be had by monitoring the agc voltage developed by the signal, whatever its source.

A standard reference for minimum usable signal in ATV is the lowest level at which the receiver's horizontal oscillator will lock the signal in. With a well-peaked average front end, this will be somewhere between 5 and 10 μV. A good preamplifier can bring the usable level down to around 1 μV, which will really help in reception of all but the stronger local signals.

RF Preamplifiers

One rarely finds top performance in either uhf or vhf home TV, in part because of the wide tuning ranges that must be covered by the rf circuitry. We are interested in a relatively narrow band, so a simple transistor preamplifier for the ATV frequency can help. Up to 20 dB gain is readily obtainable, with a noise figure well below that of the best manufactured home TV sets. A real joy in ATV is reception of clear high-definition pictures. A low-noise rf amplifier will extend the range over which such reception is possible.

The inexpensive rf amplifier by W6ORG, shown in Fig. 2, originally appeared in *The Radio Amateur's VHF Manual*, Edition 3, Chapter 13. Improvements made recently provide better stability under varying load conditions, and higher rejection of out-of-band signals. A 9-volt supply is recommended, whereas the earlier version used 12. In this form the preamplifier will be less susceptible to overloading from a 2-meter rig running in the immediate vicinity, which may be important in ATV communication. For still better suppression of your own TVI from 2-meter operation, add a simple strip-line filter in the line to the ATV receiver. (Suitable filters are described in all editions of the *VHF Manual*.) If insertion of a strip-line filter affects picture definition adversely, try tapping the input and output directly to the inner conductor instead of using coupling loops.

The amplifier is assembled on a single-sided circuit board 2-1/4 inches square, with a simple 3-pad pattern that can be etched, milled or cut with a sharp knife. The only critical item is to keep bypassing leads as short as possible. Ready-made boards and completed preamps ready for use are available from W6ORG.[1]

Requirements as to noise figure are not as critical in ATV work as in weak-signal DX communication. Any reasonably good rf stage will help any conventional uhf TV front end. By contrast, most receivers and converters used for 432-MHz communication are likely to be rather good already, and improving them appreciably takes some doing.

Conversion to Coaxial Input

Most home TV equipment is designed for 300-ohm balanced input. Conversion to coax and unbalanced input is desirable in ATV work. This requires modification of the TV set's uhf input circuit, also a must if an rf amplifier is used effectively. If there is no room to install a coaxial connector on the uhf tuner, the direct-connection method, Fig. 3, is recommended.

Drill a hole large enough to pass the coax inner conductor and its insulating sleeve, at a point that will permit direct connection to the first section of the tuner as shown. Tap the inner conductor on

---

[1] Ready-made circuit boards for the rf preamplifier, video modulators, and fm subcarrier generator described here are available from Thomas R. O'Hara, W6ORG, 2522 S. Paxon Ln., Arcadia, CA 91006. Send stamped self-addressed envelope for more information.

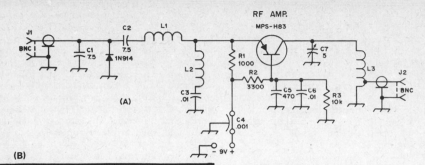

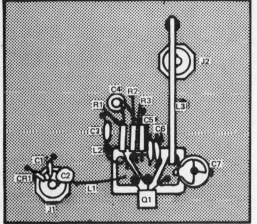

Fig. 2 — Schematic diagram and parts information for the W6ORG preamplifier, for use with uhf ATV receivers. Parts not described are numbered for text reference and identification in the layout, B.

C1, C2 — 7.5-pF disk ceramic. Lead to C2 makes L1.

C3 — .01-μF disk ceramic. Lead to C3 makes L2.

C6 — Subminiature variable, 1 to 5 pF (Johnson 187-0103-005).

L1 — 3/4-inch lead, C2 to emitter pad.

L2 — 3 turns, 1/8-inch dia, in lead from C3 to emitter pad.

L3 — 2 inches No. 20 wire 3/8 inch above and parallel to board surface. Tap for J2 at 1/2 inch from ground end.

the input circuit, adjusting the tap position in 1/16-inch increments for best response to a test signal. Precise adjustment will not be important if a preamplifier that is stable under varying load conditions is used, but optimum tap position will be desirable if the antenna feeds the tuner directly. Tinning the surface of the tuner around the hole, and also the coax braid, will help in getting a good clean bond at this point.

Warning: this grounded-input arrangement is usable only with receivers which do *not* have "hot" chassis. Also, watch for ungrounded input circuits in simple tuners having no preselection circuit (two-section tuning capacitor instead of three). If yours is a two-section front end, be sure that the low end of the mixer line is grounded directly to the frame, before installing the direct antenna connection described. In a mixer with a biased diode the cold end of the mixer line may be insulated from ground, in which case a series capacitor must be used to couple the antenna to the line. If there is room, use a small trimmer; if not, experiment with fixed values and various tap positions.

ANTENNAS AND TRANSMISSION LINES

It has been said many times, but nowhere is it more important than in the ATV station: cutting costs by using cheap transmission line is false economy. Published tables indicate that Twin-Lead

may have lower loss than coax, but adverse effects of weather make the advantage largely illusory, even if the convenience of coax is ignored. Equally important is the choice of coax, after the balanced-vs-unbalanced argument is settled in favor of the latter. Beware of bargains in coax. They may have inadequate shield-braid density, which you can check by visual examination, or they may be susceptible to moisture deterioration, which will be found out too late if the coax is not already in bad shape from use or storage in damp conditions.

Start with the best coax you can get. Foam-insulated RG-8/U is the minimum recommended quality, and that only for short runs. Be sure that connectors are properly installed, and taped and sprayed for waterproofing if they are to be out in the weather. Use constant-impedance connectors if you can afford them, but don't

Fig. 3 — Typical uhf TV tuner, modified for coaxial input.

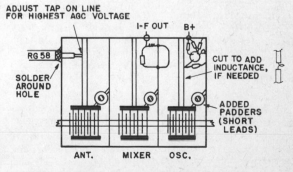

worry about the objections often raised to the inexpensive "uhf" series, PL-259 and SO-239. Properly installed and waterproofed, they will do as well as the more expensive types, for all practical purposes.

Every aspect of the transmission-line performance is vital in reception, perhaps more than in transmitting. Line losses can be offset by increasing transmitter power, to a degree, but they add to the system noise figure in receiving. Once the signal is lost or degraded through transmission line defects, there is no way to get it back.

Antenna Height and Polarization

Though horizontal polarization has demonstrable advantages on somewhat lower frequencies in certain kinds of terrain, there is little to choose from between horizontal and vertical in uhf work if everyone chooses the same, so practical considerations rule. Nearly all fm communication is with vertical antennas, to simplify the antenna problem for mobile operators. Repeaters are standardized on vertical for this reason, and in Southern California ATV is following the same course.

Height above ground is important. For practical purposes, "ground" is likely to be anything up to about 30 feet above actual earth, the the average urban residential area. Get up to at least 40 feet if at all possible, as absorption and reflections are likely to be bad below this height. Going up to 60 or 70 feet is usually helpful, but much higher may not pay off, unless very good transmission line is used. Height-gain and line-loss tables are helpful in determining your needs in these respects. (These are available in the *VHF Manual*.) Absorption by heavy foliage and reflections from buildings are very troublesome in the uhf range. A large tree or a three-story house with aluminum siding may be only an annoyance to the voice communicator, but to the ATV operator either can be disastrous, in signal loss and ghost effects.

Gain and Bandwidth

High-gain antennas are desirable in ATV work, but bandwidth is more of a factor than in other forms of amateur uhf communication. A yagi array designed for maximum gain may be selective enough to restrict the bandwidth of the ATV system, so collinears are generally preferred over yagis for medium- and high-gain systems. Corner-reflector and screen-reflector arrays are also recommended. There is plenty of information in the *ARRL Antenna Book, Handbook* and the *VHF Manual* for the ATV operator who likes to build his own arrays. One commercially available antenna that is popular with the ATV fraternity is the Cush Craft DX-420 collinear.

TRANSMITTERS

Power levels that can be generated in the uhf range economically with transistors are rather low, so the specialized modulation problems of solid-state TV transmitters will not be detailed here. For the ATV newcomer, several commercial tube-type uhf transceivers are now available at low cost on the surplus market and offer the simplest solution to the transmitter problem. The two important differences between TV and fm service should be kept in mind in choosing from the available surplus equipment. ATV bandwidth is stated in megahertz, whereas that of fm is in kilohertz. ATV modulation is a-m, so amplifier stages must be linear. The fm transmitter has no linearity requirements, so it is often designed with other objectives in mind.

The 2C39 grounded-grid triode amplifiers, such as in the Motorola T44 and GE Pre-Prog transceivers, are not well adapted to wide-band amplitude modulation. They have very low grid-drive impedance, which requires much more modulator power then grid-modulating tetrodes. These transmitters have built-in bypassing of the grid that limits the bandwidth to 2.5 MHz, or only about 200 lines of video resolution. This allows a fairly good black-and-white picture, but it will greatly attenuate fm and color subcarrier, if these are added later. The best available information on video-modulating the T44 is reproduced elsewhere in this chapter. We deal in this section with grid-modulation of tetrode amplifiers of the surplus-rig and homebuilt high-power variety. Typical tube types include the 6939, 6252, 5894, and 6907, all dual tetrodes in the low- to medium-power range, and the 4X150A and other tubes of the same general type, used for medium and high-power applications. Preferred dual-tetrode transmitters are those in the RCA CMU-15 and the Motorola U44 line. The GE Progress Line is usable, although these GE units have high-Q plate lines which limit their bandwidth to about 3.5 MHz, not enough for the fm subcarrier described later.

Converting the CMU-15

The most readily converted of the uhf fm transmitters is the RCA Carfone, CMU-15. It will put out 15 watts, with high-resolution video, at moderate cost. The receiver is not used for ATV, but it can be made to serve as a monitor for any uhf calling frequency, such as 431.5 MHz used in Southern California. Details given refer specifically to the Carfone, but the ideas can be applied to other dual-tetrode amplifiers.

There are three chassis bolted together in the Carfone. Separate them, and cut connecting wires. Transmitter power requirements are 285 volts at 280 mA, 270 at 95 mA, 270 at 20 mA, 200 at 15 mA, and minus 15 at 25 mA. The first three can come from a single high-current source of 300 volts, with the 200 being obtained from the same point through a 7500-ohm 5-watt dropping resistor. A complete supply for the high voltage and bias is shown schematically in Fig. 4. Resist the temptation to try for higher output by running higher plate voltage. The 5894 and similar tubes go bad fairly soon if run at more than 50 watts input in the 420-MHz band. The long periods of operation with continuous modulation which are characteristic of ATV testing are rough on transmitting tubes. Cooling fans are not commonly used, but may be helpful in extending tube life.

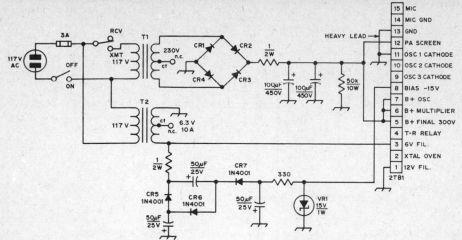

Fig. 4 — Schematic diagram and parts information for the CMU-15 power supply. Part numbers beginning with 2 indicate original CMU-15 components; e.g. 2TB1. All capacitors are electrolytic.
CR1 — CR4, incl. — 1000 PIV, 1 A (1N4007).
CR5 — CR7, incl. — 100 PIV, 1 A (1N4001).
VR1 — 15-V 1-W Zener diode (1N4744).
T1 — 150-VA isolation transformer, 235 and 117-volt windings (Essex-Stancor P-8622 or equiv.).
T2 — 6.3-V 10-A filament transformer (Triad F-21A or equiv).

The 150-VA isolation transformer, operated backward, with its 230-volt windings series connected to form the secondary as shown in Fig. 4, provides a relatively inexpensive solution to the transformer problem. The 400 mA at 300 volts may not be easily provided, otherwise. If one is willing to do some transformer work, the existing vibrator transformer in the Carfone can be stripped of its heavy primary and rewound with 350 turns of No. 22 enamel wire for 117-volt service. If this is done, only a 6.3-volt transformer capable of delivering 10 amperes for the heaters and bias supply is all that need be added, and the original power supply wiring can be left intact, other than in the primary circuit.

Test the transmitter and tune it up in the amateur band before trying video modulation. Divide the desired operating frequency by 36 to get the crystal frequency (427 MHz requires an 11.861-MHz crystal). The crystal oven is not needed, and inexpensive crystals are good enough. One thing that is not critical in ATV is frequency tolerance; the receiver can handle the 4.5-MHz sound subcarrier with frequency variations up to 300 kHz.

Remove the 12AX7 audio limiter tube. Some areas transmit fm sound on the a-m carrier, but the sync buzz will be heard under weak-signal conditions in the fm receiver, when the limiters go in and out of saturation with video a-m. Also, sync buzz may get into the high-impedance speech-amplifier circuits, and cause sync jitter in the picture.

Test the transmitter on a *good* dummy load — no light bulbs at this frequency! The metal strip along the side of the tripler-final cage is a low-pass filter. If off-frequency components are not a problem, removing the filter will eliminate its 1-dB insertion loss. Apply power, briefly at first, and tune the stages, starting with the first tripler, for maximum negative readings at the first four test points on the meter socket. Run no more than 30 seconds at a time, with two minutes off for cooling between adjustments, until optimum adjustment has been found. The following readings were taken with a high-impedance meter, 20,000 ohms-per-volt or higher: Test Point 1 (first tripler) -13V; 2 (first doubler) -29 V; 3 (second doubler) -76 V; 4 (second tripler) -62 V.

If the voltage indication does not go *through* a peak as a circuit is tuned, add 5 pF at a time until a definite voltage peak can be passed in adjustment of the tuning. The grid inductors of the tripler and final amplifier need more inductance for best operation. Remove the ribbon leads from the grid pins, and replace them with No. 14 copper wires 1/4 inch longer. Adjust the length until tuning peaks. Recheck all adjustments for maximum power output, as indicated by a wattmeter in the line to the load, or maximum reading (about minus 1.5 V) at pin 8 of the test socket.

Check the plate current, and adjust the screen voltage for 175 mA. There may be a control for screen voltage in the unit; if not, connect a suitable resistor between the B-plus line and pin 12 of the power terminal strip. A VOM can be connected between pins 6 and 7 to measure plate current, but remember the 300 volts dc is present here. With a 20,000 ohms-per-volt meter such as the Simpson 260, a reading of 1.1 on the 2.5-volt scale indicates 175 mA (volts × 160 = mA).

Bypassing of tube and circuit elements must be done with video characteristics in mind. Electrolytic bypass capacitors, 10 μF at 450 volts, were added to the 5894 screen and the high-voltage feed to the plate circuit, to prevent video distortion. At this point we call attention to the method of identifying the parts shown in Fig. 5, to distinguish between original equipment in the CMU-15 and

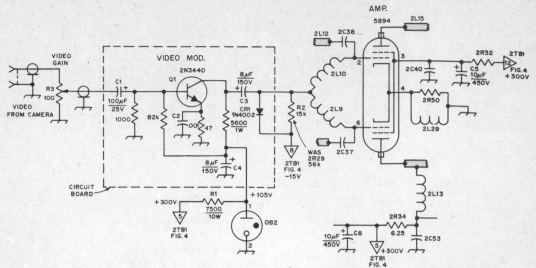

Fig. 5 — Schematic diagram of a one-transistor video modulator for use with the CMU-15 transmitter. Part numbers beginning with 2 indicate original CMU-15 components. Amplifier circuit is shown only in part, to indicate circuits where changes are made in adapting it to ATV service. Capacitors with polarity marked are electrolytic. The video gain control, R3, can be separated from the modulator by 2 feet or less, the connecting lead to be RG-59/U or other 75-ohm coax. The lead from the board to the junction of R2, 2L9 and 2L10 should be 2 inches or less in length.

those parts changed or added in the conversion process. Original components have the numeral 2 before the letter in their number. New parts used are numbered in the conventional manner. Thus, the screen bypass, above, is marked C5. It is in parallel with the original part, 2C40. The grid resistor, R2, 15kΩ replaces original 2R29, 56 kΩ. It is well to go through the tune-up procedure outlined above before the purely video changes are made, so that if trouble should develop along the line the worker will know when it started.

If the grid circuit has isolation resistors in place of the rf chokes, 2L9 and 2L10 in Fig. 5, replace them with Ohmite Z-460 or other uhf rf chokes when installing the new grid resistor, R2. If the transmitter is now operating normally, proceed with installation of the video modulator.

VIDEO MODULATION

A one-transistor video modulator suitable for use with dual-tetrode transmitters of moderate power is shown schematically in Fig. 5. A two-transistor unit of similar design for use with high-power tetrode amplifiers, such as the K2RIW kilowatt amplifier,[2] is shown in Fig. 6. Constructed on circuit board, this modulator is shown

[2] Knadle, "A Strip-Line Kilowatt Amplifier for 432 MHz," *QST*, April and May, 1972. Condensed version in *The Radio Amateur's VHF Manual*, Edition 3, Chapter 13.

in one of the photographs, attached to the back of the kW amplifier.

The modulators can be built on perforated boards or printed-circuit boards of simple design. Layout is not critical, except that high-impedance video leads should be short. For example, either modulator should be positioned so that the lead between the modulator output and the point of connection to the grid circuit should be no more than about 2 inches long. There is room for the CMU-15 modulator under the transmitter chassis. The 100-ohm gain control, R3, can be up to two feet from either modulator. The lead from its arm to the modulator input should be 75-ohm coax. The control acts as a termination for the low-impedance line from the camera, in conjunction with the modulator input impedance. As in rf lines, reflections on a video line can cause ghosts and sync instability. Monitors can be tapped on at any point, so long as the monitor input impedance is greater than 1000 ohms.

The diode, CR1, acts to charge up the coupling capacitor, C3, for dc restoration, to insure maxi-

Two-transistor video modulator of Fig. 6, mounted on the back of a kilowatt amplifier built from the popular *QST* article by K2RIW. Only minor changes were required to adapt the amplifier to video service.

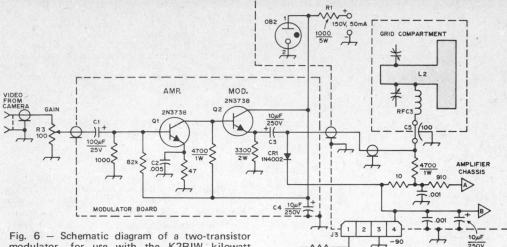

Fig. 6 — Schematic diagram of a two-transistor modulator, for use with the K2RIW kilowatt amplifier or similar high-power stages. Regulated voltage may be obtained from the screen supply, if it is capable of handling the extra load. Adjust value of R1 to suit source voltage. Basic amplifier components, where unchanged, are numbered as in the original article, Fig. 1, April, 1972, *QST*.

mum rf power output at the sync tips, regardless of average white-to-black ratio. This means that the picture will have a high contrast with varying scenes, and will insure a constant sync power level, for stable agc and sync triggering. It makes about a 3-dB improvement in weak-signal reception, because the receiver will be better able to lock up with a weak signal.

Adjusting for Picture Quality

With the modulator connected and the gain at minimum, apply power and check the output level. Then turn the gain up slowly until the output power decreases by one-third. Video modulation with dc restoration acts like downward modulation sometimes observed with a-m transmitters having low grid drive, but it is normal in this case. If everything seems to be working well, try to get another station, preferably a few miles away, to "talk your picture in." Adjusting the camera and modulation while monitoring the signal yourself will give false indications, because of overloading of your receiver. Low modulation will look fine on your monitor, but the signal received at a distance will lack contrast. Have the other fellow describe the appearance of the picture as you make adjust-

ments. Transmitting a detailed test pattern is recommended for this.

The final stage of a high-powered ATV rig can be run as a linear amplifier, driven by a CMU-15 or something comparable. In general, however, final-stage modulation makes for easier adjustment, and with grid modulation it adds little to the modulator complexity. Linearity never comes easily, and there is the extra problem in ATV of loss of bandwidth by the extra stages and tuned circuits.

Linear operation with transistors presents special problems. Often circuits must be heavily bypassed to prevent hf oscillation, and such bypassing may impose video bandwidth limitations. Useful

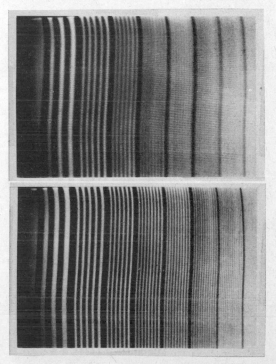

The effects of limited bandwidth are clearly apparent from these two views of a test signal. Even the broad lines at the left are a bit hazy in the upper picture, and vertical line detail is practically lost by the middle of the screen. Clear, sharp lines are plainly visible in the lower view, out to almost the right side. The same TV set and the same signal were used for both, except that a filter that limited the bandwidth to 2.5 MHz was in the circuit when the top picture was taken. Definition differences would be still more marked in direct viewing of the picture.

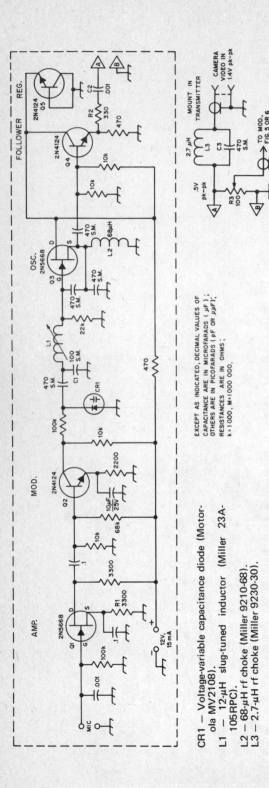

CR1 — Voltage-variable capacitance diode (Motorola MV2108).
L1 — 12-µH slug-tuned inductor (Miller 23A-105RPC).
L2 — 68-µH rf choke (Miller 9210-68).
L3 — 2.7-µH rf choke (Miller 9230-30).

Fig. 7 — Schematic diagram of the 4.5-MHz fm sound subcarrier generator. Values for R1, R2, and C1 are nominal and may have to be varied when equipment is tested. See text. Lead from C2 to R3 should be less than 3 inches. Parts not described are numbered for text reference.

application notes on simple uhf broadband amplifiers are available from several transistor manufacturers.[3]

FM SOUND SUBCARRIER

Audio can be added at the camera input to the video modulator in the form of a frequency-modulated 4.5-MHz subcarrier, if the modulator and transmitter are capable of passing the 4.5-MHz signal. The CMU-15 and the K2RIW kilowatt amplifier do a good job. The Motorola T44 will not handle this bandwidth, and the GE Progress Line transmitter is marginal. Its plate circuit may be capable of modification for lower Q, to increase bandwidth, but this has not been tried. The output filter has a bandwidth of about 8 MHz, so it is not the culprit.

The fm sound generator circuit is given in Fig. 7. Note the low-Q trap circuit, C3-L3, at the camera input. This trap keeps the long coaxial line to the camera from loading the 4.5-MHz generator capacitively. The value of the resistor, R2, in series with the generator output, is selected by experiment to give 0.5 V pk-pk, when everything is connected and operating, but with the camera switched off. R1, in the source lead of Q1, should be of such value that there will be 4 to 5.5 volts at the drain of Q1.

The oscillator, Q3, can be adjusted to 4.5 MHz by listening for it in a general-coverage communications receiver. Frequency tolerance is plus-or-minus 50 kHz. If adjusting L1 will not bring the frequency to 4.5 MHz, adjust the value of C1 as required. Do not try to tune the oscillator by listening to your own TV receiver. As with the TV picture, have a distant operator check the signal.

The only drawback with this system is that the power put into the subcarrier is taken from the video, which decreases the picture power by about 2 dB. This is a negligible difference with all but the weakest signals. The alternative is to use a separate fm transceiver 4.5 MHz above the video carrier, running on another antenna. This unit can also double as a secondary ATV calling-frequency setup, as shown in Fig. 1.

[3]*RF Power Devices* (SSD-205B), RCA Solid-State Division, Box 3200, Somerville, NJ 08876; *MX-12 Power Module*, TRW Semiconductor Products, Inc., 14520 Aviation Blvd, Lawndale, CA 90260; Motorola Semiconductor Products, Inc., 5005 McDowell Road, Phoenix, AZ 85008; *Wideband UHF Land Mobile Power Amplifiers*, (Note 2186B), CTC, 301 Industrial Way, San Carlos, CA 94070.

CAMERAS

The TV camera is usually the greatest expense in putting ATV on the air, and a primary reason that some potential enthusiasts never quite make it. The problem is not insurmountable, thanks to the boom in closed-circuit TV usage. Any closed-circuit vidicon camera with free-running sync will give very good pictures. New camera prices start around $200. Kits such as from ATV Research[4] run up from $125. Used but serviceable cameras are increasingly appearing in pawn shops, camera-equipment exchanges, and so on, as firms that have used closed-circuit TV for security purposes go out of business, or progress to more elaborate equipment. Prices generally range from $35 to $100.

Most cameras have both video- and rf-modulated outputs. The video is run to the modulator on a coaxial line, which must have a low-impedance termination at the modulator end. The gain control, R3 in Figs. 5, 6, and 7, provides this termination, as well as for adjustment of the level to the modulator. The camera output is usually an open emitter-follower requiring a dc path to ground, so do not couple it capacitively. If the camera has an rf output it can be run to a TV receiver to be used as a video monitor, by tuning the receiver to an unused channel between 2 and 6. For best resolution a separate monitor is preferred, tapped in as shown in Fig. 8. It is best to get a manual or Fotofact sheet on the TV receiver before going into it in this way.

Checking Picture Resolution

Most closed-circuit cameras are capable of 400- to 600-line resolution. The number of lines you can see determines the ability to see the video signal change from black to white. Test patterns with converging lines or groups of parallel lines of diminishing width are helpful in measuring the

[4] ATV Research, Box 453, Dakota City, NE 68731.

effect of linearity and bandwidth adjustments. A rule of thumb is 75 lines per megahertz of receiver bandwidth. ATVers soon develop a fondness for complimentary horizontal-resolution reports, in the manner of the DXer gloating over 40-over-9 reports from the rarest countries.

An excellent package of test patterns, with information on their use, is available from ATV Research. Servicing information, such as Sams, *Servicing Closed-Circuit Television*, is helpful. Many adjustments interact, making it difficult for the inexperienced ATV worker to obtain good resolution, video-to-sync ratio and contrast, without such aids.

Most cameras generate the vertical sync from the ac line frequency, and the horizontal from a free-running oscillator. The internal sync is helpful where more than one camera is used, as all will be running from the same sync source (the power line) and this will prevent picture jumping when cameras are switched.

ATV HORIZONS

Amateur television offers opportunity for expansion and development, limited only by the operator's imagination and technical skill. As an example, the Southern California ATV Club, WA6EVQ, participated in the Pasadena Rose Parade some years ago. A converted CMU-15 was installed in a helicopter of the Los Angeles County Sheriff's Office, to cover traffic situations. The police now have their own TV system, amateur radio having demonstrated convincingly the advantages of a real-time view of developing traffic problems, rather than relying solely on voice descriptions. Almost anyone entering the ATV field will quickly sense its potential for novel and challenging communication.

Information given here emphasizes simple and inexpensive approaches to ATV. By utilizing surplus components the newcomer can put a good ATV station on the air for $200 or less, with hardly more difficulty than is usually encountered in converting a commercial fm transceiver to amateur service. Current ATV activity and techniques are detailed in *A5 Magazine*, published six times yearly by Ron Cohen, K3ZKO, Box 6512, Philadelphia PA 19138.

Fig. 8 — Circuit diagram of modifications made to a typical TV receiver, to use it as a video monitor. Parts with no values given are part of the original receiver.

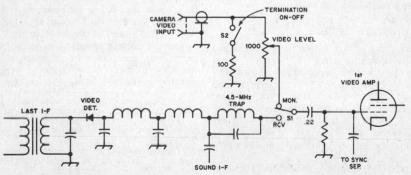

ATV WITH THE MOTOROLA T44 UHF TRANSMITTER

The Motorola T44 uhf fm transceiver, a surplus item popular with amateurs interested in 420-MHz operation, requires special attention when it is to be used for ATV work. The information below is adapted from a two-part article by F. R. McLeod, Jr., WØMZL, and originally appeared in *QST* for December, 1972, and February, 1973.

The conversion described here modifies the T44 mobile transceiver to operate from the 117-volt power line, and provides an fm transceiver for the audio link. The video is transmitted simultaneously, with the fm audio on the same carrier, using amplitude modulation, as in commercial TV stations. This provides "push-to-look" transmission capability. T44s are available from many sources, at moderate prices, depending on condition.

If your T44 has not already been converted, the first step is to procure crystals for the transmitter and receiver for the intended operating frequencies. Meanwhile it is well to check operation of the equipment on its original frequencies, using a dummy load and the power supplies and metering circuits described, to be sure that the equipment is in good order before the actual conversion work is started. Then, after installation of ham-band crystals, the transmitter and receiver can be tuned up on the new frequency and you can operate on fm, without the video modulation. This will help in understanding the equipment before attempting ATV work. Information on crystal types and frequencies is given below:

Transmitter

$$F = \frac{F_{SIG}}{24 \text{ or } 12}$$

Circuit — Motorola R-24
Temp — 85 C (for oven use)
Type — Commercial Standard
Holder — CS-05

Receiver

$$F = \frac{F_{SIG} - (\text{Mid i-f freq.})}{14}$$

Where Mid i-f = Y2 Freq. — 455
Temp — 26 C (unless rcvr has oven)
Type — Commercial Standard
Holder — CS-05

When picking a transmitter frequency, notice that the 14th harmonic of the receiver crystal frequency falls in the band, usually below 440 MHz. It may be necessary to change both Y1 and Y2 crystals of the receiver, if the 14th harmonic falls too close to the transmitting frequency. Do not be concerned if it is close to the lower sideband, as this will not bother the TV set. Be concerned only with frequencies near the upper sideband.

The camera can now be obtained, and the video modulator added as described. Now we can video-modulate, and with the fm system working as before, operate "push-to-look." Conversion of the T44 to the amateur band was described in *QST* by W8FWF[1] and WA1FSZ[2]. A schematic diagram and tuneup information can be found in *FM Schematic Digest* by S. Wolf.[3] Information given here is mostly concerned with power supply and metering changes needed for and peculiar to ATV, and for increasing the power output above the level normally obtained with these units.

ATV CONVERSION

The original three chassis modules are kept in their same positions in the conversion. An 8-3/4-inch rack panel is fastened to the power supply chassis, becoming the front. The two plates that hold the modules together and the two rails connecting the top of the plates are retained. The panel also fastens to the rail on the power supply side. The photographs show the general placement of parts. As the actual hole positions will vary with different components, no specific dimensions are given for panel layout. The general placement of the meters and video modulator should be maintained, for accessibility.

The original volume and squelch controls were taken from the control head. The speaker on the front panel is optional, as the mobile speaker that goes with the unit can be used. The voltmeter (middle of the three in Fig. 1) is also optional, but the 50-µA and 50-mA meters should not be combined in one metering circuit. The final grid current should be monitored at all times, and not allowed to exceed 50 mA.

There should be a means of cooling the converted unit for stability, longevity, and peace of mind with the higher power level. Get as much air through the 2C39 compartments as you can without excessive room noise and mechanical vibration, which can cause "fan modulation." There have been several techniques and fans used. As can be seen in the photographs, a Muffin fan is aimed at the holes in the end of the tripler assembly. The fan is nestled between the two fittings on the coax relay. Much of the air cools the outer metal parts of the 450-MHz assemblies and thus cools the 2C39s by conduction as well as radiation. Some of the air cools the 6146 in its hot little cage. The rest of the spill-over air is helpful as a general cooling agent for other hot items, particularly the power transformers, if you leave the ATV picture on for extended periods while someone peaks up a newly ATV-converted uhf TV

---

[1] Poland, "Converting Wide-Band FM Equipment for 420-MHz Service," *QST*, August, 1968.
[2] Clement, "Using Motorola TU-110 Series Transmitters on 420-MHz," *QST*, September, 1971.
[3] Wolf, S.M., *FM Schematic Digest*, available from the author, 1100 Tremont Street, Boston, MA 02120. Price $6.50 (1974). Reviewed in January, 1971, *QST*, p. 39.

Fig. 1 — Converted T44 transceiver, ready for push-to-look operation in the 420-MHz band. The video modulator is in the upper right corner, as seen in the front-panel view. Looking at the assembly from the back, the power supply is visible, next to the panel. The fan (right side of rear view) is directed at the 6146 and 2C39 multiplier assemblies. The small unit at the left rear corner is an rf amplifier for the receiver. Panel meters are l to r, 50μA, 750 or 1000 volts dc, and 50 mA.

set. The 2C39s can take all kinds of punishment. The weak part of the set after conversion is the 6146 in its hot box, as it was designed for brief transmissions.

An rf amplifier is shown mounted at the rear of the chassis in Fig. 1. It is a 417A/5842 grounded-grid stage, connected to the output of the coax relay on receive. The output of the rf amplifier has a coax T connector, its two outputs going to the converted TV set and to the T44 fm receiver antenna input. Careful peaking of the fm input rf circuits and the TV set, along with the rf amplifier plate-line output tap, can produce some outstanding increases in signal-to-noise ratio. A solid-state preamp may be better, and many good versions are now available. (A low-cost rf amplifier appears elsewhere in this chapter.)

The combination block and schematic diagram, Fig. 2, has the original T44 schematic designations for reference. There are two modifications to the transmitter module: removal of the output filter, Z5, and changing the output metering circuitry.

Modification Procedure

Remove the bottom cover of the transmitter, being careful not to lose those special screws! Locate the Z5 circuit. It is under the tripler and final stages, in their cathode compartments, fastened to the side of the chassis with screws. One end has a length of RG-58/U coax going to the output-coupling link, L13. The other lead is a stiff piece of tubing which is the outer conductor of a coaxial line to antenna post of the coaxial relay, and through R47 to the diode detector can, E1.

Before disconnecting either end, notice and remember exactly how the coax shield ends are connected. Observe the short leads at the relay end. Now remove Z5. You will need a fair amount of heat to unsolder the solid tubing end from the ground lug at the coax relay. Be sure to connect the ground exactly as it was on the final coupling link and ground lug. Run the coax tightly along the chassis corner. If the coax is allowed to raise up off the chassis, it will couple to the 2C39 cathode lines, causing reduced output, and possible oscillation if the SWR is high. Use ground lugs along the coax as cable clamps, employing screws already in the chassis.

The modified output circuitry shown in Fig. 3 provides for monitoring the waveform of the signal as it goes to the antenna, and also includes a peak sync-tip output-power detector, for peak-power output monitoring. The latter is absolutely necessary for tuning a TV transmitter, as will be seen later.

Components to the left of the dotted line in Fig. 3 should be put inside the transmitter compartment near the transmitter post of the coax relay. They should have short leads and one common ground, as shown at the original point where the length of RG-58/U was soldered to the chassis. Be careful to heatsink the 1N295 germanium detector diode while soldering, and try not to break it when bending the leads, as it is rather fragile. The 1N295 is a video detector diode used in many TV sets.

Components to the right of the dotted line are put in the compartment containing the metering socket and 2C39 grid-bias resistors. The waveform output connector is a UG-1094/U BNC coax fitting, chosen because it fits the 3/8-inch hole in the chassis nearest the side of that compartment.

Operation of the antenna output circuitry is as follows. The 1.5-pF disk ceramic capacitor couples a small amount of the 444-MHz energy across the 4700-ohm resistor, R47. The 1N295 detector diode is isolated from the rf by a 1000-ohm peak-current limiter resistor. Do not reverse these two components in their series connection! The

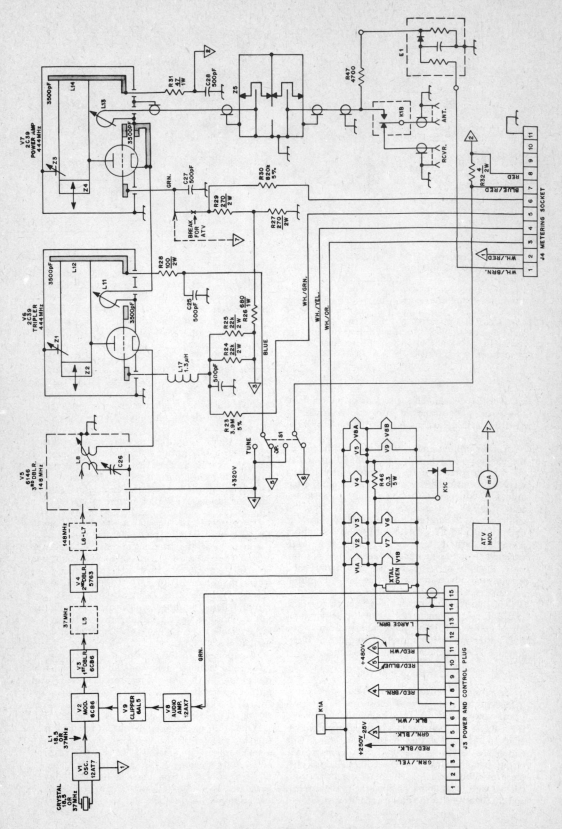

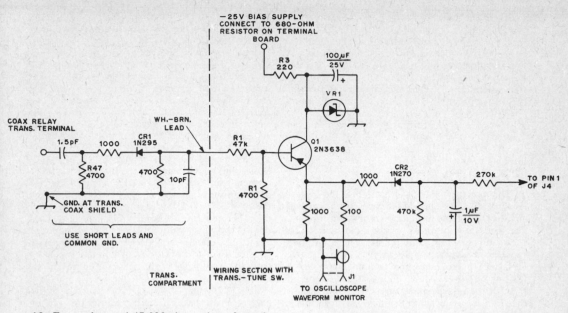

-25V BIAS SUPPLY
CONNECT TO 680-OHM
RESISTOR ON TERMINAL
BOARD

Fig. 2 — Basic block and schematic diagram of the TU204 or TU110 T44 uhf transmitter. Only those stages concerned with the conversion are shown in detail. Motorola part designations are given. Some numbers and values may vary, depending on date of manufacture. ATV modulator connection point shown at "X".

10-pF capacitor and 47,000-ohm resistor form the load for the detector and provide a video band width. This waveform signal is coupled through a resistive voltage divider to a zero-biased emitter follower. The emitter follower preserves the video bandwidth as detected, and drives a low-impedance coax cable to an oscilloscope. The follower is dc-coupled to the BNC connector so that a dc-coupled oscilloscope can be used to see where zero signal voltage occurs.

The follower also drives a peak detector. This part of the circuit is another germanium diode, that must have a high off-resistance. The high-resistance load is shunted with a high-value low-leakage capacitor. Whenever the voltage at the emitter of the 2N3638 becomes more negative than the negative charge voltage on the 1-μF capacitor, the diode turns on and rapidly charges the capacitor to the new more-negative voltage. When the peak of the signal is reached (on sync tips) and then decreases in value towards zero, the diode reverse-biases and turns off. The 1-μF capacitor now discharges through the large-value load

Fig. 3 — Schematic diagram of the waveform monitor and peak-output meter, for the antenna output circuit of the transmitter. All resistors are 1/2-watt composition. Capacitors with polarity marked are electrolytic; others are ceramic.
C1 — 1-μF, 10-volt, low-leakage tantalum.
CR1 — 1N295, glass only.
CR2 — 1N270, 1N277, 1N34, or 1N295, glass.
VR1 — 15-volt, 5-percent, 1-watt Zener diode. Adjust R3 for 10 to 15 mA of Zener current.
J1 — BNC receptacle, threaded base, UG-1094/U.

resistor at a much slower rate than its charge rate. This circuit requires that the internal leakage resistance of the capacitor be very high, so that it will not discharge itself faster than the load resistor discharges it. This voltage on the capacitor is read out as relative peak sync-tip power output. The 270-kΩ resistor takes the signal to the original pin 1 of the metering socket, J4. The signals have all been made negative, to be consistent with normal TV practice.

The Zener diode removes 120-Hz ripple from the negative bias supply. In this way, any ripple seen on the monitor oscilloscope will be as it is being transmitted. The series resistor between the bias supply and the Zener diode will depend on the value of the bias voltage (which could be anything from 18 to 28 volts). The resistance should be chosen for a Zener current of about 10 to 15 mA. The Zener voltage of 15 shown is not critical and was chosen so that up to 13 volts of peak signal could be seen on the oscilloscope and meter without saturating the 2N3638 and clipping the peak of the signal.

The 1N295 detector diodes are fairly uniform in efficiency at 444-MHz from unit to unit, but if you should happen to have one that is unusually high or low in efficiency, one of the 47-kΩ emitter-follower base resistors should be changed in value. As shown, 8 to 10 volts negative should

Nomenclature:

Older TU110		Newer TU204
C31	=	Z1
C35	=	Z3
Z1	=	Z5
ZE26 = V5		= 6146
0.5 = R46		= 0.3

be obtainable at the peak sync tips, using a 50-ohm dummy load.

R46 in Fig. 2 is shunted out by auxiliary outboard contacts on the coax relay, K1, in the transmit position on most units. Be sure that the 2C39 heater voltage does not change in the transmit and receive conditions to cause the output to drift appreciably. If it does, permanently short out R46.

Last, change R32 from 4 ohms to a 50-ohm 1-percent, 2-watt resistor.

POWER SUPPLY

The power supply modification is the biggest job. Fig. 4 shows a partial schematic of the original circuitry, after the secondaries of the transformers. This will show how it works and indicates which parts can be kept and reused. There are two supplies; the lower supply always has its negative lead tied to ground, while the top supply has a floating negative lead, which is switched to ground through the relay contacts on receive. On transmit, that lead is connected to the plus lead of the lower supply, putting the two supplies in series to obtain the 480 volts for the plates of the 2C39s, V6 and V7. The lower supply furnishes 320 volts to the

6146, V5, and 250 volts (through a 1500-ohm, 5-watt resistor) to the rest of the transmitter stages. On receive, the lower supply is not used. The top supply is now connected to the receiver through another set of the relay contacts and delivers 200 volts for the receiver. Notice that when the two are connected in series, the top negative lead of the top supply is connected to the input of the choke-capacitor filter. This way, the choke in the lower supply handles only the 320- and 250-volt currents, and the upper choke handles only the 2C39 plate currents.

The revised power supply is shown in Fig. 5. Notice the reused components. By removing transformers from old TV sets, a large saving in the cost of the power supply changes can be realized. Check the 40-40-10-μF 450-volt original metal-can capacitor before using it. Some T44s may have been sitting too long without being turned on. The capacitor actually exploded for WA0MGY, with enough force to rip the 50-mA grid-current meter from the front panel of the rig, while he was on the air with TV!

The 220-ohm, 2-watt resistor in Fig. 5 discharges the capacitors in the transmitter rapidly when going from transmit to receive. This kills the oscillator and driver stages before the receiver is energized, so that the receiver will not be momen-

Fig. 4 — Partial schematic diagram of the original T44 6/12-volt power supply. Only the secondary circuits are shown. Relay contacts are in the **RECEIVE** position.

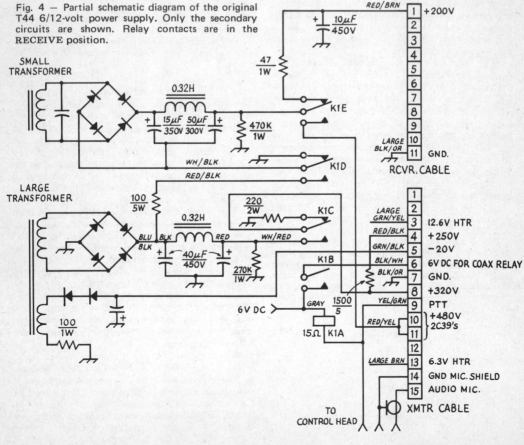

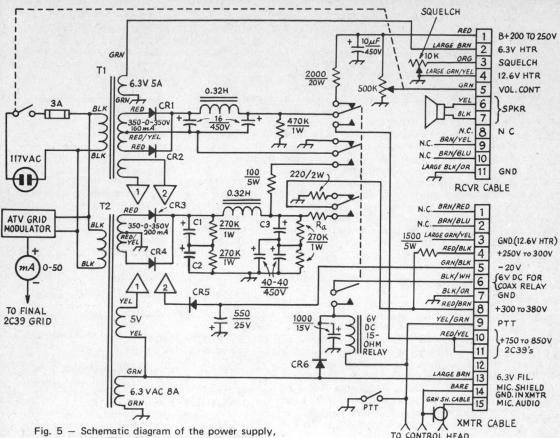

Fig. 5 — Schematic diagram of the power supply, as used for ATV. Where parts values duplicate those of Fig. 4, the original T44 components are used. Capacitors with polarity indicated are electrolytic.

C1, C2, C3 — 80-μF, 350-volt electrolytic.
CR1 through CR4 — 200-PIV, 11-A; 1N4003 or equiv.
T1 — Triad R116A, or equivalent TV transformer.
T2 — Triad R129A, or equivalent TV transformer.
Filter chokes: 0.32-H, 600-mA (Triad C-400X).

tarily overloaded and have feedback effects, causing an annoying "plop" in the speaker. The color code of the wires may not be entirely correct for all sets, and should be used mostly as a guide. In some units the volume control is not as shown. Some had the control-head volume control wired at the speaker circuit, using a low-resistance control instead of the voltage-controlled scheme as shown. If you plan to reuse this component, be sure to check its resistance to determine which control you have.

Notice the method used to obtain the minus 20- to 25-volt bias voltage for the 2C39s. The unused 5-volt filament windings on the transformers (for tube rectifiers) are series-connected in phase so that the voltages add. These are also in series with one of the 6.3-volt windings that has one lead going to ground. The value of the resistor

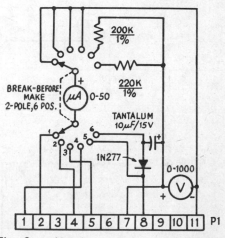

Fig. 6 — Metering circuit for the T44 ATV transmitter. P1 is an 11-pin plug to match the metering socket, J4 in Fig. 2. Switch positions: 1-Osc. output, adj. L1; 2 — 2nd doubler, adj. L5, 6, 7; 3 — 6146 output, adj. L8, C26; 4 — Relative peak out power, adj. Z1, L11, Z3, L13; 5 — final 2C39 average plate current, full scale 200 mA; 6 — Final 2C39 peak, plate current, full scale 200 mA.

marked R_a in Fig. 5 should be chosen so that the voltage to the driver stages (pin 4 of the transmitter plug) does not exceed 300. In most cases it is not needed and R_a equals 0.

The resulting power supply provides 250 to 300 volts to the initial driver stages, 320 to 380 volts to the 6146, and 750 to 850 volts to the 2C39s, on transmit, and 200 volts to the receiver on receive. The 2000-ohm resistor from the upper supply to the receiver may have to be changed in value and wattage to get 200 to 250 volts at the receiver.

The metering circuitry shown in Fig. 6 is rather self-explanatory. A 50-μA meter is preferred over any less-sensitive scale. The "peak final plate current" position is for metering the peak input current, for computing peak-input power. The regular average plate current position and the peak current position should read the same with no video modulation. The circuit is a peak detector and functions as the one in the transmitter output circuitry in Fig. 3.

VIDEO MODULATOR

The T44 is difficult to plate modulate at video frequencies without modification of the 2C39 final amplifier, because of the very large bypass capacitors in the plate and grid circuits. At the end of the plate line, L14, there is a 3500-pF sheet-mica capacitor. In addition, there is C28, 500-pF, on the same circuit outside the assembly for bypassing, a total of 4000 pF on the high-voltage lead to contend with at video frequencies. Modifying the 3500-pF capacitor is not possible without degrading the stability and efficiency noticeably. The

grid of the final 2C39 is rf-grounded by an identical 3500-pF capacitor. C27 is also 500 pF, for a total of 4000 pF to ground here also. The grid capacitor should not be changed for the same reasons. The grid voltage swing for full video modulation to zero power output is 50 volts peak-to-peak. The output-impedance requiremnt of a grid modulator for a bandwidth of 2.5 MHz at the −6dB points is 20 ohms, resistive, driving a 4000-pF load.

The above requirements are satisfied by the modulator shown in Fig. 7. It is constructed on a circuit board along with its power supply (short leads to the power supply are necessary) inside a 5 × 7 × 2-inch inverted aluminum chassis. The circuit-board layout is shown in Fig. 8, and the hole-drilling information for the aluminum chassis is shown in Fig. 9. The video modulator is a Class AB amplifier, using a complementary pair of output transistors operating as a direct-coupled output device. The output of the modulator is direct-coupled to the control grid of the final-

Fig. 7 — Schematic diagram of the ATV modulator and its power supply. All capacitors are electrolytic, values in μF. Suggested components are as follows:

C1, C2 — CDE BR-1000-50.
C3 — Sprague TE 1407.
C4 — CDE BR-500-15.
CR1-CR4, incl. — 100-PIV, 1-A; 1N4001 or equiv.
VR1 — 67-volt Zener diode (Sarkes-Tarzian VR-67).
Q1, Q2 — 2N4888 (Fairchild).
T1 — Low-voltage rectifier transformer. (Triad F-90X; use taps indicated by wire colors given); primary, 117 V ac, secondary, 21 to 24 V ac.

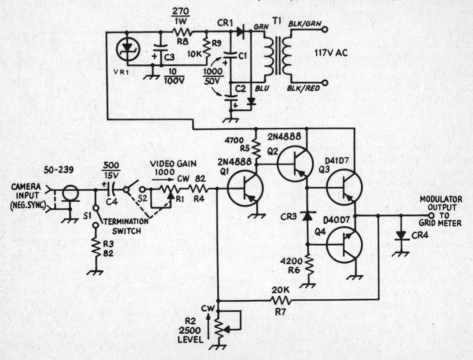

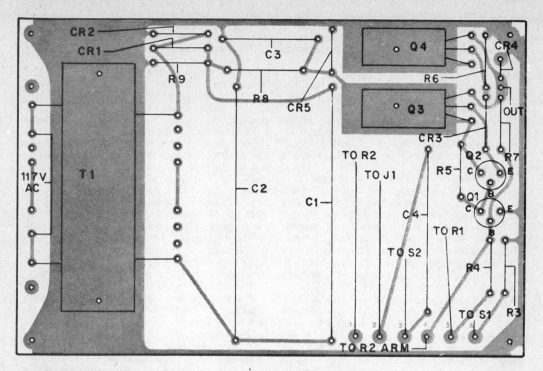

Fig. 8 — Printed-circuit board layout for the video modulator, foil side. Components are on the far side, as shown. The board mounts inside a 5 X 7 X 2-inch box, on 3/16-inch metal spacers. Parts indicated are those of Fig. 7.

amplifier 2C39. The lead from the bias resistors to C27 is disconnected, and the lead from the modulator is connected in its place. This is one video modulator that does not have to be mounted close to the grid circuit, as can be seen in the photographs.

The modulator maintains excellent phase and bias stability so long as the unit and its power supply are enclosed as shown, with the short power supply leads. This pc-board layout has been reproduced successfully many times.[4] Dc bias stability is established by negative feedback to the base of Q1, which ensures stability of the output operating point. This operating point, or average grid bias, is variable by R2, called the level-adjust control because it is used to set the average power output level, as will be seen later. R2 can vary the output potential from 0 to −67 volts. In order to acheive the low output resistance at video frequencies, low feedback capacitance, C_{ob}, (capacitance from collector to base) and high-Ft transistors must be used. Such devices are usually limited to a relatively low breakdown voltage. The Fairchild 2N4888 and the GE D40D7 and D41D7 have the necessary low capacitance and high breakdown voltage (−150 volts for the 2N4888, and 75 for the D40D7 and D41D7).

Crossover distortion in the output transistors, Q3 and Q4, is minimized by maintaining a small

[4] A circuit board for the modulator is available from Spectronics, 1009 Garfield St., Oak Park, IL 60304.

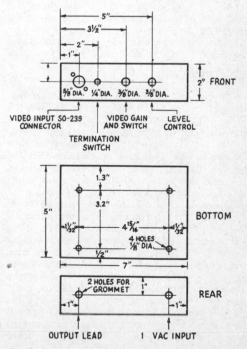

Fig. 9 — Hole-drilling information for the chassis housing the video modulator.

quiescent current of 15 mA with no video signal present. The overall amplifying voltage gain from the camera input to the output grid-modulating voltage is determined by the ratio of R7 to R1-plus-R4, as is the case with an operational amplifier.[5] The input ac-signal current and the feedback ac currents through R7 cancel at the base of Q1, so that this point is a virtual ground for ac. The gain of the modulator is adjustable by varying the ratio of R7 to R1-plus-R4 by making R1 the variable video-gain control. This modulator will fully modulate the T44 with as little as 0.3 volt from the camera.

There is no "dc restoration" to the video signal from the camera, since the input to the modulator is ac coupled and the modulator is dc coupled to the grid of the final 2C39. Do not mistake CR4 for a dc-restorer diode. It is installed as an arc-back protection device, in case the 2C39 has an internal discharge through the grid. These are always positive-going current pulses; hence the diode will normally be off and will turn on in case of arc-back and protect the output transistors, Q3 and Q4.

If one does dc-restore the composite video signal, maximum power output will always occur at the peak sync tips. It has been stated by some that dc restoration will always give a better contrast picture. However, it has been found that most vidicon cameras do not have the standard sync-to-video ratio of approximately 1:2. The best of them are more like 1:1, and some are around 1.5:1 or 2:1 and even lower, as the vidicon ages and loses sensitivity. Of course the ratio will depend upon lighting conditions if you have no automatic-light-level circuitry. Without any dc restoration, the dc coupling to the grid allows the sync tips of the composite video signal to be clipped off at the peak power level as much as desired, using the LEVEL and VIDEO GAIN controls.

ADJUSTMENTS

Tuning the T44 for normal fm operation only is straightforward. You should get familiar with the tuning adjustments and the magnitude of the various meter readings, using the original crystal, before beginning new frequency operation. One change in the procedure is recommended for limiting the final plate current. In the original Motorola instructions, all the driver adjustments, L1, L5 through L8, and C26, are peaked for maximum at their respective metering positions. Then the 2C39 tripler and final are tuned for maximum power output, and the output coupling link, L13, is used to limit the plate current of the final 2C39 to no more than 80 mA, in the same manner that the familiar loading control of a pi network on most ham transmitters is used. Instead, continue to peak the final tuning, Z3, and coupling, L13, for maximum power output, and if the plate current of the final exceeds 80 mA, the 6146 output-coupling control, L8, should be decreased to limit the final current. A point will be reached

[5] Pike, "The Operational Amplifier," Part I, *QST*, August, 1970.

while adjusting L13 where, if further increases in coupling are made (clockwise rotation), less output will be obtained with 80-mA plate current.

When the new crystals are installed, the 2C39 plate lines must be lengthened by means of the movable shorting bars. In Fig. 2, these are Z2 at the end of L12, in the tripler, and Z4 at the end of L14, in the final. They are accessible through the assembly tops, by the holes at the ends opposite from the coupling adjustments. They are adjusted after all the other driver adjustments are repeaked. The tripler is adjusted first, while metering at the grid of the final, and then the final is adjusted while the output power is monitored. Use an insulated tuning tool. The tuning adjustments, Z1 and Z3, should yield maximum output when the screwdriver slots *on the top* of the assemblies are at the 45-degree position. Be careful when lengthening the shorting bars not to slide them all the way out, as they will touch the end of the assembly. Remember that the shorting bars are at the 2C39 plate potential! If you do happen to hit ground, R28 or R31 will act as a fuse, so you will know it! R28 or R31 will also blow if the tops of the 2C39 assemblies are accidentally put on backward, so that the plate-tuning adjustments, Z1 or Z3 touch the tube anode.

Once the video modulator has been connected, the transmitter tune-up procedure for ATV is only slightly different than for fm operation alone. The video signal from a camera or other source with negative-going sync is connected to the modulator input. The gain and level controls of the modulator are preset at minimum (fully ccw). After the transmitter is turned on, the gain and level controls are turned up until the peak-output power meter reading no longer increases. The peak sync tips will be slightly clipped at this point. Assuming all the driver adjustments are peaked up, the 2C39 tripler adjustments, Z1 and L11, and the final adjustments, Z4 and L13, are tuned for maximum peak-output power. Be certain during all of these adjustments that the final grid current does not exceed 50 mA. Preferably is should be held around 30 mA. The level control of the modulator is used to keep the grid current down.

After peaking the above four adjustments, turn the level control down (ccw) so that the output signal reads a minimum on the meter. If the signal does not go all the way to zero, adjust the tripler coupling, L11, clockwise (increasing coupling) until the output just reads zero. Turn up the level control on the modulator to bring the output power reading up to maximum again. Readjust the three other 2C39 adjustments, Z1, Z4, and L13, for maximum once again. From here on, the procedure is to repeat the above two steps, alternately peaking Z1, Z4, and L13 with the level control turned up, and then turning the level control to minimum and adjusting L11 so that the output just reads zero.

The above procedure can best be done with an oscilloscope monitor. The photographs in Fig. 10 show the results. Fig. 10A shows the zero-output line at the top of the picture and the adjustments peaked, but the tripler coupling, L11, is not

Fig. 10 — Oscilloscope waveforms showing the effects of 2C39 tripler coupling
adjustment on modulation percentage.
The coupling is adjusted for maximum
amplifier output in A. In B, the tripler
coupling is adjusted clockwise so that
modulation will be 100 percent. Peak
power is the same in both cases. Increasing power is downward, with zero watts
at the top.

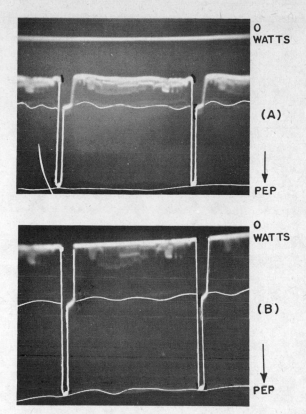

properly adjusted for ATV when peaked.
Under this condition, the most negative
video signal voltages (corresponding to
white) at the final grid will not fully cut
off the output power, resulting in less
than 100-percent modulation. In Fig.
10B, the L11 adjustement has been
turned clockwise to the point where the
grid voltage will cut the power output to
zero. Now the modulating voltage will
100-percent modulate the output power
for the best possible ATV picture.
Notice that this adjustment of L11 has
not varied the peak-power level of the
signal. If you have a normal rf power
meter in the coax line to the load, you
will see a reduction in the average output
power, but the peak-output meter will
not vary.

Use the 6146 output coupling adjustment, L8, as discussed above, to limit
the final 2C39 average plate current
(which will vary with the video signal
content) to the desired value of under 100 mA.
The peak plate current will run around 175 mA.
With 800 volts on the plate of the final, this is 140
watts of peak input power. The measured output
power on most converted T44s indicates approximately 45-percent efficiency, or 63 watts of peak
power output. For more output, add a linear
amplifier with external-anode tubes. This amplifier
should have a means of indicating peak power
output — and most of all — the output waveform,
as was done here, to tune up the amplifier properly
for ATV.

OPERATION

Try to run as high a video gain setting as
possible without appreciable "hooking," "bending," or "whiting out." The ATV operator at the
other end of the transmission path can observe for
you, if your own set gives a false picture because of
overloading. To understand what these terms
mean, turn the level and gain controls of the
modulator down while transmitting a picture. Now
increase the level control and observe that you first
get a synchronized picture without any video
information. Then, slowly, the blackest portions of
the picture will be seen, with the rest of the picture
a white area. This white area is clipping at the
zero-power level and is called "whiting out."
Increase the level control until there is no whiting
out, and then increase the gain control. You may
get some more whiting out, but now notice the top
of the picture and the straightness of the picture in
the vertical direction. If you have sufficient gain
and run the level control up high enough, the top
of the picture will first start to bend right or left.
This is "hooking," when the sync pulses are
beginning to be almost all clipped off. Further
increase in the level control will cause vertical lines
to wrinkle. The video information is getting into
the sync circuitry because of lack of enough
sync-pulse amplitude. This is a form of bending.
The optimum operating point is found when the
level control cannot be turned either up or down
without observing either hooking or whiting out.

The above procedure is best followed while
observing a dc-coupled oscilloscope connected to
the waveform-monitor BNC connector on the
transmitter module. Fig. 11 shows some of the
various waveforms obtained with a variety of level
and gain settings. A low gain setting with the level
up fairly high is shown in Fig. 11A. Notice the
sync-to-video ratio. This waveform produced a
washed-out picture, as the signal was riding up
around the high-power level. If the level control is
turned down so that the percentage of modulation
is increased, even though the actual power level has
diminished, the observer at the receiving end will
comment that the quality is better and that there is
actually less snow in the picture! Fig. 11B shows a
higher gain setting over Fig. 11A, and the level is
turned down slightly for less average power output.

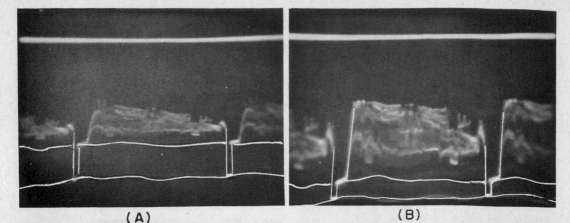

(A)   (B)

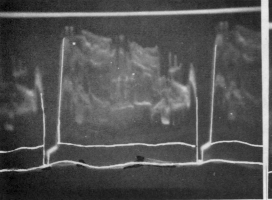
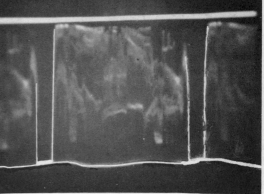

(C)   (D)

Fig. 11 — Oscilloscope patterns with various modulator gain and level settings. Increasing power is downward, with zero watts at the top. Whites are at the top; blacks are lowest in the video waveform. Sync pulses are at the bottom (peak power level).

This improves the received picture, but further decreasing the level control and increasing the gain will produce the picture you desire, and this waveform is shown in Fig. 11C. Notice how the sync is compressed. No sync instability will be noticed with this waveform, and this includes some very old TV sets.

The waveform shown in Fig. 11D is one that should be noted carefully. See how the whites come all the way to zero watts (top line). The sync information is completely gone. Notice, however, that no video information at the black level extends more than 90-percent of the way down the waveform, so there is a 10-percent margin of

blanking pulses left for the receiver to sync its horizontal and vertical circuits. Most TV sets will have no problem displaying a steady picture with this type of waveform (10-percent margin of sync). A little hooking was noticed on some sets but was not objectionable. This was also a snow-free picture. Compare this with the one in Fig. 11B, which was not entirely snow-free, even though both are at the same peak-power level. For ATV DXing, you may even want to increase the gain to a higher setting and allow the picture to bend somewhat, as a trade-off for the ability to see large-lettered signs.

A TUNER FOR ATV RECEPTION

Reception of ATV signals can be handled in several ways. The low end of the frequency range used for home uhf television is just above the amateur 420-MHz band, so padding down the tuning range of the family TV set immediately suggests itself. This can be done fairly easily, merely by adding capacitance across the tuned circuits of the TV receiver rf, mixer, and oscillator stages. While this usually works after a fashion,

much better results can be obtained with a more extensive conversion.

Peter Bertini, K1ZJH, described two such TV tuner conversions in separate *QST* articles.* The

*Bertini, "A Tunable 440-MHz FM Receiver," July, 1961, *QST*, page 26. Condensed version in *The Radio Amateur's VHF Manual*, 3rd edition, p. 213. Also, "A Tuner for ATV Applications," *QST*, p. 34, October, 1973.

information below is condensed from both, and deals specifically with the Sickles Model 228 uhf tuner, found in many home TV receivers. Other makes of tuners can be converted to amateur service in generally similar ways. Many tuners use the same basic electrical and mechanical layout, the only differences being in the dial drive arrangement made for a particular TV receiver. These tuners do not have trimmer capacitors for alignment, such as were used in earlier uhf converters. Alignment is done with specialized test equipment, by precisely bending the rotor plates in the tuner. Most tuners are linear within plus or minus one TV channel, over the entire uhf TV spectrum, when they leave the factory.

Uhf Tuner Modifications

Getting this type of tuner to cover the upper portion of the amateur band is best done by adding trimmer capacitors across the tuner circuits. The photograph of the original tuner, and a sketch of the tuner as modified, Fig. 1, should help to make clear how this is done. Start by removing one of the two rotor plates in the oscillator compartment (bottom section of the photo and Fig. 1). The mixer and antenna circuits will not require tuning across our small intended frequency range, so the

ATV tuner built by K1ZJH has its own power supply, rf, and i-f amplifiers.

rotor plates in the two upper sections of the tuner can all be removed.

Mount three 16-pF glass trimmers on the tuner walls, parallel to the three lines and as close as possible to them. See Fig. 1. Connect the trimmers to their respective lines with short pieces of heavy wire or copper strip. By bending the one oscillator rotor plate away from its stator carefully, the tuning range can be reduced to as little as 15 MHz.

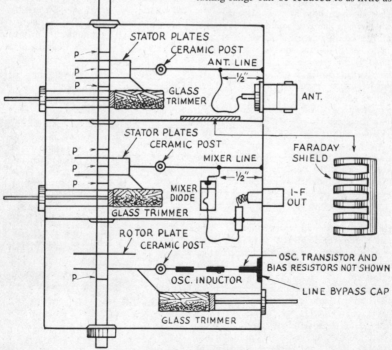

Fig. 1 — Bottom view of the uhf TV converter, as modified for use in ATV or fm reception. Only the oscillator circuit is tuned by the vernier dial, all rotator plates in the mixer and preselector circuits having been removed. One rotor place is left in the oscillator section. Positions of plates to be removed are indicated by the letter P.

Typical uhf TV tuner, in its original condition before modification.

Remove the 300-ohm connector and coupling loop from the antenna section, by drilling out the mounting rivets in its insulating support. Enlarge the hole, and mount a phono jack or a BNC fitting for antenna connection. Run a 1/8-inch copper strip from a point on the antenna line, 1/2 inch from the wall, down to as close to the coupling port to the mixer compartment as possible, then up to the connector, as shown in Fig. 1. If the port is not merely an open hole in the wall separating the sections, but is a Faraday shield, as in the 228 tuner, remove the shield to improve interstage coupling. This shield is not visible in the tuner photo. If used, it is a comb-like insert in the port, as shown in enlarged form in Fig. 1.

One lead of the mixer diode in the 228 tuner runs through a small port between the oscillator and mixer sections. The other diode lead, barely visible in the tuner photo, is parallel to the mixer line and is connected to the right-hand wall of the tuner. Cut it at this point and solder the lead to the mixer line, about 1/2 inch from the wall, as shown in Fig. 1. In some of the better tuners the mixer diode is reverse-biased, and does not go directly to ground in the mixer section. This was done for improved noise figure, and should be left the way it is.

Most tuners are designed to terminate in an i-f input circuit which is at dc ground potential. If the receiver to be used does not provide a dc path, an rf choke should be connected from the tuner i-f output to ground to provide a dc path for the mixer crystal current. The ground end of the choke can be lifted to measure crystal current, which should be at least 100 μA.

The tuner conversion detailed above was done primarily to provide coverage of the upper portion of the 420-MHz band. In this application the i-f and audio system was part of a Motorola crystal-controlled commercial-fm receiver. The conversion information is the same for ATV applications, except that in the latter a low-noise rf amplifier is made an integral part of the converted tuner, and

an i-f amplifier is added, for improved reception of weak signals.

The antenna circuit of the tuner was used for the collector output network for the rf amplifier, giving a lower noise figure and better sensitivity than when a remote preamplifier was used. With 14 dB of mixer noise being typical for these tuners, it is quite obvious *what* the rf stage is expected to overcome and improve upon!

Some of the later model 228 uhf tuners use a biased hot-carrier diode in the mixer. These are readily identifiable by the clear glass diode package which has a single black band, and by locating the resistor from the eimtter of the local oscillator transistor, which provides the dc biasing for the diode. The lower noise figure of the hot-carrier diodes allowed these tuners to produce pictures with a better degree of "quieting," or less snow, at comparably lower signal levels than with tuners using the conventional germanium mixer diodes. These are generally 1N82 diodes in the Sickles tuners, and are identified by a clear glass diode package with a single gray and a single red band.

A slight improvement in sensitivity is possible by increasing the coupling between the mixer and antenna cavities of the tuner. The removal of the Faraday shield (if present) as described above partially acheives this, and the coupling can be further improved by moving the antenna line closer to the coupling port. This is best done by the removal of the rigid line originally used, and by substituting an equal length of No. 14 bus wire in its place.

The rf amplifier, Fig. 2, uses a Texas Instrument TIXM101 germanium uhf transistor, designed for low-noise amplifier applications up to 1200

Layout of the ATV tuner. The preamp compartment is visible in the upper left-hand portion of the photograph. Q1 is mounted in the side wall between the glass trimmer and the air trimmer. Leads to Q1 should be kept as short as possible.

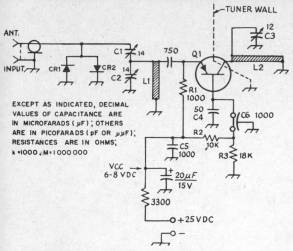

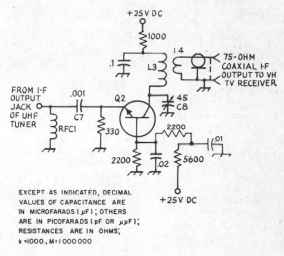

Fig. 2 — Schematic diagram of the 439-MHz preamp. Resistors are 1/4- and 1/2-watt composition.
C1, C2 — 14-pF trimmer, E. F. Johnson pc type mount.
C3 — 12-pF glass trimmer.
C4 — 50-pF button mica.
C5 — .001-μF button mica.
C6 — .001-μF feed-through.
CR1, CR2 — 1N914. (May be eliminated in receive-only applications.)
Q1 — TIXM101. (See text.)
L1 — 1.5-inch (3.81 cm) length of No. 16 wire in a "U"-shaped coil.
L2 — 1.5-inch (3.81 cm) length of No. 14 wire. Antenna line in tuner rf cavity.

MHz. They are expensive and may be difficult to obtain, but any of the more common uhf pnp transistors will work equally well, with usually no more than a small change in base biasing being required.

The transistor body is mounted in a 3/8-inch hole drilled through the left side-wall of the antenna tuner cavity, just below the glass trimmer used to pad the antenna tuning line. This provides a convenient, ready-made shield for the preamp, and the shield lead of the transistor should be directly soldered to the tuner sidewall. For stable operation, the 50-pF base bypass capacitor is soldered as close to the transistor body (on the base lead) as is physically possible, and to the tuner wall, using extremely short leads. The collector lead is too short to reach the glass trimmer, and is lengthened with a short piece of 1/8-inch copper strap. It is possible for this rf stage to become

regenerative under certain conditions of tuning in the presence of a reactive antenna load.

The tuner is mounted on a piece of heavy double-sided pc board. The tuner sidewall associated with the rf stage is seam soldered to the pc board where the two meet at right angles. The pc board surrounding the tuner case provides a convenient surface on which to build the remaining converter circuitry.

A noticeable improvement in overall performance was obtained with the inclusion of an i-f amplifier stage. The circuit diagram is shown in Fig. 3. A 2N2222 transistor was used as a grounded-base amplifier. The input to the i-f stage is untuned, and the purpose of the 330-μH choke is to provide a dc-return path for the mixer diode current. Any i-f between Channel 2 through 6 may be obtained, dependent upon the tuning of the i-f output and the operating frequency of the local oscillator. The coil information shown is for an i-f which corresponds to Channel 5. The i-f output is designed to feed an unbalanced 75-ohm line, and vhf TV sets equipped with only a 300-ohm input will require a 4:1 balun, or conversion of the vhf input circuit to unbalanced (coaxial) input.

Fig. 3 — Schematic diagram of the i-f preamp. Resistors are 1/4- or 1/2-watt composition.
C7 — .001-μF disk ceramic.
C8 — 7 to 45-pF trimmer.
L3 — 5 turns No. 24 enameled wire on 0.5-inch (12.7 mm) OD toroid (red "E" core).
L4 — 3 turns No. 24 enam. over L3 cold end.
Q1 — 2N2222.
RFC1 — 330 μH

A SYNC GENERATOR FOR INTERLACED SCANNING

Many of the inexpensive cameras available today, and most of the units made by do-it-yourself addicts, employ random scanning in the sweep circuits. The vertical rate is synchronized to the ac line frequency, usually 60 Hz, and the horizontal scan is more or less free-running, being adjusted only to the extent that it will provide a stable picture on a normal TV receiver or monitor.

Random scanning will produce a quite usable image, one with good resolution in both vertical and horizontal video information. However, there are purists in the field who would like to emulate the "commercial" stations in picture quality, insofar as it is practical. To achieve this definition and quality of reproduction, interlaced scanning is used. That is, the scanned lines of one frame

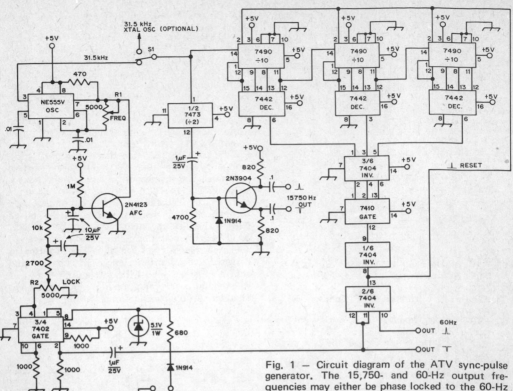

Fig. 1 — Circuit diagram of the ATV sync-pulse generator. The 15,750- and 60-Hz output frequencies may either be phase locked to the 60-Hz power-line frequency or derived from an external crystal-controlled oscillator. Selection is made with S1. Resistances are in ohms; k = 1000. Capacitances are in microfarads; capacitors with polarity indicated are electrolytic. All ICs are dual-in-line type. The 7400 series of ICs are of the TTL family, available from various manufacturers or as surplus. Motorola part numbers are prefixed by *MC* and suffixed by *P*. Texas Instruments parts have an *SN* prefix and an *N* suffix. Signetics ICs have an *N* prefix and an *A* suffix for 14-pin ICs, a *B* suffix for 16-pin ICs. For example, Motorola's MC7402P is equivalent to Texas Instruments' SN7402N or Signetics' N7402A.

(picture) fall between those of the previous frame, greatly enhancing the detail that can be reproduced in the picture.

To obtain this precision of positioning of the electron beam, in both the camera and the receiver, requires that the oscillators providing the vertical and horizontal sync information be quite stable, and preferably locked (in phase) to each other. In the sync generator described here, this stability is obtained by phase locking the master oscillator to the ac line frequency. It requires only a few more components than does a system of free-running or random synchronization. Provision is also made to lock the sync to a crystal oscillator, in case there is a need for portable TV operation.

Outline

As shown in Fig. 1, the basic frequency-control part of the circuit is an NE555 oscillator, operating at 31.5 kHz. Output from this stage is applied (through S1) to the input of a divide-by-two IC, this providing 15,750 Hz for horizontal synchronization. The 31.5-kHz signal is also applied to the input of a divider chain consisting of three 7490 ICs. This chain, with the aid of three 7442 BCD-to-decimal decoders, divides by 525, thus providing 60-Hz pulses for vertical synchronization.

Output from the three decoder ICs is used to drive an inverter and gates which simultaneously provides a reset pulse to the divider chain and a vertical-pulse output. A portion of the energy from

the vertical-pulse stage is connected to a phase comparator (a 7402 NOR gate), where it is matched against a sample of the 60-Hz ac line input. The phase-difference voltage, if any, is applied to the 31.5-kHz oscillator through the 2N4123 transistor in such a manner as to correct the frequency slightly, bringing the two 60-Hz components in phase with each other. Thus, the 31.5-kHz oscillator is phase-locked to the 60-Hz line frequency.

Construction

An etched-board layout was used to assemble the generator, but most of the other techniques common to digital circuitry will work as well. No attempt was made to produce an overly small package since the objective was to provide a working model of the sync generator. An idea of parts placement may be obtained from Fig. 2. For such low-frequency and digital circuitry, parts

Fig. 2 — The synchronizing pulse generator is on a board that measures 3 × 4-1/2 inches. The NE555 phase-locked IC oscillator is at the upper left, with the frequency-adjusting potentiometer just to the left of it. The control at the top is the afc lock range adjustment. Top row of ICs, from left to right, are the 7402, 7404, and 7410. The 7442 decoders are in the center row, while the 7473 and three 7490s are in the bottom row. The generator provides both positive-going and negative-going output pulses at frequencies of 15,750 and 60 Hz.

location is not critical and may be modified within reason to fit the needs of the builder.

It is advisable to use sockets for the ICs, especially if the builder intends to make use of the stock available at many of the suppliers of "bargain   solid-state devices. In testing this unit in the ARRL Lab, it was found that a 50-percent backup supply of ICs was needed in order to get things working right. Some of the decoder ICs would not work well with certain 7490s, although neither 7490s nor 7442s appeared defective by themselves. This type of compatability problem may be at the root of many troubles that beginners have with seemingly fool-proof circuits. (It may also account for the large number of low-priced devices on the market.)

A CHARACTER GENERATOR FOR ATV

Recent years have seen much growth in the use of artificially synthesized video. Computer terminals and airport information displays are two familiar examples. These developments, like many others in present-day electronics, have resulted from the availability of inexpensive digital ICs. Information in this section is a result of the work of Thomas M. Ellison, Jr., WA4JNA, and originally appeared in *QST* for July, 1974.

The circuit presented here uses TTL ICs to produce an 11 by 40 grid of rectangles, any of which can be made black or white, resulting in two lines of up to six characters each, as shown in the photograph. The characters are programmed simply by including or omitting diodes in the diode matrix to correspond to the video display. Sixteen standard ICs and four transistors are required. A 5-volt supply requires an additional voltage-regulator IC. Total cost is about $50, less power supply, if IC sockets are used and $40 if sockets are omitted. Construction techniques are noncritical, as the highest frequency in the circuit is 1 MHz.

Theory of Operation

The circuit is divided into five sections: a clock generator, a set of position counters, a video diode matrix, a sync generator, and a final video combiner (see Fig. 1). The clock generator is crystal controlled and operates at a frequency of 1006.08 kHz. This drives the horizontal-position counter which divides by 64, giving a horizontal-repetition frequency of 15.72 kHz. This signal then drives a set of scan counters and bar counters, whose overall effect is to divide by 262 scans per field, resulting in noninterlaced scanning, which is quite adequate, considering the size of the characters being generated. The relations of the codes in the horizontal, scan, and bar counters (denoted H,S, and B) are explained in the diagram of Fig. 2.

The horizontal and bar counters drive the video diode matrix, which generates actual video seen on a TV screen. The three horizontal driver ICs (74154s) convert a 6-bit binary code to one of 64 possible horizontal positions, of which only about 40 may be used for actual video (the other 24

The information in this section describes an artificial video generator which is capable of providing two lines of up to six characters each, enabling an amateur to generate his call, and "TV," "ATV," "CQ ATV," or a similar expression, as shown by this photograph of a monitor display. Because it is completely solid state, the device can run continuously without consuming vidicon time, and can be built into a small package. Output of the generator is standard negative-sync video.

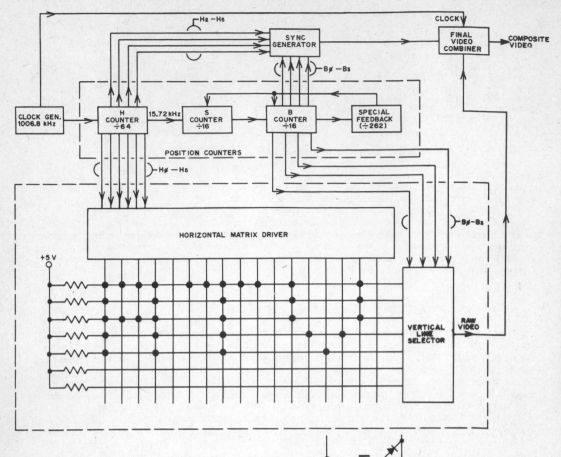

Fig. I — A functional block diagram of the character generator. The letters H, S, and B in the position counters denote Horizontal, Scan, and Bar counters respectively.

DOTS INDICATE DIODES AS SHOWN ⟶

Fig. 2 — A "state assignment" map to illustrate the method of determining diode positions in the matrix. Note that the aspect ratio of this drawing is not the same as will be seen on a tv screen. Each video field is generated by a sequence of 16,768 operations. Each operation corresponds to a location on the state map and is assigned a number between 0 and 16,767 in binary form.

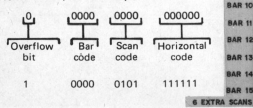

0	0000	0000	000000
Overflow bit	Bar code	Scan code	Horizontal code
1	0000	0101	111111

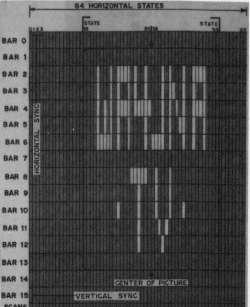

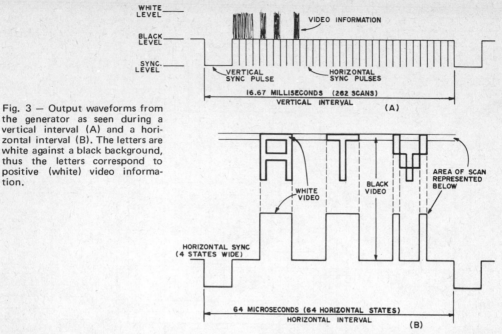

Fig. 3 — Output waveforms from the generator as seen during a vertical interval (A) and a horizontal interval (B). The letters are white against a black background, thus the letters correspond to positive (white) video information.

positions being near the edge, off-screen, or during the retrace interval). The cycling of the 6-bit code causes a low voltage to sweep across the matrix from left to right, occupying each line of the matrix for about 1 microsecond, or 1/64 of a horizontal interval. Each controllable horizontal bar of video consists of 16 scans, and each horizontal line of the video matrix represents a horizontal bar of video. The circuitry located to the right of the matrix determines which matrix line will be sampled, and the sampling is controlled by a 4-bit bar code. Raw video is found at the output of this circuit. Raw video, in television parlance, refers to picture information (video) without any synchronizing or blanking pulses included. After these pulses have been added, the result is termed composite video.

In order to make this video fall at the correct place on the screen, both horizontal- and vertical-syncing pulses must be generated, and at the proper time. The horizontal-syncing pulse is 4 clock pulses wide, or about 4 microseconds in duration. A vertical-syncing pulse is 16 horizontal intervals in duration, somewhat longer than broadcast specifications call for, but this length results in positive sync action. Since the display consists of white letters on a black background, the screen is in a blanked condition; thus no blanking pulses are required during horizontal or vertical retrace. This system also deviates from the standard broadcast waveform, but it is used in some commercially made character generators, and greatly simplifies the design without affecting performance noticeably.

Video Generation

Composite video is generated by the final video combiner (Fig. 8), the only analog circuit in the project. This converts a digital code into one of three voltage levels corresponding to white, black, and sync, to give negative-sync video at 4 volts peak-to-peak. The composite waveform is shown in Fig. 3. This signal can be used as is to drive a transmitter modulator, or can be attenuated to 1 volt peak-to-peak to drive a monitor. Various means of attenuation may be used in place of the one shown here, but the 4-V signal point should not "see" an overall load impedance of less than 200 ohms. A lower impedance will interfere with the video-to-sync ratio, and this requirement does not allow loading the 4-V output with the standard 75-ohm termination.

Construction Details

Construction is fairly straightforward. The 7400 family of TTL circuits is used throughout, available from many sources. Those used here came from a bargain distributor, and all functioned with no apparent discrepancies from published specifications. Layout is not critial, but good bypassing throughout the circuit is essential, for both low and high frequencies. It is recommended that each chip be bypassed with a .01 μF or larger capacitor, and that several electrolytics of about 20 μF also be used. A well-regulated 5-volt dc supply is also essential, or 60-Hz hum-bar drift may appear on the picture. IC regulators which provide a 5-volt output from 9- to 12-volt supplies are readily available. Fig. 6 shows a suitable power supply circuit, but any supply capable of supplying 5 volts at 400 mA will be adequate. It is recommended that the power for the final video combiner be separate from the main 5-volt supply, as shown in Fig. 6. The final combiner requires relatively little current, and its voltage may be regulated by means of a Zener diode, rather than an additional regulator IC.

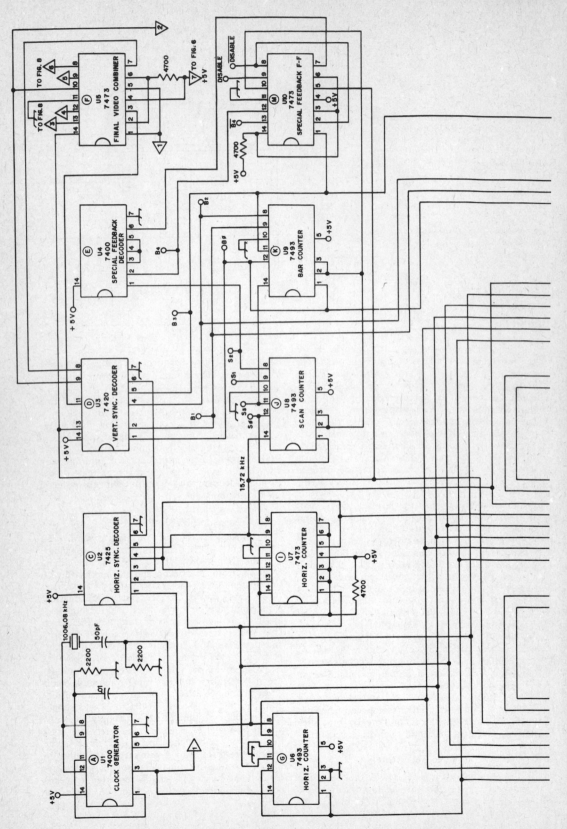

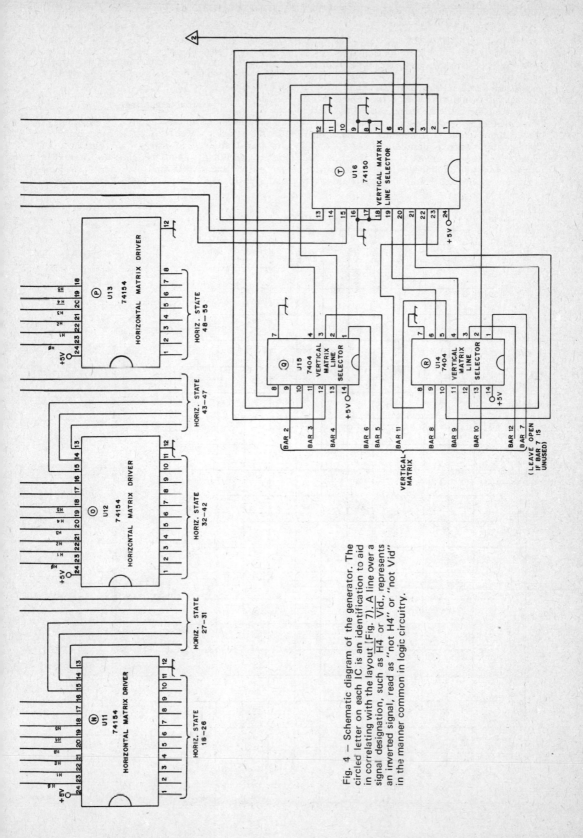

Fig. 4 — Schematic diagram of the generator. The circled letter on each IC is an identification to aid in correlating with the layout (Fig. 7). A line over a signal designation, such as H4 or Vid., represents an inverted signal, read as "not H4" or "not Vid" in the manner common in logic circuitry.

Programming

In order to program one's call, a grid of blocks, 11 vertically by 40 horizontally should be drawn, and those squares needed to form a picture marked. Generally, characters will be 5 squares high, and 4 or 5 squares wide, as needed, with the middle horizontal bar left blank. Once this is completed the call can be marked lightly on that part of the perfboard where the matrix is to be built, and a diode is soldered in at each square where white video is desired. An average of 100 diodes will be required, if this format is used. Bargain-pack silicon diodes may be used, provided each one is checked before using. Do not try to make the call appear as black on white by reversing the diode pattern. Because of the circuit design, those areas near the edge of the screen are not controllable by the diode matrix, and will appear black, which would detract from the appearance of the picture.

Troubleshooting

No alignment of the circuit is required, and it should be ready to go as soon as construction is finished. If the desired display is not obtained, the clock generator should be checked first. The output of 1006.08 kHz can be heard in a broadcast radio positioned near the circuit. If this is obtain-

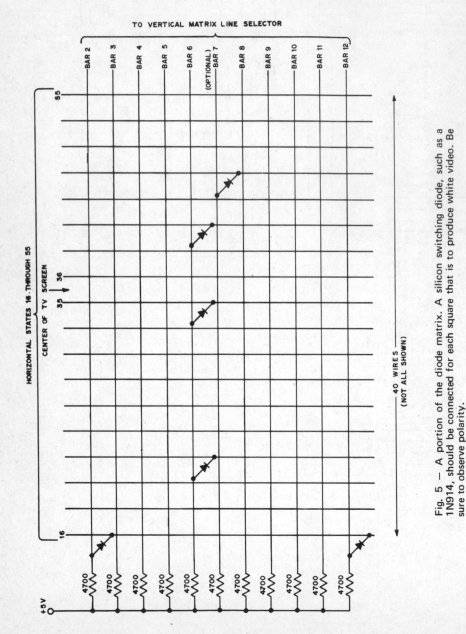

Fig. 5 — A portion of the diode matrix. A silicon switching diode, such as a 1N914, should be connected for each square that is to produce white video. Be sure to observe polarity.

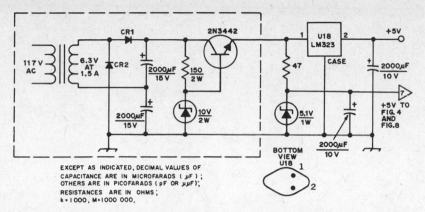

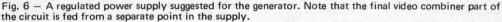

Fig. 6 — A regulated power supply suggested for the generator. Note that the final video combiner part of the circuit is fed from a separate point in the supply.

ed, check for the 15.72-kHz signal, either on a scope or aurally, for those who can hear that high (headphones can be capacitively coupled to the 15.72-kHz and lower-frequency dividers, in the absence of an oscilloscope). If results so far are good, check the 60-Hz signal. To check that the counters are dividing properly, the scope can be synchronized to the power line, and the 60-Hz signal from the character generator monitored. The drift across the screen should be slow, if the scan and bar counter combination is dividing by 262 as it should.

If all counters give the proper output, check the video and sync. Video should give a complex waveform with a repetition frequency of 60 Hz, and sync should give a combination of 15.72-kHz

and 60-Hz sync pulses. If either of these is improper, check the sync circuitry and the video matrix, respectively. The video matrix may be checked by examining the waveform on any of the horizontal matrix lines, looking for a complex waveform with a repetition frequency of 15.72 kHz. If horizontal lines exhibit good signal but there is no video, check the wiring of the 74150 and associated 7404s. If video and total sync are good, but final video output is improper, check the 7473 and the four transistors in the final video combiner.

Possible Modifications and Improvements

The prototype generator was built on perfboard, which resulted in a slightly tedious wiring

Fig. 7 — Physical layout of the generator. The circuit is assembled on perfboard, although an etched board will work as well. Q1 through Q4 may be mounted on a small board or bracket, placed conveniently near U5, although lead length is not particularly critical.

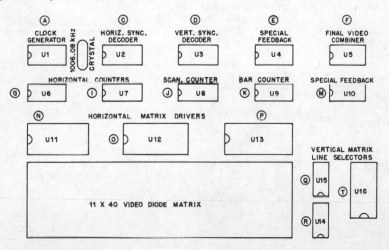

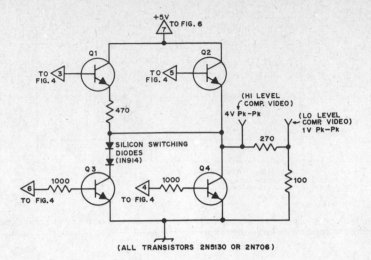

Fig. 8 — The final video combiner portion of the generator. Video-to-sync ratio may be changed by varying the number of diodes connected between Q1 and Q3.

task. If etched pc board were used, the expensive sockets could be omitted, and much needless work involved with soldering small wire to IC sockets could have been avoided. The only difficulty in using pc board is that the etching pattern would be fairly complicated and would probably require foil on both sides of the board.

A circuit modification that can be considered is to add the option of blinking to either or both of the lines of video. This can be accomplished by replacing the two 7404s in the diode-matrix circuit with three 7402 quad 2-input NOR gates, and gating either of the two groups of 5 bars each by means of a slow astable multivibrator. This option can be added for less than $2, and gives an interesting effect.

In order to give the best picture on the greatest number of television sets and monitors, the builder may want to vary the video-to-sync ratio. A high ratio will give high contrast to the picture, but it may result in raster-bending in some television sets, because the set will interpret part of the video as sync information. On the other hand, if the video-to-sync ratio is low, sync will be good on virtually any television set, but the contrast will be low. This ratio is about 2.5:1 in broadcast television, but should be slightly less in such a video source as this, as the receiver is more likely to be disturbed by "black and white only" than by the smooth waveforms caused by normal half-tone video from a camera. To control the ratio, the builder can change the number of series diodes between Q1 and Q3 in the final video combiner, as shown in the schematic diagram. The addition of diodes will result in more sync and less video. Based upon tests with several television sets and monitors, two diodes seem to be a good compromise.

An improvement upon the sync waveform would be to make it more nearly like broadcast sync, by interrupting the vertical-syncing pulse to permit inserting horizontal-syncing pulses. As designed, the vertical sync is 16 scans in duration and uninterrupted, but this has caused no apparent problems, as the horizontal sync has several scans to "get in step" before the first video information appears.

Another improvement, considered but not yet tried, would be to speed up the clock by a factor of about 10 times, and use the smaller horizontal

An early version of the character generator. Layout is similar, but not identical to that of the character generator in this section.

increment to generate 20 lines of 40 characters each. For such a project, one would probably want to use some sort of read-write memory to store the character codes, so that the message could be changed at will. The actual character generation would probably be accomplished by stock character-generator read-only memories, currently available for around $20. Although there are no final design plans as yet, it is felt that such a display generator could be built for a little over $100, not counting a keyboard from which to type in messages. However, such a device would drop its message each time the power was turned off; the present simple design has the advantage of having its message hardwired.

The design presented in this article, although simple and definitely not state-of-the-art, operates upon the same basic principles used by commercial character generators, and could, in theory, be expanded. It is a minimum-cost design which will allow the beginner in ATV to transmit a high-contrast picture of his call. While no substitute for a camera, it could substitute for a flying-spot scanner, and would be ideal for use in continuous-transmission beacons. It easily could be used for portable or mobile operation with a transistorized 440-MHz transmitter, due to its low power drain. The project has produced good pictures with both closed-circuit and rf transmission. It worked virtually the first time from an on-paper design.

Slow-Scan Television

The slow-scan TV (SSTV) aspect of amateur radio has grown considerably since experimentation began in the 1950s. Most of the work at the start of this amateur era was done by Copthorne Macdonald, WØORX. Early on-the-air tests took place in the then-available 11-meter shared band, the only hf amateur band where "facsimile" transmissions were permitted. The video information was transmitted as amplitude modulation of a 2000-Hz subcarrier tone, which in turn was fed into the speech-amplifier circuits of a conventional transmitter.

After the loss of the 11-meter band, much of the SSTV activity decreased, until special permission was granted by the FCC to conduct tests on 10 meters and eventually 20 meters. Different modes were tested, such as a-m, fm, and ssb, until suitable standards were obtained. Most of the standards in use today are based on those established during early experimentation.

Since the early days of SSTV, commercial interest has increased to the point where cameras and monitors are readily available. This chapter deals in the basics of SSTV and some practical circuits for transmitting and receiving pictures. All circuits described herein were built and proved by amateurs.

Since August 1968, narrow-band A5 and F5 emissions (SSTV) have been permitted in the Advanced and Extra Class portions of 75, 40, 20 and 15 meters, in all but the cw-only portions of 10, 6, and 2 meters, and the entire amateur range above 220 MHz. The regulations permit the transmission of independent sidebands, with picture information contained in one sideband and voice in the other. Few amateurs today are equipped for this type of operation, however. The usual practice is to intersperse picture transmissions with voice transmissions on single sideband.

A stipulation in the U.S. regulations limits the bandwidth of A5 or F5 emissions below 50 MHz; they must not exceed that of an A3 single-sideband emission, approximately 3000 Hz. This precludes the use of an a-m transmitter with the standard SSTV subcarrier tones. Most amateurs operating in the hf bands feed the video information as a varying-frequency tone into the microphone input of an ssb transmitter, and with carrier suppression, a mode that is indistinguishable at the receiver from F5 emission results. A seldom-used but quite feasible alternative is to frequency modulate an rf oscillator with video signals from the camera.

Because of the narrow bandwidth used, tape recordings of SSTV video signals can be made with an ordinary *audio* tape recorder running at 3-3/4 inches per second. Nearly every slow scanner preserves some of his on-the-air contacts on tape, and most prepare an interesting program to be transmitted. A good number of amateurs begin making two-way picture transmissions while equipped with nothing more than a receiving monitor and a tape recorder, in addition to ordinary station equipment. In lieu of a camera, they enlist the aid of a friend having the proper equipment to prepare a taped program which is sent during transmissions. Because of the slow frame rate with SSTV (one picture every 7 or 8 seconds), live pictures of anything except still subjects are impractical. Viewing a series of SSTV frames has frequently been compared to viewing a series of projected photographic slides.

Experiments are currently being made with the transmission of color pictures by SSTV. Various techniques are being used, but in essence the process involves the sending of three separate frames of the same picture, with a red, a blue, and a green filter successively placed in front of the camera lens for each of the three frames. At the receiving end of the circuit, corresponding filters are used and each frame is photographed on color film. After a tricolor exposure is made, the photograph is developed and printed in the normal manner. The use of Polaroid camera equipment with color film is popular in this work because it affords on-the-spot processing. Color reproduction by this technique can be quite good.

Transmission

There are two basic ways that pictures can be transmitted: flying-spot scanners and vidicons. The simpler system employs a flying-spot scanner which can produce quality pictures at considerably less cost than the vidicons. All the stages following the camera are the same in most instances. Fig. 1 describes in block diagram form the system components. Practical models using the flying-spot and vidicon scanner follow. The first system, used in Macdonald's early work makes use of this less expensive scanner technique. It did not use present-day SSTV standards.

FLYING-SPOT SCANNER SYSTEM

The important system characteristics are listed below:

Number of lines: 120
Aspect ratio: 1:1 (square picture shape)
Vertical repetition rate: 6 seconds
Horizontal frequency: 20 Hz.
Modulation: Amplitude-modulated 2000 Hz subcarrier. (White level, 0-20 percent of maximum amplitude; black level, 50 percent to 75 percent of maximum; sync level, maximum amplitude.)
Passband required: 1000-3000 Hz.
Synchronization: Maximum-amplitude carrier bursts coinciding with retrace periods. (Approximately 0.015 second for vertical pulse and 0.0015 second for horizontal.)

Many possible combinations of sweep times, aspect ratios, and audio carrier frequencies were studied in an attempt to find the most suitable combination. The maximum possible vertical sweep time is limited to about 6 seconds because the brightness of the P7 phosphor on the receiver cathode-ray tube face decays too rapidly to retain bright picture detail much longer than this. The 1:1 aspect ratio is a picture shape which makes efficient use of a round cathode-ray tube screen, and does not favor the viewing of horizontal objects as the usual 4:3 aspect ratio does. The bandwidth requirements of the flying-spot scanner video output are dc to approximately 1000 Hz. The 2000-Hz subcarrier frequency was chosen because it permits the upper video sideband to fall within the 300-3000 Hz passband considered representative of amateur practice, and provides at least two cycles of carrier for each cycle of modulating frequency.

Modulation polarity was selected to make low level represent white and high level represent black, for two reasons. First, the synchronizing pulses, being at the infrablack level, will blank the cathode-ray tube retrace if the receiver retrace and sync trigger time is less than the duration of the sync pulse. Second, strong noise pulses appear black rather than bright white as they would if high amplitude represented white.

Simple rectangular pulses lasting the duration of the retrace period permit synchronization of the receiver sweep oscillators. Since the vertical pulse is only about one-third the length of a scanning line, it is completed well before the next horizontal sync pulse starts. This avoids the need for serrating the vertical sync pulse to prevent upsetting the horizontal sweep, as is necessary when the pulse is over one line in length. The simplified block diagrams in Fig. 1 represent the circuit connections.

Picture Transmission

The flying-spot scanner consists of a light-tight aluminum box with a 908-A cathode-ray tube (V2) mounted at one end. The tube faces the other end where a 931-A photomultiplier tube (V1) is mounted so that light from the cathode-ray tube will strike it. A slit in the side of the box directly in front of the cathode-ray tube allows insertion of a slide, which consists of a size 120 or 620 photographic negative mounted on a 3 × 5-inch cardboard frame. The slide is held in position in the scanner by its cardboard edges in such a way that the transparent portion of the slide is in intimate contact with the glass face of the 908-A cathode-ray tube. Thus, any light which appears on the surface of the 908-A passes through the photographic negative before it strikes the photocathode of the photo-multiplier tube, some 8 inches away.

In operation, a small bright spot on the cathode-ray tube face is caused to sweep across the tube in raster fashion by the horizontal and vertical sweep voltages. The 908-A is a 3-inch electrostatically deflected tube with a P5 very-short-persistence screen, whose brightness decays to 1 percent of its original value in 35 microseconds. The spot, therefore, remains a spot at the sweep frequencies used and does not leave a "tail" of undecayed brightness behind it as it sweeps across the tube. The spot faintly illuminates the cathode of the 931-A photomultiplier, and the intensity of the illumination is inversely proportional to the photographic density of the negative at a point directly in front of the spot. The small photocathode current is amplified approximately 40,000 times by the secondary-emission action of the dynodes. The voltage across the multiplier anode load resistor is, then, a video signal whose instantaneous amplitude follows the variations in picture brightness as the negative is scanned.

Plate-coupled 6SN7 multivibrators are the heart of the sweep and sync generation circuits. The 20-Hz horizontal multivibrator (V17) is synchronized with the 60-Hz power line, not only as a convenience in keeping its frequency constant, but

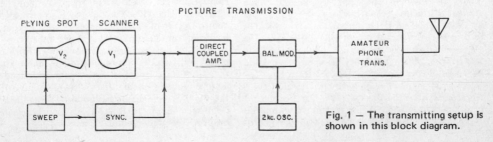

PICTURE TRANSMISSION

Fig. 1 — The transmitting setup is shown in this block diagram.

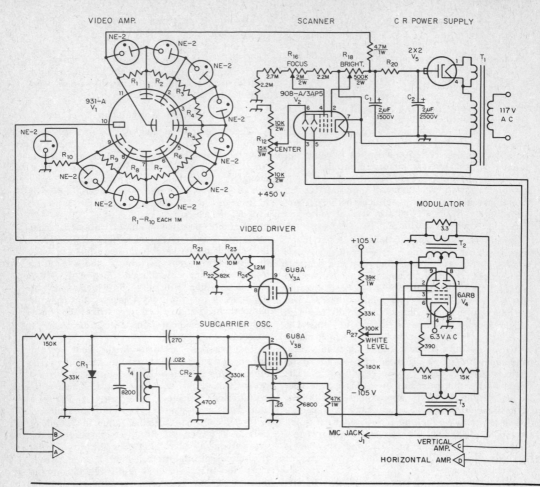

to insure that any hum in the video will result only in variations in picture shading, not diagonal hum patterns. The vertical multivibrator (V14), with a period of about 6 seconds, is triggered by the horizontal oscillator during a horizontal retrace period. This assures that the vertical retrace will always occur at the beginning of a line, which is necessary for proper positioning of the vertical sync pulse.

Sweep capacitors, charged through resistors from B+, are discharged during retrace periods by current from the multivibrators, channeled through isolating diodes (V15). The sawtoothed voltage developed across each capacitor is coupled directly to the grid of its associated sweep amplifier, half a 6SN7 (V16). One of the horizontal and one of the vertical deflection electrodes of the 908-A are internally tied to the tube's anode which is returned to a positive centering potential. The other deflection electrodes are connected to the V16 plates, putting the varying sawtoothed plate potential directly on the deflection electrodes.

The rectangular pulses developed by the multivibrators during the retrace periods are combined in a dual-diode tube (V12) to form a composite sync signal. This signal is coupled to the photo-multiplier load resistor where it is added to the video signal. The grid of a dc amplifier (V3A — triode half of a 6U8) is also connected to this point. Since the sync pulses drive the triode beyond cutoff, the output voltage consists of video during the sweep period and of sync pulses, clipped to constant amplitude, during the retrace periods. The ratio of sync level to video level is controlled by the cathode-ray tube's brightness control, increased brightness raising the video level and reducing the ratio.

Since the video signal at this point has important components from dc to 1000 Hz, it is evident that it cannot be applied directly to the ordinary transmitter modulator which attenuates frequencies below about 300 Hz. To surmount this difficulty, the video is directly coupled to the control grid of a 6AR8 sheet-beam used as a balanced modulator (V4). This tube can be thought of as a miniature beam tetrode with two plates and two deflection electrodes. In operation, the 2000-Hz output of a synchronized electron-coupled Hartley oscillator (V3B — pentode half of the 6U8) is applied in push-pull to the deflection electrodes in the 6AR8. This causes the electron beam to be deflected back and forth from one

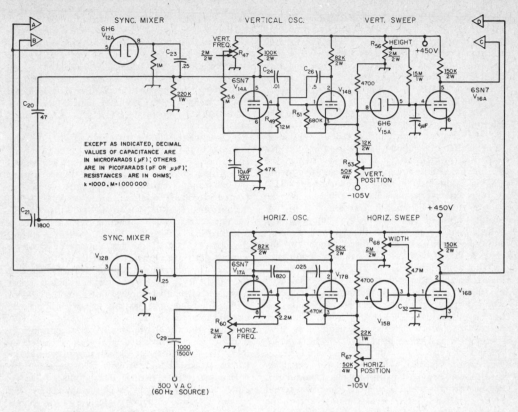

Figs. 2 and 3 — Signal-generating circuit for slow-scan picture transmission. Unless otherwise indicated, capacitances are in pF, resistances are in ohms, fixed resistors are 1/2 watt, variable resistors are composition potentiometers, 1/2 watt. Capacitors marked with polarity are electrolytic; others may be paper, ceramic, or mica as available or convenient. With the exceptions listed below, component designations are primarily for text reference.

C5 — See T4.
C10 — See text.
CR1, CR2 — 1N34 or equivalent.
J1, J2 — Microphone-type connectors.
L1 — 12 henrys, 20 mA. (Thordarson 20C52).
R20 — 1 to 2 megohms, 1 watt (see text).
R84 — Slider type resistor.

S1 — Spdt toggle or rotary.
S2 — 2-pole 5-position rotary (Centralab PA-2019).
T1 — Scope transformer, to deliver approx. 2000 volts dc; see text (Thordarson 22R40; 1800 volts at 2mA; 2.5 volts at 2.2A or 6.3 volts at 0.6 A.).
T2, T5, T6 — Audio output transformer, push-pull plates to voice coil.
T3 — Audio interstage or small modulation transformer, single plate to push-pull grids, ratio not critical (Triad M-1X).
T4 — Autotransformer or tapped inductance; see text. C5 may be varied to suit any available tapped coil to resonate at 2000 Hz.
T7 — 6.3-to-6.3-volt isolation transformer, 1.2 A (Stancor P-8191).
V5 — 2X2, or to suit filament voltage available on T1.

plate to the other at the 2000-Hz rate. The beam current is controlled by the grid voltage and is therefore proportional to the level of the video signal. The output is taken from the plates through a push-pull transformer. The balanced push-pull connection prevents the original 0- to 1000-Hz video signal from appearing in the output, the only output being the 2000-Hz carrier and its sidebands. This output may be connected directly to the transmitter modulator. It should be noted here that, although the image source is a photographic negative, signal polarities have been handled so that the transmitted image is positive — that is, a clear negative is black level, and a dense area is white.

Transmission Circuitry

The diagram of the transmission apparatus is shown in Figs. 2 and 3. The cathode-ray tube (V2) and the photomultiplier tube (V1) require a high negative voltage for operation. A scope-type transformer with an electrostatically shielded 2.5-volt filament winding for the V2 heater is used in conjunction with a half-wave rectifier to develop approximately 2000 volts dc. If the transformer (T1) suggested in the parts list is used the rectifier should be a 2X2; other transformers may require a different tube. R20 should be selected to provide 1300 to 1500 volts across filter capacitor C1, and will have a value of 1 or 2 megohms. The photomultiplier tube is quite sensitive to voltage changes so NE-2 neon lamps were wired across the voltage-dividing resistors to regulate the dynode voltage at about 65 volts per dynode stage. The 450 volts B+ can be obtained from any supply capable of delivering approximately 200 mA. The +105 and −105-volt supplies were regulated by 0C3/VR105 regulator tubes.

The grid resistor (R24) of V3A is also the photomultiplier anode load resistor; thus the grid of V3A is at some negative potential, the actual value depending upon the setting of the V2 brightness control (R18) and the density of the picture being scanned. The large negative pulses coming from the sync-combiner diode (V12) during retrace periods are attenuated by the R21-through-R24 network but are still of sufficient amplitude to drive V3A beyond cutoff. The voltage-dividing network in the V3A plate circuit and V4 grid circuit permits direct coupling of the video and sync signals to the balanced modulator.

The white-level control (R27) should be adjusted so that the tone output of the balanced modulator is close to zero during the scanning of white portions of the picture. A scope connected to the output jack (J1) during transmission will permit this adjustment to be made, as well as setting the maximum black level at about 50-75 percent of sync level with R18. Fig. 4 illustrates the correct output wave form. No balancing control was provided in the balanced modulator, because the unwanted 0-1000 Hz video was found to be 20 dB below sync level when checked on the scope with the 2000-Hz carrier cut off.

The kHz oscillator (V3B) is an experimental circuit which permits the horizontal sync pulse to control the oscillations. It was felt that maintaining a constant time relationship between the sync pulses and individual cycles of tone might permit slightly more accurate synchronization than would be possible with a random relationship between the two. The results were inclusive, however, with any advantage being a slight one. A standard oscillator circuit would probably serve just as well and would

have a better output wave form. In the circuit used, T4 is a high- to low-impedance headphone autotransformer. The CR2-R36 combination improves the output wave form by limiting the negative grid-voltage swings so the tube is not driven to cutoff. This "gimmick" can also be applied to other types of oscillators. The oscillator output transformer (T3) can be a small modulation transformer or single plate to push-pull grid interstage unit.

The horizontal multivibrator (V17) is synchronized at a submultiple of the power line frequency by a voltage fed from the power transformer (external) through C29. R60 controls the horizontal frequency and permits frequencies from 15 to 60 Hz to be selected. The picture width is controlled by R68, which regulated the charging current of the sweep capacitor, C32. On retrace, V17B is cut off and a heavy discharge current through V15B pulls the grid voltage of V16B to some negative value which depends on the setting of R67. The charging rate during sweep is such that the grid never goes positive. A highly linear sawtooth wave, therefore, appears on the grid of V16B; the tube amplifies this voltage, and it is fed directly to pin 5 of V2.

The vertical multivibrator has a sweep range of 1 Hz to 1 cycle every 7 seconds, controlled by R47. The oscillator receives a sync pulse from the horizontal oscillator through C20 during every horizontal retrace period. These pulses have no effect until the vertical oscillator approaches the triggering point, at which time one of the pulses triggers the oscillator. The rest of the vertical sweep circuit is similar to the horizontal, with R56 controlling flying spot scanner raster height and R53 the vertical position. R12 is used to center the raster on V2 and R16 focuses the flying spot.

The rectangular pulses developed during the multivibrator retrace periods are coupled to the cathodes of V12, where they are combined to provide the video sync pulses fed to R21. The sync pulse for the 2-kHz oscillator is coupled from V17A through C21.

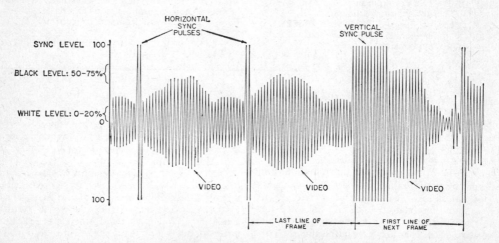

Fig. 4 — Wave form of modulated 2000-Hz tone. There are approximately 100 cycles of 2000-Hz carrier per line.

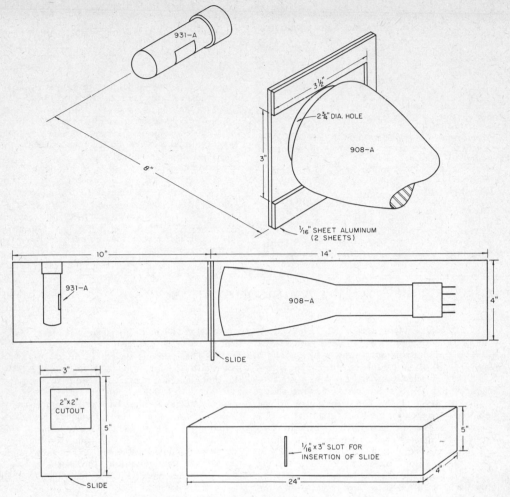

Fig. 5 — Some mechanical details of the flying-spot scanner.

Many substitutions can be made in the picture transmission circuits. While there is no inexpensive substitute for the 931-A, any cathode-ray tube with a P5 phosphor is suitable for V2. The 5CP5 and 5JP5 are sometimes available on the surplus market. Miniature equivalents of the octal-base tubes can be used, of course. Generally speaking, the R and C values in the sweep and sync circuits are noncritical; however, the time constants in the grid circuits of the multivibrators (C24-R51, C26-R49, etc.) should be adjusted for proper timing. Several balanced modulators were tried, but most failed to remain in balance over the wide range of control-grid voltage swing. The 6AR8 circuit was the most satisfactory in this respect, and it also provides plenty of output. If the output voltage from J1 overdrives the first stage in the transmitter modulator, a pot or fixed pad may be installed to cut the gain.

Mechanical Details

The flying-spot scanner has the 6U8, 6AR8, and voltage-regulating neon lamps mounted on the back. The important constructional points are illustrated in Fig. 5 and in the photographs of the scanner. While this scanner has a framework of machined aluminum and sides of 1/16-inch thick aluminum sheet, equivalent results can be obtained with a much less elaborate arrangement. Actually, the first tests of the system were conducted with the scanner tube and photomultiplier in a cardboard box made light tight with masking tape, and with a negative taped to the face of the 908-A.

The aluminum scanner box was made as light tight as possible. A strip of felt covers the slot where the slide is inserted in order to reduce the amount of light entering here, and the interior is painted black to reduce reflection. Since it is desirable to have the negative directly against the face of the scanner tube during operation, the tube was mounted on a movable carriage, operated by a cam arrangement. This permits the 908-A to be moved back to allow a slide to be inserted, and to be moved forward under spring tension directly against the slide for scanning. This relatively elaborate arrangement has proved unnecessary in

TABLE 3-I — Amateur Slow-Scan Standards

	60-Hz Areas	50-Hz Areas
Sweep Rates:		
Horizontal	15 Hz	16 2/3 Hz
	(60 Hz/4)	(50 Hz/3)
Vertical	8 sec.	7.2 sec.
No. of Scanning Lines	120	120
Aspect Ratio	1:1	1:1
Direction of Scan:		
Horizontal	Left to Right	Left to Right
Vertical	Top to Bottom	Top to Bottom
Sync Pulse Duration:		
Horizontal	5 millisec.	5 millisec.
Vertical	30 millisec.	30 millisec.
Subcarrier Freq.:		
Sync	1200 Hz	1200 Hz
Black	1500 Hz	1500 Hz
White	2300 Hz	2300 Hz
Req. Trans.		
Bandwidth	1.0 to 2.5 kHz	1.0 to 2.5 kHz

practice. Satisfactory results are obtained by rigidly mounting the tube so that there is just enough space to insert the slide between the face of the tube and the aluminum plate which backs up the slide.

Since it is impossible, because of the thickness of the glass covering the face of the tube, to lay the negative directly against the phosphor in the 908-A, some parallax is present which could reduce the scanner resolution if precautions are not taken to minimize the effect. To help the situation, the 931-A was mounted about 8 inches from the face of the scanner tube, and the glass envelope of the 931-A was painted black, except for a 1/2 × 1/2-inch square section in front of the cathode which was left clear. The angle formed by imaginary lines drawn from the extremes of the exposed cathode area to the spot of light on the scanner is kept small in this way, thereby keeping down the parallax.

A VIDICON SYSTEM

The second system uses a WL-7290 vidicon made by Westinghouse. This tube is not readily available and suitable substitutes will work with slight modification to the circuit (6326, 7038, 7735, etc.). An electro-mechanical shutter synchronized with the vertical retrace exposes the photoconductive layer of the slow-scan vidicon to the light and dark areas of the scene for a fraction of a second at the beginning of each frame scan. This exposure establishes charge patterns in the photoconductor that are scanned off by the electron beam. In addition to giving rise to a varying electrical output signal, the beam also erases the previous scene's charge patterns and readies the tube for another exposure. Conventional vidicons act in a similar manner when scanned at 30 frames per second, but are unsatisfactory when the scan rates are slowed down because the charge patterns leak away too rapidly, even with the tube in the dark.

Those readers who have followed amateur slow-scan activities know that the system presently in use is an attempt to reach an optimum compromise between three interrelated factors; bandwidth, transmission time per picture, and picture detail. The present system requires an audio bandwidth extending between 1 and 2.5 kHz, transmits one picture every 8 seconds, and presents a picture with 120-line resolution in horizontal and vertical directions. Figs. 1A and 1B are one-frame time exposures of a monitor display of live images picked up by the slow-scan vidicon camera. The sharpness of the images is due to the high "aperture response" of the vidicon and cathode-ray tube at 120 lines resolution. In other words, the fact that vidicon and CRT are capable of a "limiting" resolution much higher than 120 lines insures that the system resolution is determined only by bandwidth and line structure. Since bandwidth and line structure are sharp-cutoff effects, the images have a crispness of detail that even some old hands in the TV field say they never expected to see with a 120-line system.

Building a television camera is not a task for the beginner. Prior construction of a slow-scan monitor and flying-spot scanner represent a practical mini-

Fig. 1 — Live images picked up by the slow-scan vidicon camera.

(A)

(B)

mum of experience. Thorough understanding of what *should* be going on, and sufficient test equipment to see what *is* going on, are absolute musts before the expensive vidicon is ever plugged into its socket. A dc-coupled scope, with either a calibrated preamp and time-base, or an uncalibrated dc-coupled scope with some external means to calibrate it, is required. A frequency-calibrated audio oscillator is almost a necessity, although there are ways to get by without it if one cannot be begged or borrowed.

Cameras using this basic circuit but completely original mechanical planning, layout, and construction techniques were built by Bob Mangold, K3BWW; Robert Gervenack, W7FEN; and Don Miller, W9NTP.

CIRCUIT DESCRIPTION

Sweep Generation

A block diagram is given in Fig. 2 and the complete circuit in Fig. 3. The horizontal multivibrator, V3 generates a 15-Hz sawtooth waveform and retrace pulse that is used for blanking. During the greater part of a cycle V3B is cut off and C2 charges toward B+ through R13. The 300-volt ac applied to the string of NE-2s causes the bulbs alternately to fire and extinguish at a 60-Hz rate. The firing of the bulbs on positive alternations of the 60-Hz sine wave produces sharp positive spikes that are coupled to pin 7 of V3B through C3. When one of these spikes raises the grid voltage above cutoff, V3B conducts (discharging C2) and the multivibrator switches to the other state. The duration of this retrace state is determined by R14

and C4. R11 adjusts the oscillator period to the proper subharmonic of 60-Hz. A sawtooth wave form appears at the cathode of cathode-follower V4A. The horizontal-centering pot, R12, is used to set the voltage at the red yoke lead to the average dc level of the sawtooth applied to the black lead. This centers the sweep by providing that the yoke current swings positively and negatively about an average value of zero.

The vertical sweep circuit is similar to the horizontal. Synchronization of the vertical retrace with a horizontal retrace is accomplished by feeding the video synchronization signal to the vertical multivibrator at pin 2 of V1B. A height control, R9, shunts a portion of the drive current around the yoke to permit equalizing horizontal and vertical size.

Vidicon Beam Control

The vidicon output current is very low (about 0.003 μA) and the impedance of the target circuit is high (1 megohm). Such a combination invites hum problems. To minimize hum effects, the vidicon beam current is chopped at a 10-kHz rate, and the vidicon output is amplified in a *bandpass* amplifier that has very poor low-frequency response. V11 is a free-running multivibrator with a frequency of about 10 kHz. The 10-kHz square-wave output is coupled to the vidicon grid No. 1 clamp circuit (C4, R15 and CR1). The beam control, R7, adjusts the magnitude of positive-going 10-kHz signal that is added to the −105-volt bias. It is adjusted for adequate beam current to charge down the target, but not so much that resolution suffers.

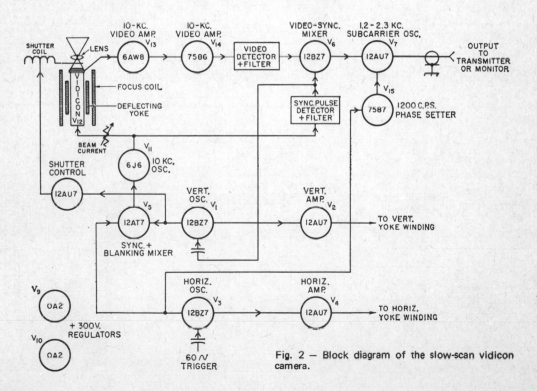

Fig. 2 — Block diagram of the slow-scan vidicon camera.

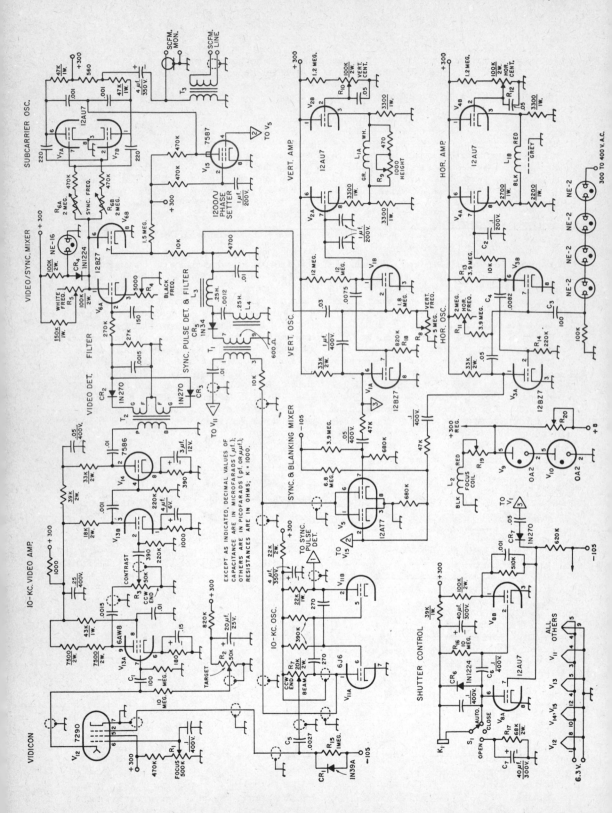

Fig. 3 – Circuit diagram of the vidicon slow-scan camera. Component designations not listed below are for text reference. Unless otherwise specified, capacitors are 400- or 500-volt dc ceramic, paper, or mica (type not critical), except those with polarity indicated, which are electrolytic. All resistors are 1/2-watt composition unless otherwise specified.

K1 – Potter & Brumfield type PW5LS, modified as shown in Part II.

L1A – 100-mH. vert. winding of deflection yoke.
L1B – 500-mH horiz. winding of deflection yoke.
L2 – 385-ohm focus coil. (Above coils available from Cleveland Electronics, Inc., 1974 East 61st St., Cleveland 3, Ohio, Yoke and Focus Coil Kit VK-300.)

R1, R2, R4, R8, R9, R11 – Composition control, linear taper.
R3 – Composition control, audio taper.
R5, R7, R10, R12 – 2-watt control, linear taper.
R6 – Dual 2-megohm control, linear taper.

R19 – Voltage-dropping resistor to give focus-coil current of 20.5 mA. Wattage rating of resistor should be chosen to be several times the actual power dissipated (for maximum focus-current stability).

R20 – Adjustable resistor of adequate wattage rating, set to give current of about 25 mA, through V9 and V10, with camera operating properly.

S1 – Rotary, 1 pole, 3 positions; or spdt toggle with neutral center, such as Arrow-Hart & Hegeman 82022-HD.

T1 – Audio transformer, 22K to 600 ohms; type TF1A19 (available from Arrow Electronics, Inc., 900 Broad Hollow Rd., Farmingdale, N.Y.).

T2 – Audio, 15K single plate to 80K p.p. grids (UTC type A-19. Less expensive transformers such as the Stancor A-53-C should be satisfactory).

T3 – 1:1 audio transformer (Knight 64G174 or equivalent). Vidicon socket is Cinch-Jones type 7VT (Allied Radio catalog No. 41H349).

During retrace, positive-going pulses from the sweep oscillators drive the two halves of V5 into conduction. The conducting V5 section loads down the 10-kHz multivibrator, dropping its output sharply. The reduced output keeps the vidicon beam cut off for the duration of the pulse, thus blanking the sweep retrace. The output of V11 is coupled through T1 to a rectifier-filter circuit where dc-referenced synchronization pulses are formed at the grid of V6B.

Video Amplification

The vidicon delivers its output current to a relatively high impedance load for best signal-to-noise ratio. The video amplifier is similar to an audio preamp except for coupling and cathode bypass capacitors, which are kept small to keep 60-Hz amplification low. Since the vidicon beam current is chopped at a 10-kHz rate the output current contains two spectra: the desired 10-kHz carrier with video sidebands that are amplified in the video amplifier, and an undesired dc-to-approximately-1-kHz video signal that is attenuated by the small coupling capacitors. After amplification by V13 and V14, this modulated 10-kHz signal is rectified by CR2 and CR3, filtered to remove 20-kHz ripple, and fed to the video-sync mixer, V6A. The subcarrier-fm multivibrator, V7, oscillates at a frequency determined by the voltage at the plates of V6A and V6B. The sync-frequency pot, R6, is adjusted to produce a 1200-Hz output when V6B conducts heavily during sync pulses. The black-frequency and white-frequency controls, R4 and R5, are set to limit the black excursion to 1500 Hz and the white excursion to 2300 Hz maximum. Proper video balance between black, white, and intermediate shades of grey is determined by the light level, lens "*f*" opening and contrast-control setting.

Without V15 the phase of the 1200-Hz synchronizing waveform would be random with respect to the horizontal sweep. This would cause "jitter" in the synchronization of a directly triggered monitor horizontal-sweep circuit because of the small number of subcarrier cycles per cycle of modulating (video) signal. V15 sets the phase of the subcarrier oscillator to 0 or 180 degrees at the start of each horizontal retrace, thus eliminating the jitter problem. The 600 ohm/600 ohm transformer, T3, is necessary only if one wishes to feed a balanced audio line such as a telephone circuit.

Shutter Control

V8 is a monostable multivibrator triggered by the vertical retrace pulse. Conduction of V8A (hence opening of the shutter) is initiated by a positive-going retrace pulse at pin 8 of V8A. The duration of the "shutter open" period is determined by the R16-C6 time constant. The values shown produce an "open" period of about 1/2 second. This time may be reduced by reducing the resistance of R16.

A center-off toggle switch was used for S1. When S1 is thrown to the "open" position, C7 provides the high surge current necessary to open the shutter, while the steady drain through R17 is sufficient to keep it open.

Power Supply

Focus coil current of approximately 20.5 mA is required if the vidicon is to focus with the focus control, R1, set at +75 volts (midrange). Focus-coil (L2) resistance is about 385 ohms; thus any well-filtered (and preferably regulated) supply putting out over 8 volts and having the required current capability could be used with a suitable series dropping resistor. The black focus coil lead should be connected to the negative terminal of the supply. The series dropping resistor should be wire-wound and of higher than necessary wattage rating to minimize resistance change (and thus focus change) with warmup.

The −105-volt supply should be regulated if line voltage changes are expected.

V9 and V10 provide adequate regulation from an unregulated +400-volt dc supply. They may, of course, be eliminated if an electronically regulated +300 volt supply is available.

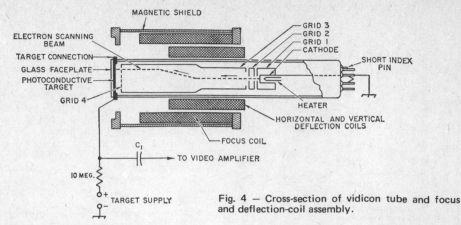

Fig. 4 — Cross-section of vidicon tube and focus and deflection-coil assembly.

Part Substitution

Having read this far, you have possibly already given some thought to cutting costs. Unfortunately, the major components do not have ready substitutes. The 7290, and other related tubes also manufactured by Westinghouse, are the only vidicons that will perform as described with low dark current at this scan rate, and low lag when shuttered. Most vidicons will not perform at all. The deflection yoke is higher than normal impedance (many turns of fine wire) and building a good one requires know-how and facilties not possessed by many.

Conventional miniature tubes can be substituted for the nuvistors. A 6CL6 with suppressor grounded can be used instead of the 7587, if space permits. One half of a 6BQ7 should be a satisfactory substitute for the 7586.

MECHANICAL DESIGN

Four versions of the camera are described in the following text. Several approaches are shown to solve the various constructional problems.

The WA3BTK Camera

The first camera built was housed in the case of an obsolete Dage video switcher unit. The self-contained +300 volt power supply was retained, as were the tube sockets and some electrolytic capacitors; the rest of the circuitry was removed. The vidicon-yoke/focus-coil assembly was mounted at the bottom front of the unit since this was the coolest location. It is vital that no heat-producing components be placed under the focus-coil assembly and that hot air does not circulate around the assembly, since the vidicon will not operate at its best above about 100°F and will be permanently damaged if the temperature rises above 113°F.

The preamp input tube, V13, is mounted close to the front end of the focus coil. An inch or two of shielded hookup wire connects the target side of C1 with the focus-coil vidicon target contact. The first-stage lead dress was watched to minimize pickup from the 10-kHz multivibrator located at

the rear of the camera; even so, without the sides fastened up, pickup is excessive. In this regard, it is also essential to shield the vidicon grid No. 1 lead right up to the vidicon socket; the only path for the 10-kHz chopping wave form to pass from V11 to V12 should be through the vidicon itself.

The shutter mechanism is shown in Figs 4 and 5. The relay mechanism can be removed from its can by heating the solder seal around the base *rapidly* with a hot, high-wattage soldering iron or fine torch flame, and pulling the can and base apart with two pairs of pliers. The operation should be performed quickly to avoid overheating the relay mechanism. Once the cover is off, the electrical contacts and the 7-pin base should be removed. The armature should be bent up slightly to give greater angular rotation when the relay is actuated. A piece of 18-gauge copperweld wire soldered to the armature serves to increase the lever arm considerably. (A light-weight plastic rod attached with epoxy could be substituted for the wire.) A piece of 3-mil thick shim brass soldered to the other end of the wire acts as the shutter diaphragm. Short pieces of wire soldered to the brass

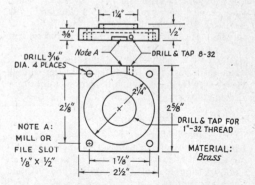
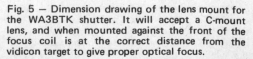

Fig. 5 — Dimension drawing of the lens mount for the WA3BTK shutter. It will accept a C-mount lens, and when mounted against the front of the focus coil is at the correct distance from the vidicon target to give proper optical focus.

diaphragm serve as stops and also act to stiffen the diaphragm. The 1-inch/32-thread hole in the lens mount accommodates any "C-mount" 16-mm movie camera lens. Since the weight of the focus coil makes it undesirable to mount the coil by one plastic end plate alone, four pieces of threaded 8-32 brass rod with nuts on both sides of the back plate were used to provide a sturdy mounting arrangement.

The relay coil was mounted next to T2. The magnetic field from the relay coil initially induced voltage transients in the secondary of T2 and also displaced the vidicon scanning beam slightly when energized. Two layers of 5-mil mumetal sheet wrapped around the coil solve the problems. Since mumetal sheet is not normal ham shack stock, a better solution would be to move the relay coil nearer the top of the camera housing and to locate T2 and associated components several inches from the relay coil.

The power transformer in this camera was an additional source of trouble; 60-Hz magnetic fields produced a slight waviness of horizontal lines in the transmitted picture. More disturbing, however, was the heat generated by the transformer and other power supply components. Some parts in the camera were too hot to touch after a few hours operation, and some drifting of electrical adjustments was the natural result.

K3BWW's Camera

Bob Mangold's camera is shown in Fig 6. Bob's answer to the heat problem was to put the circuitry into two units; the power supply in one, and the remainder of the circuitry in the other. A Bud WA-1540 Portacab was used to house the power supply.

The camera case was made of bent and riveted 1/16-inch aluminum. This very professional-looking cabinet shows the type of construction possible if one has access to the proper tools for sheet metal work.

W7FEN's Camera

Gervie's camera departs from the original design in several respects. His camera unit contains only the video amplifier and detector in addition to the vidicon and associated components. This results in a very cool-running head in spite of the fact that the Bud CU-1099 utility-box cabinet has no ventilating louvers or holes. His shutter mechanism (Figs. 7 and 8) is also different. He uses a standard plate-circuit relay mounted at the rear of the cabinet in conjunction with a very long lever-arm arrangement to get the necessary shutter blade travel.

The rest of the circuitry is mounted on a Bud CA-1228 amplifier foundation. Video detector output and vidicon grid No. 1 connections between the units are made with 52-ohm coax, using two different types of connectors to prevent accidental interchanging. The rest of the leads are fed through a cable terminated with 11-pin Amphenol connectors.

Fig. 6 — The K3BWW camera, shown open for access to components. The power supply is built as a separate unit to isolate the camera from the heat the supply generates.

Fig. 7 — The shutter used by W7FEN is similar to WA3BTK's, but is operated by a long throw and pivot arrangement that greatly multiplies the mechanical travel of the relay armature.

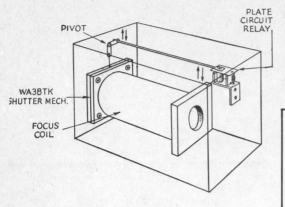

W9NTP's Camera

Don Miller's camera is shown in Fig. 9. By hinging two Premier 17 × 10-inch chassis and mounting the parts on Vectorbord, Don comes up with a very neat looking yet simple-to-build package. Note the ventilating holes in top and bottom as well as the luggage-type clasp to hold the two chassis bases together.

Lens Selection

If the lens mount is threaded with a 1 inch/32 thread it will accept any standard C-mount 16-mm movie camera lens. For shuttered operation with normal room illumination the lens should have a

maximum opening of $f/1.9$ or, even better, $f/1.4$. The recent trend to automatic iris control on movie cameras had led to much trading-in of older 16-mm cameras. Used lenses and even complete cameras can often be found for less than $25. Any focal-length $f/1.9$ lens can be used for any given field of view if one is free to select his lens-to-subject distance. With the raster size used in the vidicon in this camera (5/16 × 5/16 inch) the relationships in Table 3-II apply. For example, if one wanted the image of a 2-foot-wide object to fill the screen he would set his lens-to-subject distance at 6 feet if using a 25-mm lens.

TABLE 3-II	
Lens Focal Length	Approximate Field of View
15 mm (wide angle)	1/2 of lens-to-subject distance
25 mm (normal)	1/3 of lens-to-subject distance
50 mm (telephoto)	1/6 of lens-to-subject distance

SETUP AND OPERATING PROCEDURES

Because of the slow scanning rates, a slow-scan TV camera requires much more time and patience to adjust initially than does a conventional closed-circuit TV camera. With normal TV, 30 complete pictures come along every second and one can see the results of an adjustment immediately. Not so with slow-scan TV; one must wait at least 8 seconds to see the results of many adjustments. Patience and a systematic setup procedure are essential for proper operation of the equipment and the sanity of the operator. Fortunately, if good-quality components have been used and attention has been paid to adequate ventilation, the adjustments need not be made frequently.

Setup and Alignment

The vidicon can be permanently damaged by the application of improper voltages, or by lack of scan if the beam current is high. To prevent this the step by step setup procedure outlined below should be followed *before the vidicon is installed*.

1. Check all points where waveforms are given, with a calibrated dc-coupled scope. The given sawtooth amplitudes across the yoke windings (Figs. 10A and B) will produce a square raster approximately 5/16 × 5/16 inch. If the positive excursion equals the negative excursion (as shown) the raster will be centered on the vidicon, if not, readjust the centering controls.

If the period in waveform A is not 66.7 ms. adjust R11 until the horizontal multivibrator locks in at 15 Hz. If the vertical period is not 8 seconds, adjust R8.

The pulses in waveform C should be 5 ms. wide at a 15-Hz repetition rate and 30 ms. wide at 1/8-Hz repetition rate. The horizontal pulse width can be adjusted by changing R14 and the vertical rate pulse by changing R18.

The beam control, R7, should be set at full counter-clockwise position for waveform D, and

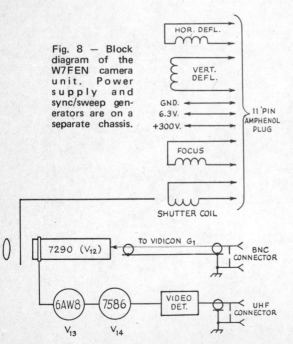

Fig. 8 — Block diagram of the W7FEN camera unit. Power supply and sync/sweep generators are on a separate chassis.

Fig. 9 — The camera built by W9NTP uses two chassis hinged together to make the complete enclosure. This arrangement is easy to build and makes all parts readily accessible.

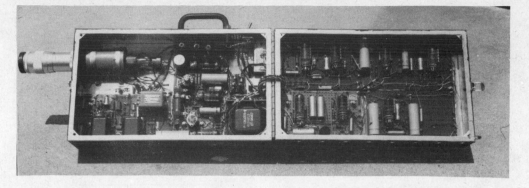

full clockwise for waveform E. The high frequency square wave between blanking intervals should be approximately 10 kHz, though this is not at all critical.

Waveforms F, G, H, and I are given to aid trouble-shooting.

2. The subcarrier frequencies are set next:

A. Set up a scope and audio oscillator or other means to check the audio frequency at the "scfm monitor" jack.

B. Ground pin 7 of V6B. Adjust R6 for an output frequency of 1200 Hz. Unground pin 7.

C. Pull V6 out of its socket. Adjust R5 for an output frequency of 2300 Hz. Replace V6.

D. Short the primary of T2. Adjust R4 for an output frequency of 1500 Hz. Unshort the primary of T2.

3. Check the current in the red focus coil (L2) lead. Adjust R19 until the current is 20.5 mA.

4. Check voltages at the vidicon socket with a vacuum-tube voltmeter.

Between pins 1 and 8 — 6.3 volts ac
Pin 7 to ground — 0 volts
Pin 5 to ground — +300 volts dc

Pin 6 to ground — Adjust R1 for a reading of +75 volts.

Center arm of R2 to ground — Adjust R2 for a reading of +10 volts.

5. Make a bar pattern test chart by applying strips of 3/4-inch-wide black electrical tape to white cardboard. Make the white spaces between strips of tape equal to the tape width. Determine the proper vidicon-to-lens distance by setting the lens focus adjustment at the shortest distance marked on the lens barrel (2' 6" for example). Position the bar pattern that same distance in front of the lens. With a piece of white paper held at the rear of the lens to pick up the test pattern image, check lens-to-paper distance for best focus on the paper. Put the lens to face-plate in its normal mount and position the vidicon in the yoke-focus coil assembly so that lens to face-plate distance is 0.1 inch less than the optimum lens to paper distance determined above. With the test pattern the same distance away from the lens, optical focus will not be approximately correct. Orient the pattern so that the bars are vertical.

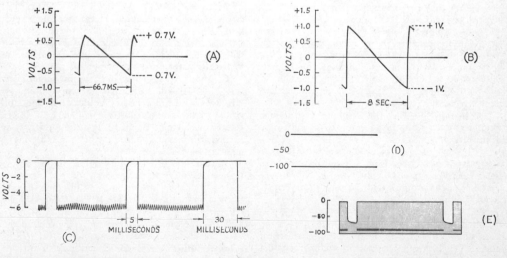

Fig. 10

Fig. 10

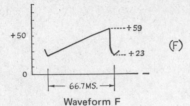

Waveform F
Measured between pin 8 of V4 and chassis.

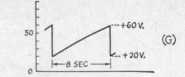

Waveform G
Measured between pin 8 of V2 and chassis.

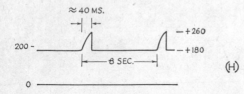

Waveform H
Measured between pin 6 of V1A and chassis.

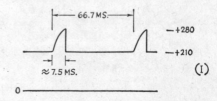

Waveform I
Measured between pin 1 of V3A and chassis.

6. With vidicon socket still disconnected check the operation of the video amplifier by monitoring pin 2 of V6A with a dc-coupled scope. Turn R3 fully clockwise. The voltage should be very close to zero. Wrap a piece of insulated hookup wire around the lead going to pin 1 of V11. Bring this lead close to the vidicon target or target lead. The voltage at pin 2 of V6A should go several volts negative if the amplifier-detector circuit is working properly. Remove the wire.

7. Shut off the power to the camera. Connect the vidicon socket to the vidicon, being careful not to disturb the lens-to-faceplate distance set previously. Set R7 (beam control) fully counterclockwise. Set R6 (contrast control) fully clockwise. With normal room illumination on the test pattern, set the lens at $f/1.9$. Monitor pin 2 of V6A with a dc-coupled scope. Turn on the camera power. Allow a 5-minute warmup period. Set S1 in the "auto" position; the shutter should open every 8 seconds for about 0.5 second period.

8. Cap the lens. The voltage at pin 2 of V6A should be near zero. Advance R7 clockwise just beyond the point at which the V6A pin 2 voltage goes sharply negative. After a minute or so the voltage should return to zero; if not, increase R7 a little more. (If the output still does not drop to zero, stray light is probably reaching the vidicon faceplate. Check for light leaks in the camera housing.)

9. Uncap the lens. Some voltage variations should now be seen on the scope as the vidicon is scanned.

10. View the picture on a monitor. A course bar pattern should be visible if monitor contrast is set properly. Rotate the yoke until the bars appear vertical on the monitor and the top of the scene is at the top of the display.

11. Electrical and optical focus should be touched up to give the sharpest picture. Move the vidicon *a little at a time* to optimize electrical focus. This is a rather tedious procedure since the effects of an optical focus change do not show up

until 8 seconds later. It cannot be rushed. However, if the adjustment is made by moving the vidicon, and if lens-to-test-pattern distance is the same as the lens focus setting, the lens focus distance calibration will be correct for all settings once the focus procedure has been completed.

12. With a monitor contrast and brightness controls set so that 1500 Hz gives a just-barely black picture and 2300 Hz gives the desired "white" brightness, view some scene at proper focus distance. Adjust "f" stop and contrast control, R3, for the most pleasing picture.

Camera Operation

A few rules of thumb are:

A. If the picture "white" areas are too dim, open the lens, turn R3 farther clockwise, or increase the light on the scene.

If dark areas in the picture are too bright, do the opposite.

B. Operating with low video gain (R3 near the ccw end) and high light level can degrade resolution. For this reason, and also to permit lens settings giving maximum depth of field, operate with the R3 near the clockwise end, and adjust the "f" stop for the most pleasing picture.

C. Vidicon sensitivity depends on target voltage. The +10 volts suggested in step 4 should be satisfactory in most cases. Should white spots be visible in the monitor display, reducing the target voltage may eliminate them. If more sensitivity is needed, the target voltage may be increased, but in no event beyond +15 volts.

D. Do not operate with R7 more clockwise than is necessary to produce a good picture, since the additional beam current may produce shading effects, and vidicon damage if the sweeps should fail.

E. If the vidicon is removed, replace it in the same position so that the same raster area is scanned; otherwise, shading may appear due to "raster burn" effects.

F. If the shutter is kept in the "open" position, much less light will be required; of course, one cannot view moving objects in this mode.

For vidicons other than the 7290 type, the following modifications should be made:

The phase setter (V5) and shutter stages (V8) and their associated circuitry are omitted. Pins 3 and 6 of the vidicon socket should be tied together. This last step allows proper electrical focus to be achieved if a 6326 vidicon is used, and in no way affects the operation with other pickup tubes. Slow-scan focus and deflection coils from ATV Research (see *QST* ads) were used in place of the coils specified, at a considerable saving in cost. The only other deviation consisted of a revised procedure for adjusting the black frequency. Rather than shorting out the primary of T2 as specified, the following procedure was used:

1) Cap the lens.

2) Adjust the black frequency control (R4) to the low end of its frequency range.

3) Increase the contrast (R3) until the subcarrier output is 1500 Hz. *Leave* the contrast control at this setting.

4) Recheck the sync and white frequencies as specified in the article — readjust if required.

RECEPTION OF SSTV

RECEPTION OF SSTV WITH CONVENTIONAL TV SETS

An individual just becoming interested in SSTV might ask the question of himself, "Why not convert a regular TV set for reception of SSTV?" With many "retired" TV sets available at low cost, this approach would at first seem to offer an advantage in economy. Unfortuantely there is no economical way to make the conversion, even if the acquisition cost of the TV set is low. Because the picture of an SSTV transmission takes 8 seconds to transmit from direct viewing, the picture tube of the monitor must be one which will glow for longer than 8 seconds after the information has been "written" on the screen. With a conventional TV picture tube, the image will fade away within a fraction of a second, and all that the viewer will see is a bright line moving from top to bottom in 8 seconds. By eye, the viewer would never be able to see a complete picture at a single glance, and the mind cannot remember the information it receives in this form. Thus, for suitable viewing with the regular picture tube, some form of image storage system must be included as an accessory or as an integral part of the conversion. The cost of replacing the picture tube with one having long persistence would be prohibitive, and most likely the required replacement type would be one that is not even manufactured.

Image storage systems are of two forms, photographic and electronic. Photographic recording of the image from a regular TV picture tube is possible, but if viewing of the received information is by this means only, there is the nuisance of having to complete the photo processing before the image can be seen.

Electronic conversion systems can be built to "store" the picture information as it is received via SSTV, and to scan the storage memory electronically at a rate which is compatible with an existing TV set. Thus, the set itself requires no modification other than making provision for a direct video input. Suitable storage systems using digital-logic memories have been designed and built by enterprising amateurs, but require a large number of integrated circuits. The cost of construction is reported to equal or surpass that of a new commercially built SSTV monitor. A more feasible approach from an amateur standpoint is to use a video storage tube. Such tubes on occasion may be available new from manufacturers as "rejects," at prices below $100. Although rejected because they fail to meet some broadcast TV specification, they are quite suitable for amateur work. These tubes receive the video image at one end, and the image is then scanned from the other end in a manner similar to that used in a vidicon type of tube.

In this section four basic designs of monitors are described that will function very nicely with a conventional amateur receiver that has an audio passband of 300- to 3000-Hz. The first is by Macdonald, two by Tschannen, W9LUO, and the last by Briles, W7ABW, and Gervenack, W7FEN.

THE BASIC SSTV SYSTEM

The SSTV system now used universally in amateur circles incorporates an fm-subcarrier audio channel. In this system shown in Fig. 1, an audio-subcarrier is modulated so as to be 1200 Hz during sync pulses, 1500 Hz at black level, and a maximum of 2300 Hz at peak white. The shades of gray needed to constitute useful pictures are included in the 1500- to 2300-Hz region. Thus, at peak white the instantaneous frequency does not appreciably exceed that normally used for good voice communications. The signals are usually transmitted by modulating a conventional ssb transmitter with the fm subcarrier developed by a camera, flying-spot scanner, or recorded audio tape. When received on a conventional ssb receiver, the output signal is processed by the monitor to produce the slow-scan image.

The unit described here uses standard off-the-shelf components throughout. This makes it readily reproducible, though perhaps somewhat more expensive than if surplus components had been used. The monitor features a self-contained power supply with an accessory output to power an external flying-spot scanner if desired. A 5-inch diameter flat-faced cathode-ray tube is used and the unit is designed to take a commercially available light-shield hood. The accelerating potential on the cathode-ray tube is about 3 kV, insuring adequate brightness. Since subcarrier frequency modulation is used, the unit will accommodate a wide range of input level variation with no picture degradation. The monitor requires no adjustment in the course of normal operation.

Fig. 1 — Block diagram of the slow-scan monitor. Circled letters indicate section of Fig. 2 in which circuits shown will be found.

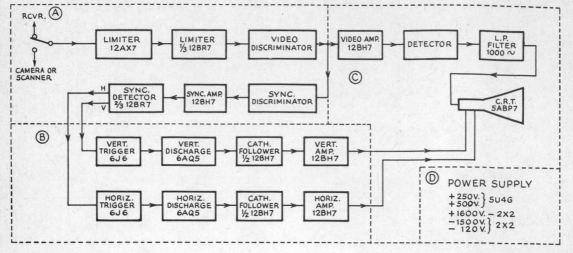

Circuit Description

A block diagram of the monitor is shown in Fig. 1. The complete schematic diagram is shown in Fig. 2. An scfm signal from communications-receiver output, tape recorder, or other source, is fed to the grid of the first limiter stage, V12, through transformer T1. The output of V1A is amplified by V1B and again by V2A. When the audio input level is greater than 10 millivolts or so, one or more of these first three stages will limit, rendering the output level at the plate of V2A, one third of a 12BR7, constant regardless of input level variations.

The limiter output is fed to the video and sync discriminators, similar to those described previously. The output of the video discriminator is amplified by V13, detected, filtered, and used to modulate the beam current of the 5ABP7 (or 5ADP7) cathode-ray tube, thereby producing brightness variations. The output of the sync discriminator is amplified by V3 and rectified by V2B. The rectified 1200-Hz subcarrier voltage appearing across R2 is used to control triggering of V4, the horizontal monostable multivibrator. V9 is the vertical trigger multivibrator and receives its triggering signals from the output of integrating network R3-C1. The low-pass filter action of the integrating network prevents the short horizontal sync pulses from triggering V9, but permits the longer vertical sync pulses to do so.

Referring to the horizontal sweep circuit, V4 acts to deliver a positive drive pulse to the horizontal discharge tube, V5. The horizontal sawtooth voltage is generated across C2 by the charging current through R5. R6 and V6 form a protection circuit which keeps the voltage across C2 from rising above 90 volts or so, in the event that synchronization signals are not being received. V7A is a cathode follower which provides correct bias and a sawtooth of proper amplitude for the horizontal sweep amplifier, V8. V8 is a cathode-coupled amplifier or "long-tailed pair" which gives direct-coupled push-pull output with single-ended drive.

The operation of the vertical sweep circuitry is quite similar, the vertical discharge pulse being somewhat longer.

The power supply is quite conventional. Power at various voltages is brought out to J4. A dummy plug, P1, wired as shown, must be used when the unit is not supplying power to an external unit. The reason for this is that the dropping resistor, R21-R22, for the neon-bult regulators would be replaced by the normal flying-spot scanner CRT and photomultiplier bleeder resistors in an external flying-spot scanner. R24 is adjusted to produce 250 volts across C4 with normal load on the +250-volt bus.

Mechanical

The monitor is housed in an 18 × 11-1/8 × 11-inch Bud Portacab (WA 1543). The parts are mounted on a 17 × 10 × 4-inch chassis. Layout is relatively noncritical, with the exception of transformer placement and high-voltage considerations. To prevent ac magnetic field deflection of the cathode-ray-tube beam, an annealed mumetal shield (Millen 80805-HZ) is used. Power transformers T5 and T6 should be mounted well away from input transformer T1 to minimize hum pickup. They should be mounted as far from the cathode-ray tube as possible — preferably toward the rear.

High-voltage wire is used to wire the +1600- and −1500-volt circuits. The focus and brightness pots are mounted with Millen 39023 insulated high-voltage couplings, T3, T4, L3 and associated small components are mounted on a sturdy Bakelite insulating board under the chassis. These parts are floating at approximately −1500 volts, so care should be used to avoid personal contact during checkout of the unit.

While not high-voltage circuits, excellent insulation must be used in the sawtooth-forming networks because of the high impedances involved.

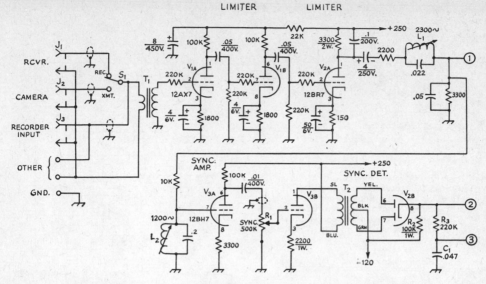

Fig. 2 A — Limiter and sync section. In this and the following sections, capacitances are in µF; capacitors with polarity marked are electrolytic; others are paper tubular, ceramic or mica as convenient. Resistances are in ohms; resistors are 1/2 watt except as indicated. Circled numbers connect to identically labeled points in other sections of circuit. Component designations not listed are for text reference.

J1, J2, J3 — Shielded jack, microphone type (Amphenol 75-PC1M), mounted with insulating washers.

L1, L2 — Approx. 200 millihenrys (Stancor WC-14, slug fully inserted).

R1 — 0.5-megohm linear control.

S1 — Spdt toggle.

T1 — 600-ohm line to grid transformer (UTC A-12).

T2 — Audio, push-pull plates to push-pull grids; 3 to 1, secondary to primary (Thordarson 20A19).

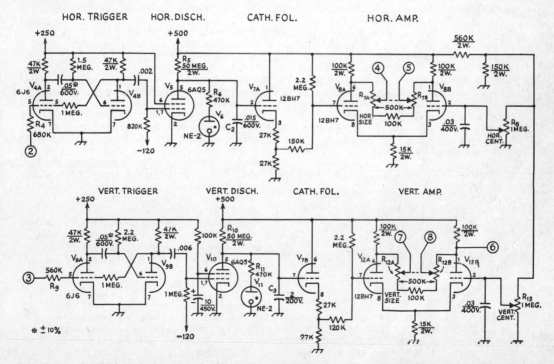

Fig. 2B — Vertical and horizontal deflection circuits.

R7, R12 — Dual 0.5 megohm control, linear taper.

R8, R13 — 1 megohm control, linear taper.

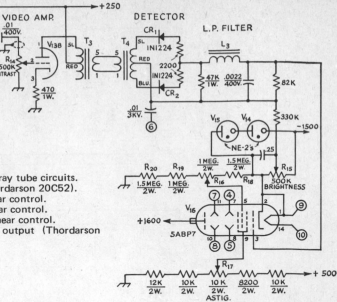

Fig. 2C — Video and cathode-ray tube circuits.
L3 — Approx. 10 henrys (Thordarson 20C52).
R14, R15 — 0.5-megohm linear control.
R16 — 1-megohm, 2-watt linear control.
R17 — 10,000-ohm, 2-watt linear control.
T3, T4 — Universal audio output (Thordarson 24S60).

Individual Teflon or ceramic standoffs are recommended at the junction of R10, R11 and C3, and at the junction of R5, R6, and C2. Ceramic tube sockets are preferred for V5, V7, and V10.

A Tektronix viewing hood, bezel, and yellow light filter are used in front of the cathode-ray tube. These items are Tektronix parts No. 016-001, 200-025, and 378-502, respectively. Total price for all three items is about $6.15. The sweep size and centering pots are mounted in the four corners of the bezel. To do this, it is necessary to make cutouts in the four mounting ears of the tube shield with a "nibbler" tool. Mounting the pots directly in the holes is impossible because of mechanical interference between the pots and the mounting brackets. Standoff bushings are used to space the pots away from the front panel. A U-shaped equipment handle with banana plugs attached to the two ends is used as a removable foot to raise the front end of the monitor to a more convenient viewing angle.

Operation

The input signal, from a communications receiver or other source, should have an amplitude somewhere between 10 millivolts and 10 volts, for proper operation of the monitor. Brightness and contrast controls are set to give desired brightness when a 2300-Hz tone is being received, and beam cutoff (zero brightness) when a 1500-Hz tone is being received. Focus and astigmatism controls are adjusted for best overall focus. Size and centering controls are adjusted for the desired raster size.

The sync control is adjusted for proper triggering of the vertical and horizontal sweep circuits. The sweep circuits should trigger properly as the sync control, R1, is adjusted over a considerable range of values. If they do not, or if horizontal and vertical sweeps do not trigger at the same settings

of R1, the values of R4 and R9, or both, should be modified to produce horizontal and vertical trigger ranges that overlap. (Variation of component values within their normal tolerances is the reason why this trimming may be necessary. Designing the unit to guarantee tracking of the trigger circuit would have required the use of expensive precision components.) If the transmitted signal has the proper subcarrier frequencies for sync, black, and white, and if the sync pulses are close to the proper duration, the controls will not have to be touched during operation. A considerable deviation from perfection in the transmitted signal can be accommodated through adjustment of the controls. The main precautions to observe with regard to communication operation are that carrier insertion is at the proper frequency when using ssb, and that receiver audio output (noisy as it may be) does not drop below 10 millivolts even during a severe fade.

The sweeps are of the driven type; that is, a received sync pulse is necessary to initiate each scan. This system has the advantage that if a sync pulse is missed, the scanning beam moves off the screen and stays there until the next pulse comes along. The phosphor screen is thus not covered with out-of-sync picture information during deep fades. Because of this driven sweep arrangement, no raster will appear on the cathode-ray tube unless a slow-scan signal is being received.

Modifications

A number of modifications could be made to reduce the cost of the unit significantly. The magnetic shield may be eliminated if the power supply is built on a separate chassis and if the cathode-ray tube is located at least three feet from any power transformer. Less expensive tubes may be used; a 5CP7A or 3FP7A would require no

Fig. 2D — Power supply circuits.
I1 — Pilot lamp, NE-2.
J4 — Octal socket.
L4 — 10.5 henrys, 110 mA (Stancor C-1001).
R23 — 50 megohms, 5 watts (five 10-megohm 1-watt resistors in series).
R24 — 7500-ohm 50-watt slider; set for 6000

ohms.
S2 — Spst toggle.
T5 — Oscilloscope power transformer; 880 volts ct, 125 mA; 1250 volts, 5 mA; 2.5 volts, 1.75 A; 2.5 volts, 1.75 A; 5 volts, 3 A; 6.3 volts, 0.6 A (Triad R-41C).
T6 — Filament, 6.3 volts, 6 A (Stancor P-3064).

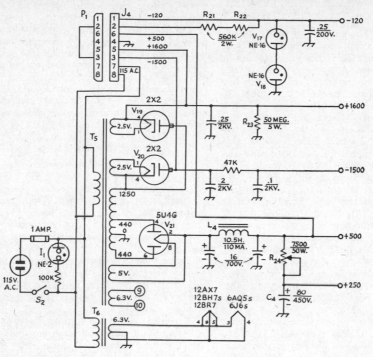

modification of the circuitry. If a 5CP7, 3FP7, or 5JP7 is used, the CRT bleeder must be modified to supply additional current to the tube. If R15, R16, R18, R19 and R20 are made one-half of the indicated resistance value, and R21 and R22 are doubled, defocusing with modulation should not be excessive.

T1 may be eliminated if an audio signal of at least 0.1 volt is available, and if connection to circuits carrying dc is never anticipated. Cabinet style is, of course, unimportant and the unit may be packaged in any desired manner. The viewing hood should be retained, however, if the unit is to be operated in a normally-lit room.

One final suggestion: bushings for recessed mounting of the size and centering pots can be fashioned easily from electric-lamp hardware available at any electrical supply store. The standard thread is 3/8-32, the same as used on pots, and the threaded tubing has an inside diameter somewhat greater than 1/4 inch.

SOLID-STATE SSTV MONITORS

The next two versions (Mark I and II) by Tschannen use solid-state techniques. The physical layout is more condensed and the units run cooler than the older tube type of monitors.

Electrostatic vs. Magnetic Deflections

The pros and cons of electrostatic versus magnetic deflection are varied and many; however, a few general comparisons are interesting. Magnetically focused and deflected CRTs provide excellent resolution and may usually be operated at somewhat higher accelerating voltages than their electrostatic counterparts. The magnetically focused and deflected tubes require external com-

ponents on the neck of the tube (yoke and focus coil); however, the deflection circuitry is ideally suited to being driven by solid state devices. Electrostatically-deflected tubes require no external components on the CRT, but need deflection voltages of several hundred volts peak-to-peak in order to produce a normal raster size on a 5-inch CRT. The sweep voltage necessary usually requires power supply voltages from 400 to 600. Deflection is usually produced by vacuum-tube amplifiers because solid-state amplifiers with adequate voltage capability are expensive. The approach used in the monitor described here is that of magnetic deflection and focus.

Description of the SSTV Monitor Circuit

The monitor is simple, and consists of several limiters, a discriminator, sync and video detectors, video amplifier, and display CRT. The sync separator is followed by one-shot (monostable) multivibrators, discharge circuits, and deflection circuits. A power supply provides several different operating potentials and uses a high-voltage pulse system.

The circuits may be understood by referring to Figs. 1A and 1B. Transistors Q1 and Q2 provide limiting of any amplitude variations which may be present on the signal. The emitter follower, Q3, drives a simple discriminator that consists only of a parallel-resonant circuit. An fm-subcarrier input to this circuit results in a subcarrier output which is amplitude modulated. The signal splits at the output of the discriminator and is detected by two separate full-wave detector systems. (Note that full-wave detection doubles the subcarrier frequency, permitting more effective filtering of the video and sync signals from the subcarrier.)

The video detector output passes through a low-pass filter, and the video amplifier, before reaching the CRT. (It should be noted that dc coupling is used from the video detector to the CRT, and also that direct coupling is used all the way from the limiter through the sync amplifier, and through all of the deflection circuits.)

The sync system is designed to provide good performance in the presence of noise and other undesired signals. The 1200-Hz bursts which appear across the 1200-Hz tuned circuit in the collector of Q6 drive the full-wave sync detector and the sync clipper. Only peaks of the detected signal Q8 forward-bias so that sync pulses and unfiltered subcarrier appear at the collector of Q8. Separate horizontal and vertical integrators provide clean sync pulses to the two integrated-circuit monostable multivibrators. These multivibrators provide the discharge pulses from which the sawtooth sweeps are derived. The sync level control in the emitter of Q6 permits the operator to adjust the clipping level, in the event he has to cope with some unusual type of interference. In general the control can be set and left alone.

Good noise immunity can be obtained only if direct coupling is retained throughout the sync and deflection system. For example, if additional charging paths are present in the sweep-generation system there will be a tendency for the trace to take several sweeps to stabilize after a burst of noise or interference. This condition is intolerable, particularly in the vertical deflection circuit where several sweeps would require a total time of 16 or more seconds. The 2- and 10-μF capacitors shown in the discharge circuits must be tantalum or paper types. The conventional aluminum electrolytic capacitor in this application has too much leakage.

The principle of operation of the horizontal and vertical sweeps is the same. The output of the monostable multivibrator provides a positive pulse. The tantalum timing capacitors charge until a positive pulse drives the discharge transistors, Q10 and Q16, into high conduction. This immediately discharges the capacitor, and the process begins again. A sawtooth wave is, of course, the result. The junction FET transistors, Q11 and Q17, present high impedances at their inputs and do not discharge the sawtooth forming capacitors via their input circuits. By setting the operating point of the FET, centering of the trace is achieved. This scheme is simple and does not degrade the sweep linearity when used within the normal range of centering.

Complementary-symmetry transistors in the output system provide a convenient means of maintaining dc balance through the deflection coils. The two diodes permit both output stages to remain in conduction during the "overlap" region near the center of sweep. In other words, an offset bias between the two transistors is provided so that neither of the two transistors will cease conduction before the other takes over.

Deflection Yokes and Focus Coils

A variety of deflection yokes can be accommodated in a circuit of this type. The 5FP7 tube has a deflection angle of 50 degrees and therefore the preferred yoke should at least closely match the contour of the glass envelope. However, 70-degree yokes have been used with good success. The 50-degree yokes are available from old TV sets using CRTs of the 10BP4 or 12KP4 type. The 70-degree yokes are of the type used with picture tube types such as 17CP4, 16TP4, 16RP4, 14EP4, etc. Several types of radars which made use of the 5FP7 tube are good sources for the yoke and focus-coil assembly.

The focus coil is a Syntronic Type F10. Also satisfactory for this application are units such as the "Focalizer" magnetic focus assembly made by Quam-Nichols. This type of unit was used in many early magnetically focused TV receivers.

Power Supply

Many monitor units utilizing vacuum tubes have incorporated 60-Hz high-voltage power supplies that are lethal in nature because of the large amount of energy stored in the filter capacitor. The self-oscillating pulse-type supply used here permits operation in the 12- to 15-kHz region. This high operating frequency permits the use of small capacitors for adequate filtering. A flyback transformer from a solid-state television is readily adapted to the self-oscillating circuit. The only modification required is the addition of a few turns of wire on the side leg of the transformer. A solid-state doubler provides an output of approximately 6 kV.

Low-Voltage Power Supply Systems

Several voltage sources are required for operation of the monitor. The supplies of plus and minus 10 volts are stabilized by a simple regulator system. A 35-volt supply is used to operate the pulse high-voltage oscillator. Another bridge circuit provides plus and minus voltages on the order of 300 volts, which supplies the CRT and discharge circuits. The low-voltage supplies are conventional in design and use readily available transformers.

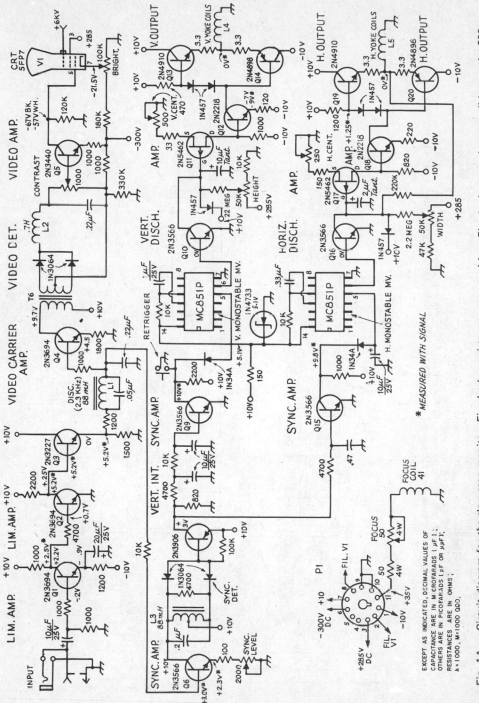
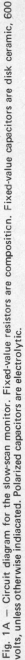

Fig. 1A — Circuit diagram for the slow-scan monitor. Fixed-value capacitors are composition. Fixed-value resistors are composition. Fixed-value capacitors are disk ceramic, 600 volts, unless otherwise indicaadvised. Polarized capacitors are electrolytic.

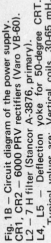

Fig. 1B — Circuit diagram of the power supply.
CR1, CR2 — 6000 PRV rectifiers (Varo VB-60).
L2 — 7 H filter (Stancor A-3876, primary).
L4, L5 — Deflection yoke for 50-degree CRT.
Typical values are: Vertical coils, 30-65 mH,
30-60 ohms dc resistance. Horizontal coils, 8-30
mH, 12-45 ohms dc resistance.

T1 — Power transformer (PC 8418 Stancor)
T2 — 25.2 V, 1A (Knight 54D1421).
T3, T4 — 12.6 V, 1.5 A (Knight 54D1420 or Triad
F25X).
T5 — Flyback transformer (RCA 116122).
T6 — Interstage, 500 ohms (Knight 54D4174).

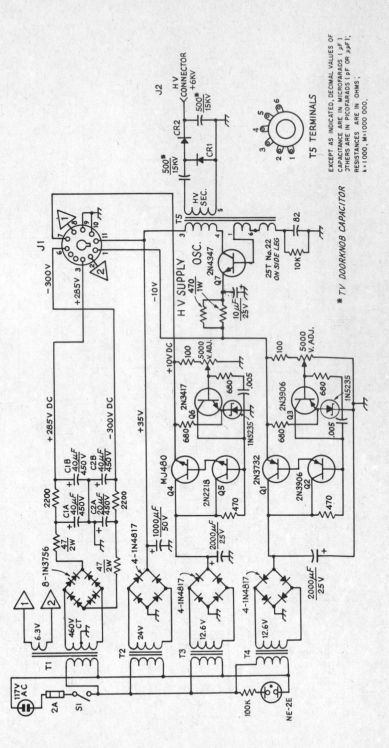

Mechanical Details

Both the monitor and power supply chassis are 12 × 7 × 3-inch aluminum. A flat panel with CRT cutout is mounted on the front of the monitor chassis. A protective shield is used to cover the power supply chassis. Eleven-pin connectors are used on each end of the low-voltage power cable and a separate cable is used for the high voltage. The use of individual chassis for power supply and monitor is advisable since stray 60-Hz fields must be minimized. Several transformers are used in the power supply and it is desirable to have the flexibility of removing stray fields from the display device.

Adjustment

The design is such that if components for the tuned circuits are selected with reasonably close tolerance, very few adjustments will be required. The essential item needed in the adjustment is a SSTV signal. It is suggested that a tape-recorded SSTV signal be used, making it possible to replay the material as often as needed. The sync-level control is adjusted so that clean horizontal and vertical pulses are obtained at the outputs of Q9 and Q15. These pulses should be free of subcarrier. The pulse at Q9, of course, will appear only once in about 8 seconds. Clean positive-going pulses should also appear at terminal 6 of each of the integrated circuits.

The height, width, and centering controls should be adjusted for a square raster centered on the face of the 5FP7. If excessive height and width are obtained, resistive loading across the horizontal and vertical yoke coils may be used. Starting values will be of the order of 10 to 15 ohms.

THE MARK II VERSION

The Mark II version of this monitor offers improved performance and further simplification. The new unit employs more integrated circuitry and has an improved sync separator, horizontal phase-locked loop, operational amplifier drivers for the deflection outputs, and a simplified power supply system. The design aim was improved performance with simplicity.

Signal Handling

The effective use of the fm-subcarrier mode of transmission in SSTV requires signal processing with adequate selectivity and bandwidth, good limiting, and faithful demodulation and reproduction of the video. Simultaneously, the sync and deflection circuits must provide accurately timed sweeps, good scan linearity, and be as immune to interference and noise as possible.

The majority of good-quality ham receivers provides sufficient selectivity with adequate bandwidth for SSTV reception. Greater selectivity and bandwidth reduction are normally neither desired nor necessary. All of the remaining fm-subcarrier process functions are conveniently handled in the monitor.

Video and Sync Circuits

With reference to Fig. 1, three inputs are provided on the monitor to provide patch-through connections for other slow scan equipment, as well as a monitor test point. The inputs are connected to a single op-amp limiter state, U1. Effective limiting action begins with input signal levels of about 0.25 V pk-pk. A simple LC discriminator circuit, equivalent to the one used in the original monitor, follows the amplifier-limiter. The parallel-resonant circuit consisting of L1-C2 is tuned to 2300 Hz. This permits slope detection of fm-subcarrier signals up to 2300 Hz. The discriminator output is split into two paths to (1) drive the push-push sync separator, and (2) drive the video subcarrier amplifier.

The tuned circuit, L2 and C3, is adjusted for 1200-Hz resonance. This circuit provides a voltage gain at the sync subcarrier frequency. A small amount of damping is used with this circuit in order to produce a selectivity characteristic that is wide enough to accommodate a modest range of sync-frequency variation. The push-push sync separator is forward biased by positive peaks of sync, and an output is developed across the 5600-ohm load resistor on terminal 1 of U2, the CA3046 integrated circuit. A sync level control permits adjustment for optimum sync stability. Sync pulses are integrated in separate networks for application to the horizontal phase-locked loop and vertical monostable multivibrator.

The video subcarrier amplifier (which is another part of U2) drives the video detector through T1. High-frequency components of the subcarrier which are present after the detection process are removed by C6, L3, C4, and C5. The video amplifier, Q1, is connected to drive the cathode of the CRT, thereby minimizing cathode degeneration in the CRT stage.

Horizontal Phase-Locked Loop

U3, a Signetics NE565 IC provides a convenient phase-locked loop (PLL) for low-frequency operation. The advantage of the PLL over one-shot triggered sweeps is appreciable. The oscillator continues operation at very nearly the correct frequency, even though several sync pulses may be lost because of interference or noise. C7 determines the amount of integration in the control path of the VCO. The 100-μF value was chosen as a good compromise between reasonable noise integration and capture range.

The square-wave output of the PLL is clipped and then differentiated in another section of U2 and is then applied to Q2 as a positive discharge pulse. C9 is discharged by this pulse at a 15-Hz rate to provide a sawtooth wave form to an op-amp driver, which in turn drives a complementary pair of transistors, Q3 and Q4. These transistors drive the horizontal deflection coils.

Vertical Deflection System

Vertical sync pulses, supplied from a two-section integrator, trigger the SN74122 monostable multivibrator, U5. The narrow positive output

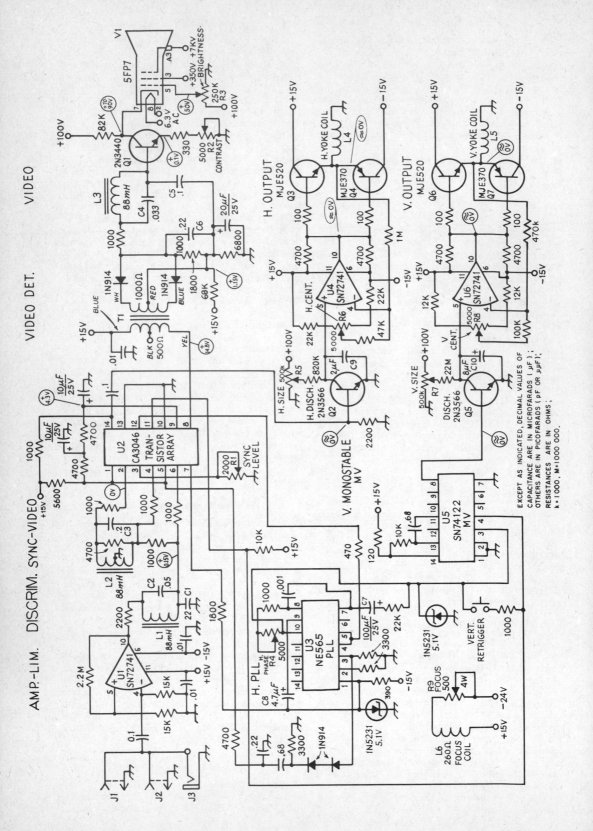

Fig. 1 – Schematic diagram of the SSTV Monitor
– Mark II.

C1-C6, incl. – Mylar or polystyrene.
C7 – Electrolytic.
C8, C10 – Tantalum.
C9 – May be either Mylar or tantalum.
J1, J2 – Phono jacks, rear-panel mounted.
J3 – Phone jack, front-panel mounted.
L1, L2, L3 – Surplus 88-mH toroids.
L4, L5 – Deflection-yoke coils. See text.
L6 – Focus coil. See text.
Q2, Q5 – Transistor type 2N3566. HEP55,
2N3392, or HEP736 also suitable.
Q3, Q6 – Motorola transistor. HEP245 or 2N4910
also suitable.
Q4, Q7 – Motorola transistor. HEP 700 or 2N4898
also suitable.
R1-R8, incl. – Linear-taper controls, low wattage.
T1 – Audio driver transformer, 1000-ohms ct to
500 ohms ct, Calectro type D1-728. See text.
U1-U6, incl. – See text.
V1 – Cathode ray tube, type 5FP7.

pulse at pin 8 turns Q5 on which discharges C10, thereby providing a field-rate sawtooth at 1/8 Hz. The vertical op-amp driver and output system are similar to the horizontal system.

Centering System

DC offset in the input of the op-amp drivers provides offset to the output amplifiers and in turn controls the dc through the yoke coils. This is a simple and stable means of obtaining picture centering.

Power Supply System

The original monitor used a total of five transformers in order to provide the six different dc supply voltages needed for operation. The Mark II power supply provides six different supply voltages with two transformers. The voltages provided are +5, –15, +24, +100, +350, and +7000. The 15-volt supplies were designed around Signetics NE550 voltage regulators. Excellent regulation and hum filtering are achieved in these supplies, shown in Fig. 2 at A.

A μA723 regulator may be used in place of each NE550 regulator which is shown at A of Fig. 2. From checks made with a breadboard version using these regulators, performance appears to be identical provided that the proper component changes are made. For the positive regulator with a μA723, the values of R11 and R12 shown in Fig. 2A should be changed to 3300 and 3000 ohms, respectively. For the negative regulator, the connections are as shown in Fig. 2B. Points B and D in this section of the diagram correspond with those shown in Fig. 2A.

A dual 15-volt regulator is available from Motorola, the MC1486L. A breadboard circuit using this regulator is shown in Fig. 2C. A single MC1486L may be used in place of both NE550 ICs, with the alternative circuit connected at points A, B, C, and D, as indicated. C11 and C12 should be located as close to the MC1468L as possible. A 0.1-μF ceramic capacitor may be required at each

point, A and B, if the regulator is located an appreciable distance from the filter capacitors.

T2 is a rewound power transformer incorporating two low-voltage secondaries. One is a 35-V ct winding; the other is a 6.3-volt winding for the CRT filament. The transformer uses the original primary of a small power transformer which had about a 60-VA capability. The turns per volt required for each of the secondary windings was determined by counting the turns used on the 6.3- and the 5-volt filament windings as they were removed. The wire size used for the 35-volt winding was No. 18, while No. 22 was used for the 6.3-volt winding.

For the less adventuresome builder who is not interested in the rewinding chore and not concerned in space saving, a Triad type F54X and a Triad type F13X may be used to supply the correct voltages. Whether the single or the pair of transformers is used, *it is imperative* to place the transformers as far as practicable from the CRT neck. It is also necessary to determine a transformer position where the stray-field influence upon the CRT is minimum. This condition was obtained in the original monitor by using a separate power supply. This type of construction is worth considering if small size is not an objective. The single rewound power transformer, mounted in the position shown in the bottom view of the chassis, produced negligible stray-field influence on the CRT.

The horizontal flyback transformer, T-3, is used to supply 7 kV, +350 V, and +100 V. The transformer is connected as a self-oscillating circuit which operates at a frequency of approximately 20 kHz. Because the 5FP7 CRT requires very low current for the No. 2 grid voltage of the CRT then tracks the second-anode potential, regardless of beam current. The regulation of the high-voltage supply is somewhat better than that of the original monitor. A simple voltage doubler and Zener regulator provide +100 volts to the video amplifier and sweep charging circuits.

Obtaining the Parts

Many builders are likely to desire information on component substitutions. The parts lists accompanying the schematic diagrams provide some such information, and the following paragraphs may also help the would-be builder in finding suitable components at low cost.

L4 and L5 are deflection yoke coils such as those used on old 10-, 12-, and 16-inch TV receivers. The minimum recommended inductance for the horizontal coils is 10 mH. The inductance of the vertical coils should be no less than 30 to 40 mH.

L6 is a focus coil from an old magnetic-focus TV set, having 260 ohms dc resistance. Usable substitutes include the focus coil from 1P41/ARR-27 or 1D30/APS-2 radar indicators. High-resistance focus coils (20,000 ohms) require a supply of 190 volts at 11 mA for proper focusing. Also suitable are permanent-magnet assemblies, some of which are called Quam Focalizers. An excellent-quality but higher priced unit is the

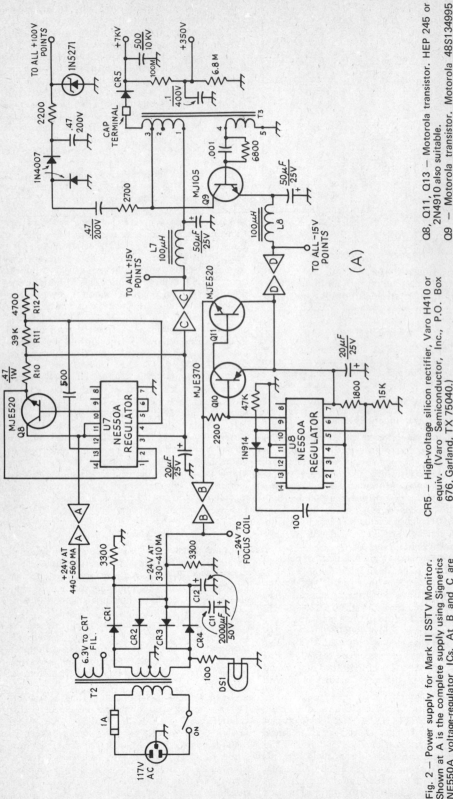

Fig. 2 — Power supply for Mark II SSTV Monitor. Shown at A is the complete supply using Signetics NE550A voltage-regulator ICs. At B and C are suitable alternative regulator circuits using other IC types, as discussed in the text.

CR5 — High-voltage silicon rectifier, Varo H410 or equiv. (Varo Semiconductor, Inc., P.O. Box 676, Garland, TX 75040.)
DS1 — 12-V pilot lamp.
L7, L8 — Rf choke, 100 μH (J. W. Miller 4632 or equiv., Newark Electronics No. 59F289).
C11,C12 — For text reference.
CR1-CR4, incl. — 1N4002 or equiv.

Q8, Q11, Q13 — Motorola transistor. HEP 245 or 2N4910 also suitable.
Q9 — Motorola transistor. Motorola 48S134995 also suitable.
Q10, Q12 — Motorola transistor. HEP700 or 2N4898 also suitable.

Fig. 2 — (Continued)
R10, R13, R14 — 5 ft. No. 30 enam. wire wound on 1000-ohm or higher value 2-W resistor.
R11, R12 — For text reference.
T2 — See text.

T3 — Horizontal output transformer. Motorola type 24D69828A04. (Obtainable from Motorola Chicago Co., 25 E. Howard Ave., Des Plaines, IL 60018.)
U7-U10, incl. — See text.

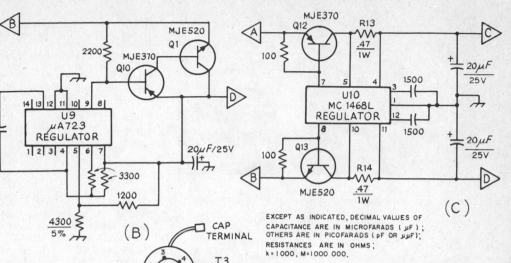

Syntronic F10C 360-ohm focus coil, obtainable from Syntronic Instruments, Inc., 100 Industrial Rd., Addison, IL 60101. A higher cost type 5AHP7 electrostatic-focus cathode ray tube may be used for V1, thereby eliminating the need for a focus coil.

T1, the audio transformer in the video detector stage, may be obtained at many electronics outlets for approximately $1.10, or from Calectro, GC Electronics, Div. of Hydrometals, Inc., 400 S. Wyman St., Rockford, IL 61101. (Note that the 1000-ohm winding is connected to the 1N914 diodes.) Also usable for T1 is a Thordarson TR-213, 1500 ohms ct to 600 ohms ct, Newark Electronics No. 5F1527.

If the Triad transformers are used in place of T2, as mentioned earlier, they may be obtained from Newark Electronics, 500 N. Pulaski Rd., Chicago, IL 60624. Their stock number for the F54X is 5F1378, and for the F13X, 3F958.

The NE565, NE550, 74122, and 741 ICs are all available from Solid State Systems, P.O. Box 773, Columbia, MO 65201, and also from many other suppliers. Other transistor and IC types are available from Newark Electronics.

Mechanical Details

The number of integrated circuits used in the monitor may prompt some to consider printed wiring for the monitor. This should offer an interesting exercise for those who enjoy this aspect of construction. A main chassis is required, in any case, for mechanical support of the yoke, CRT,

power supply components, and so on. Therefore, with a little additional hand wiring the unit is complete and readily modified if, indeed, one cares to experiment after the monitor is initially "completed."

The unit is constructed on a 10 × 12 × 3-inch aluminum chassis. A wooden support with a cutout corresponding to the CRT maximum bulb diameter is used to cradle the bottom of the 5FP7. A flat aluminum panel about 10 × 7-1/2 × 1/8-inch is used with an appropriate CRT cutout. A light-shield cover (not shown), extending several inches beyond the front panel, may be formed easily from stock aluminum material and used to reduce the glare from overhead lighting. A coat of dull black paint on the front panel and on the inside of the light shield helps to reduce reflections.

The high-voltage pulse transformer (also called "flyback" transformer) produces a very substantial high-frequency field which can have influence on the low-level signal and sync circuitry. It is necessary, therefore, to supply good shielding for the pulse transformer and high-voltage rectifier system. A rectangular-shaped tin can, such as shown in the top view of the monitor, will serve nicely for this purpose. Soldering lugs may be bent into right-angle shapes, soldered to the bottom of the can, and used to secure the can to the main chassis. All MJE520 and MJE370 power transistors are bolted to the bottom of the chassis using the mica insulating washers supplied with the transistors. The high-voltage oscillator transistor, Q9, is mounted in a TO-3 socket on the top of the chassis.

Top view of the Mark II Monitor chassis. The ICs are located in sockets, which, in turn, are mounted in rectangular openings cut into the chassis. C11, C12, and the shield for the high-voltage circuitry are prominent in the upper portion of this photograph.

Alignment

Discriminator alignment is accomplished by connecting an accurately calibrated audio oscillator to the input terminals of the monitor and connecting the vertical input leads of an osilloscope across C1. The value of C2, which tunes L1 to 2300 Hz, is then carefully selected so that a minimum output voltage is indicated on the scope when the audio frequency input is 2300 Hz. The scope vertical terminal is next connected to either side of L2 and the value of C3 selected to produce a maximum voltage when the audio oscillator is set at 1200 Hz.

The adjustment of sync, contrast, brightness, size and centering controls is best accomplished with a tape-recorded SSTV signal that can be played continuously until the desired control settings are found.

PARTS SUBSTITUTION FOR THE MARK I

There are literally hundreds of types of silicon npn transistors that will function satisfactorily in the sockets of Q1, Q2, Q3, Q4, Q6, Q9, Q10, Q15, and Q16, as well as Q6 in the power supply. Substitutes, if used, should preferably have betas of at least 100. The same comment regarding beta is true of the 2N3906 pnp silicon type. Transistor Q5 must have a V_{CEO} of 300 V, in order to handle the supply voltage used. HEP803s may be used in place of the 2N5462s in Q11 and Q17. Types MJE520 and MJE370 can be used respectively as low-cost replacements for the 2N4910 and 2N4898 complementary pair.

There are several substitutes for the MC851P. Some are the TI SN74121 and SN74122. A dual monostable MV is also available in the SN74123. The manufacturer's data sheet should be checked for basing differences. The MC851P is available from two supply houses: Semiconductor Specialists, 195 Spangler Ave., Elmhurst Indistrial Park, Elmhurst, IL 60126; and Newark Electronics, 500 N. Pulaski Rd., Chicago, IL 60624. Yokes and focus coils of the type needed are available from old TV sets employing the 10-, 12-, 14- and 16-inch tubes with 50- or 70-degree deflection. Many TV service shops can get these items.

ADAPTING AN OSCILLOSCOPE FOR SSTV MONITORING

The system for monitoring SSTV described here was developed for use with a modified standard oscilloscope. Adapters have been used successfully with several oscilloscopes, including the Tektronix 514, Dumont 304, Heathkit IO-18, Heathkit IO-10, and a navy surplus scope, OS-8B.

Oscilloscope Requirements

The oscilloscope's horizontal scan must be able to synchronize from an external trigger at 15 Hz. The scope should have a dc vertical input that will accept 10 volts. If the scope does not have a dc input, the vertical deflection amplifier may be able to be driven directly. The circuit shown in Fig. 1 was used with the Heath IO-18. This arrangement should be adaptable to other scopes not having a dc input, but R1 and R2 would have to be scaled to provide proper centering.

Most oscilloscopes have cathode-ray tubes with a P1 phosphor. The P1 phosphor is of short persistence, which is not suitable for slow-scan TV. Therefore, the P1 tube should be replaced with a P7-phosphor tube which has the long persistence required. The last two characters of the CRT type usually indicate the phosphor, and most types are available in several different phosphors. The Heath IO-18 uses a 5UP1 which was replaced with a 5UP7 at a cost of less than $15.00. If a direct substitute cannot be found, it may be possible to find a surplus CRT of another type which will function. The Dumont 304 used a 5ABP1 CRT, which was replaced with a 5CP7A. This CRT was

Fig. 1 — Amplifier circuit to provide a dc vertical input for the IO-18. A similar conversion can be used with other ac-only oscilloscopes. Unmarked components are parts in the Heath's original circuit. Capacitors are ceramic, and resistors are 1/2-watt. The switch, S1, may be any convenient type. The operational amplifier, U1, is a Fairchild μA709. R1 and R2 should be adjusted in value to give proper centering, if necessary.

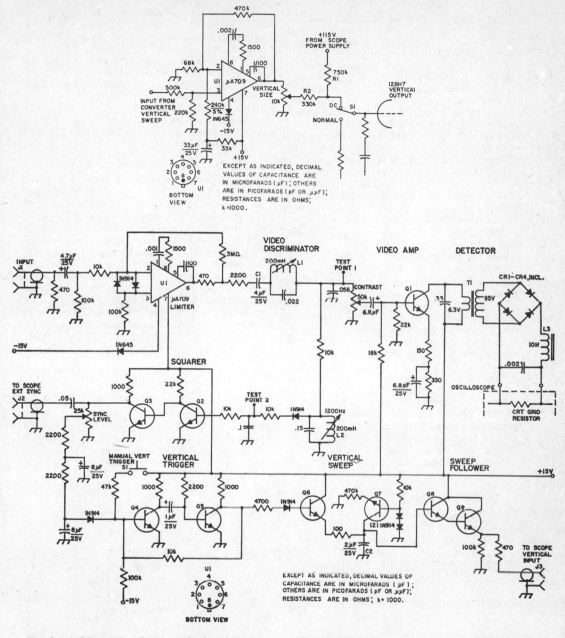

Fig 2 — Schematic diagram of the slow-scan adapter. Capacitors with polarity indicated are electrolytic, others are ceramic or paper, except as indicated. Variable resistors are composition controls, linear taper. Resistors are 1/2-watt.
C1 — 4-μF, 25-volt, nonpolarized tantalum.
C2 — 2-μF, 25-volt, Mylar.
J1-J3 incl. — Phono jack.
L1, L2 — Variable inductor, approx. 200 mH

(Miller 6330, UTC HVC-6, or Stancor WC-14).
L3 — 10-H low-current choke, 3000-volt insulation (B-A 18A959).
Q1-Q9 incl. — 2N718, 2N697, 2N2222, or 2N3641-3.
T1 — 6.3 volt, low current, 3000-volt insulation.
U1 — Operational amplifier (Fairchild μA709, Texas instruments SN6715 or Motorola SC4070G).

obtained on the surplus market for less than $5.00. If the purchase of a new oscilloscope is anticipated, a P7-phosphor cathode-ray tube should be requested.

Adapter Circuit Design

The schematic diagram of the slow-scan TV converter is shown in Fig. 2. The slow-scan signal from the audio output of a communications receiver, tape recorder, or other source is fed into the input of an integrated-circuit operational amplifier having a gain of 300. Therefore, a 0.1-volt ac peak-to-peak signal causes the amplifier to limit at the supply voltages, and the limited output will be approximately 28 volts ac peak-to-peak. The limited signal is then fed to a series video discriminator. The output of the video discriminator is fed to Q1, a video amplifier with a 6.3-volt ac filament transformer as a collector load. The transformer is used to provide voltage step-up. A transformer with 3000-volt insulation from ground is used, as the CRT grid circuit has a 1400-volt potential which must be insulated from ground. The video is then full-wave rectified and fed to a 1000-Hz filter. The output video dc is then connected across the scope CRT's series grid resistor to modulate the CRT intensity.

The output of the video discriminator is also fed to a 1200-Hz sync discriminator. This circuit passes only the 1200-Hz sync pulses. The 1200-Hz sync pulses are then rectified, filtered and fed to a two-stage amplifier, Q2 and Q3. The output of this squarer provides 15-volt sync pulses.

A 5-volt sawtooth voltage is required for vertical sweep on the oscilloscope. This voltage should have a very fast rise time and a linear decay. A sync separator circuit is used to separate the 30-ms vertical pulses from the 5-ms horizontal pulses. The vertical pulses are fed into the vertical trigger, a one-shot multivibrator. Provision is made for manually triggering the vertical sweep with a front-panel push button, S1, in case a vertical sync pulse is missed. The multivibrator triggers a transistor switch, Q6, that instan-

taneously charges C2 every time a vertical sync pulse is received. This capacitor is discharged at a linear rate through Q7. The base of Q7 is biased by two diodes at 1.2 volts. Thus, the current through the 0.47-megohm emitter resistor is held at a constant value, giving a linear voltage discharge across C2. This sawtooth voltage is sampled by a Darlington transistor follower, Q8 and Q9, whose output will sweep from 10 to 5 volts dc when receiving slow-scan TV. The value of 5 volts was chosen so that when a signal is not present, the dot on the scope CRT will be off the screen.

If the capability for high contrast is desired, the video signal level may be increased by adding a 2N718 transistor ahead of Q1, as shown in Fig. 3A. For those who wish to use 88-mH toroids in place of the variable inductors, L1 and L2, the circuit of Fig. 3B may be used.

Construction

The layout is relatively noncritical with the exception of the 6-volt ac filament transformer which will have high voltage on the secondary, so necessary precautions must be taken. It should be mounted away from the power transformer to minimize hum pickup. High-voltage wire is used to bring the CRT grid connection into the unit. Sockets were used for the IC amplifier and transistors; however, the components can be soldered directly into the circuit. The vertical-scan output lead should be shielded. Several types of transistors may be used; the circuit was designed for devices with a minimum beta of 50. A variety of integrated operational amplifiers may be used; however, the 709 was chosen because of its low cost and availability.

Scope Modification

The potential between the CRT control grid and the cathode varies the intensity. The control grid usually has an isolation resistor in series with the negative voltage lead. Video from the converter is connected across this resistor to vary the intensity of the CRT. This resistor should be at

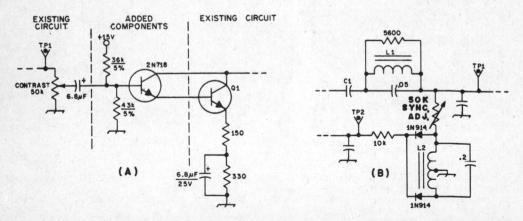

Fig. 3 — At A, a circuit which may be added to increase the contrast of the SSTV adapter, and at B, an alternative circuit using surplus 88-mH toroidal inductors for L1 and L2. If the circuit of A is used, the 18,000- and 22,000-ohm resistors shown connected to the base of Q1 in Fig. 1 are unnecessary.

Fig. 4 — Power supply for the adapter. Capacitors are electrolytic. Resistors are 1/2-watt unless otherwise specified.
CR1-CR4 — Silicon type, 200 PRV or more, (Motorola 1N4002, 1N4004, or 1N4007).

CR5, CR6 — 15-volt, 1-watt Zener (Centralab R4128-4, Unitriode Uz715).
P1 — Fused line plug.
S1 — Toggle.
T1 — 40-volt ct, 100 mA (Triad F90X).

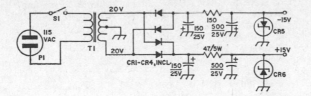

least 100 kΩ. If it is not this large in the existing scope circuit, it should be changed to 100 kΩ. This will have no effect on the scope operation, since this control grid draws no current. There is usually ample room on most scopes to install two additional insulated jacks on the terminal board that has the direct deflection-plate connections.

Adjustment

1) Connect the scope vertical input to test point 1.

2) Connect a 2350-Hz signal to the input and adjust the video discriminator coil L1 for minimum indication on the scope. This is usually with the slug fully inserted.

3) Connect the scope to test point 2. Change the input to 1200 Hz and peak the sync discriminator coil L2 for maximum indication on the scope. Connect a dc voltmeter between the collector of Q3 (sync level) and ground. With a 1300-Hz tone fed to the input of the adapter, adjust the 50,000 ohm sync adjust control to the point where the dc voltmeter just reads +15 volts.

4) Make the connections from the adapter to the oscilloscope external sync, vertical input, and the CRT grid.

5) Connect the adapter input to the receiver or tape recorder.

6) Set the contrast control at midposition and the sync control to maximum.

7) Adjust the scope sweep to 15 Hz for trigger lock.

8) Adjust the size of the raster with the scope horizontal and vertical size controls until a square raster is obtained.

9) Adjust the adapter contrast and the scope intensity controls until a clear picture is obtained. If the picture is negative, the connections to the CRT grid should be reversed.

10) When a picture is obtained, the sync level should be adjusted to a point just before sync is lost. This will eliminate false triggering when copying weak signals and, if a vertical sync pulse is missed, the manual trigger can be used.

STORAGE TUBES

One of the major problems with reception of SSTV is the lack of persistence of screens in CR tubes. The use of storage tubes in monitors is a distinct improvement over the older techniques. The information concerning this method is contributed by W. C. Smith, K6DYX.

Interior view of W7ABW's adapter. The transformer near the rear is in the power-supply circuit. The phono jacks on the rear deck are for connections to the oscilloscope and receiver — one is a spare. Two banana jacks are used for the CRT connections. The large transformer near the front panel is in the video detector circuit.

The commonly used P7 phosphor has a purplish-blue flourescence during excitation and a yellowish-green phosphorescence which persists for several minutes after excitation is removed. The initial decay of the phosphorescence is, however, very rapid, decreasing to 10 percent of its original value in a matter of five seconds. Thus, as the picture is drawn on the screen at the rate of one raster in 8 seconds, the top fades to quite a low intensity while the picture is still being drawn by a bright blue line at the bottom. A yellow filter or simply a sheet of yellow plastic may be used to remove the disturbing blue line, but nonetheless, most amateurs operate their monitors in a very subdued light or preserve the illusion of persistence.

Storage-type CR tubes operate on a principle that is ideally suited to slow-scan television. A Hughes Tonotron, type H-1192AP20 has been used in a monitor with very satisfactory results. The picture is drawn in the normal manner; in fact the trigger, sweep, and video-detection circuits may be quite standard. The picture appears, a line at a time, at full brightness with good gray scale and remains on the screen until erased. An erase pulse, generated by the vertical trigger pulse, completely destroys the picture when the next frame starts. An additional feature makes it possible to hold a picture on the screen for up to five or ten minutes.

Electrical and Mechanical Characteristics

The Tonotron (RCA type 6866 seems similar) is a five-inch, electrostatic-deflection CR tube, shorter than the 5ABP7, with a P20 aluminized phosphor having yellow-green fluorescence and phosphorescence. The useful screen diameter is 3.8 inches, only slightly less than for the 5ABP7. It has an integral magnetic shield and may be readily installed in a surplus Tektronix 511A CRO chassis. The electrode potentials are different from those of the 5ABP7 because of the principle of operation.

Video information is drawn by a writing gun and deflection electrodes on a storage surface exactly as in the case of the P7 CR tube monitors. Another gun, see Fig. 1, is used to project a collimated beam of electrons through the storage surface to a viewing screen. Areas of the storage surface which have not received electrons from the writing gun inhibit the passage of the low-energy

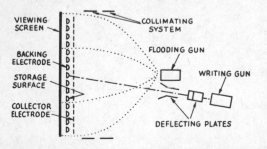

Fig. 1 — Storage-tube structure. See text for description of operation.

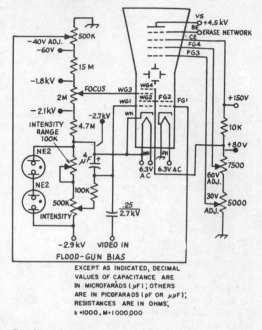

Fig. 2 — Circuit for providing electrode potentials for the storage tube.
VS — Viewing screen.
BE — Backing electrode.
CE — Collector electrode.
FG — Flooding gun.
WG — Writing gun.
FH — Flooding-gun heater.
WH — Writing-gun heater.

EXCEPT AS INDICATED, DECIMAL VALUES OF CAPACITANCE ARE IN MICROFARADS (μF); OTHERS ARE IN PICOFARADS (pF OR $\mu\mu F$); RESISTANCES ARE IN OHMS; k =1000, M=1 000,000

flooding electrons. Areas which have been charged by the writing-gun beam permit the flooding electrons to pass through. They are then accelerated toward the viewing screen and cause it to glow brightly until an erase pulse, applied to a backing electrode of the storage surface, causes it to be charged uniformly to a slightly negative potential, thus blocking out the flooding electrons from the viewing screen. The retention time of stored information is limited by the slow dispersion of the charge written on the storage surface. Charge leakage is mainly caused by positive ions, which come from residual gas molecules within the tube. In practice this seems to limit the hold time to about five minutes.

The average deflection-electrode potential should be about 125 volts and the deflection factor is about 35 to 45 volts per inch per kilovolt of accelerating potential of the writing gun. These figures are comparable to those for the 5ABP7. The electrode potentials used in my monitor are shown in Fig. 2.

Although the viewing screen may be operated at up to 11,000 volts, with resultant increase in brightness, the screen is bright enough for full daylight viewing and has a better gray-scale range with only 4500 volts applied. CR tubes with P7 phosphors exhibit a build-up to their phosphorescence which significantly affects their gray-scale sensitivity. This characteristic is not present with the storage tube. Consequently it is much more

Fig. 3 — Erase circuit for storage tube.
CR1-CR4, incl. — Any small-signal silicon diode.
Q1, Q2 — Silicon npn transistor, 500 mW.
S1 — Push-button type, momentary.
VR1 — Zener diode, 1N747 or equiv.

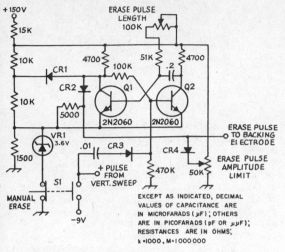

Briles and Gervenack, "Slow-Scan TV Viewing Adapter for Oscilloscopes," *QST* June, 1970.

Macdonald, "A New Narrow-Band Image Transmission System," *QST* August and September, 1958; "A Slow-Scan Vidicon Camera," *QST* June, July, and August, 1965; "A Compact Slow-Scan TV Monitor," *QST* March, 1964.

Smith, "A Storage-Tube Monitor For SSTV," *QST*, July, 1972.

Taggart, "Slow-Scan with Regular Vidicons," Technical Correspondence, *QST*, December, 1968.

Tschannen, "A Solid State SSTV Monitor," *QST*, March, 1971; "A Solid-State SSTV Monitor — Mark II," *QST*, March, 1973.

(A)

(B)

sensitive to writing beam intensity. The use of a lower-than-normal viewing-screen voltage seems to widen the range of gray-scale excitation.

Unique to the storage tube monitor is the erase operation. The circuit for this is shown in Fig. 3. The length of the erase pulse is more important than its amplitude, which must be less than 20 volts. The erase pulse is 0.4 second long at about 6 volts amplitude. This is generated when a vertical trigger pulse starts the vertical sweep. A push button on the front panel permits erase and start-over at any time. This is convenient since a vertical sweep which, once started, proceeds to the end in a little over 8 seconds, unaffected by noise or spurious trigger pulses.

The HOLD feature on the monitor is simply a relay that is operated by a negative fly-back pulse derived from the vertical sweep. The frame being drawn will be completed and held, for when the relay closes it shorts the input and applies a "black" potential to the writing gun (video) grid.

Fig. 4 shows the gradual dissolving of the image when the monitor is on HOLD. The images shown in the photographs are not time exposures. They are, rather, snapshots of the images displayed by the playback of a tape recording made directly from the receiver. Fig. 4 was made at 1/25 second at *f*8 using a Polaroid oscilloscope camera.

Bibliography

Source material and more extended discussions of topics covered in this chapter can be found in the references given below. This listing does not include every article published in *QST* on the subject in this chapter, however. A detailed bibliography of references in *QST* on SSTV will be sent on request to ARRL, Newington, CT 06111. Please enclose a business-size stamped, self-addressed envelope.

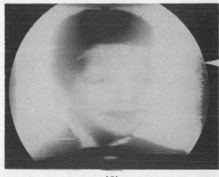

(C)

Fig. 4 — Storage-tube display with monitor on HOLD. At A is the initial presentation; at B, two minutes later; and at C, five minutes later.

Chapter 4

Facsimile

Facsimile (FAX) is an electronic or electro-mechanical process by which graphic information is transmitted by wire or by radio to a distant receiving point, where it is recorded in a permanent printed form. Common uses of FAX include the transmission of maps, schematic diagrams, drawings, photographs, and other fixed images. At the present time, amplitude modulated facsimile (A4) is permitted in the U.S. on six meters between 50.1 and 54.0 MHz, on two meters between 144.1 and 148.0 MHz, and on all amateur frequencies above 220 MHz. Frequency modulated facsimile (F4) is permitted on all amateur frequencies above 220 MHz. As the cost of new manufactured equipment is prohibitively high, virtually all amateur operation makes use of converted surplus or homemade equipment. Since few industry-wide standards exist, there are a wide variety of transmission and reception formats in current use. Most equipment is tailored to the requirements of one or two specific applications, and is therefore incompatable with hardware from other systems.

FAX TRANSMISSION

The most common method of converting written or printed images into the electrical signals used for modulating a transmitter involves photo-electric scanning. The material to be transmitted is wrapped around a cylinder or drum which is rotated about its longitudinal axis, while a tiny spot of light is projected on the surface of the material. The reflected light from the subject copy is focused on a photoconductive tube or photo-multiplier. The amplified output of the phototube is an electrical analog of the varying light intensities reflected from the information being scanned. Each rotation of the drum provides one scanning line. As the drum turns, it is slowly moved laterally by a lead screw, causing slight separation of adjacent scanning lines. In this manner, the scanning beam strikes the subject copy in the form of a helix. Alternatively, some systems use both a moving drum and a laterally moving scanning spot, while others illuminate the entire subject material evenly and focus the reflected light through a small aperture in front of the phototube. All-electronic systems use flying-spot scanning, which replaces mechanical complexities with the simplicity of a cathode-ray tube. The customary order of scanning is from left to right, and from top to bottom.

The band of frequencies that the output of the phototube occupies is called the baseband. The baseband ordinarily consists of varying dc levels (which represent the range of densities from white to black on the copy) and frequencies in the low audio and subaudio range (which arise from the rapid transitions between the various densities encountered by the scanning beam). On some systems, maximum output is interpreted as white, minimum output is interpreted as black, and intermediate values represent shades of grey. Other systems use the opposite scheme. The baseband signal may be used to vary the frequency of a voltage-controlled oscillator, in order to generate an fm subcarrier (not unlike an SSTV subcarrier) in which the highest frequency represents white, the lowest frequency represents black, and intermediate frequencies represent grey (or vice-versa). Alternatively, the baseband signal may be used to vary the amplitude of a constant-frequency subcarrier. In practice, fm is preferred over a-m wherever noise or fading due to propagation are important factors, inasmuch as the receiving techniques used for demodulating fm offer greater immunity from those effects. Another method sometimes used is to interrupt the reflected light from the subject copy by placing a chopper wheel between the light source and the phototube. If the light is interrupted 2400 times per second, the output of the phototube is an amplitude modulated 2400-Hz subcarrier. This system is used in the Western Union Telefax transceivers described later in this chapter.

RECEIVING FAX

Most FAX receiving systems available to the amateur operate on an electromechanical basis. Received a-m subcarrier signals may be demodulated with a diode or other envelope detector. Fm signals are first passed through a limiter to remove amplitude variations, and then through a discriminator and detector. The output from the detector in either case is a varying dc signal corresponding to the lightness and darkness variation in the subject material. There are several methods currently used to transfer the varying dc signal into a printed record of the original copy. Some of the more common processes include the use of electrolytic paper, electrothermal paper, and photosensitive paper.

The action of electrolytic paper is based on the change of color that results from the passage of an electric current through an iron stylus and paper treated with a special electrolyte. A sheet of paper is wrapped around a metal drum on the receiving machine, and the amplified signal voltage is applied between the pointed stylus and the drum. The variations in current caused by the signal voltage appear as variations in the darkness of the paper. The drum rotates, and simultaneously, either the drum or the stylus moves laterally, in order to separate the adjacent lines. With this system, the stylus must be replaced at intervals because it deteriorates due to the effects of electrolysis. Another method commonly used with electrolytic paper employs a stationary blade contact plus a rotating single-turn helical contact wound over a cylinder instead of the stylus and drum. The paper is drawn continuously between the helix and the metal blade. The helix cylinder makes one complete revolution for each printed line. The color change in the paper takes place at the point where the blade, paper, and helix are in contact with each other. This point moves laterally across the paper as the helix cylinder turns.

A drum and stylus are used with electrothermal paper, which has a coating that breaks down chemically when an electric current passes through it, and changes color according to the strength of the current.

A lamp replaces the stylus when photosensitive paper is being used. The demodulated signal voltage is used to modulate the intensity of the light source, which exposes the paper. The paper is usually wrapped around a rotating cylinder (as in the previous cases). After exposure, the paper must be processed in a darkroom. The paper must be protected from exposure to light sources other than the desired one until it has been processed. The optimum diameter in inches for the spot of light used to expose the paper is the reciprocal of the number of lines printed per inch by the machine (optimum spot diameter for 96 lines per inch is 1/96 inch). Any further reduction of spot size will not result in improved resolution in the printed copy, while any increase in spot diameter will lower the resolution.

Synchronization

It is important that the speeds of the FAX transmitter drum and FAX receiver drum be as close to identical as possible. Failure to match the speeds will result in diagonal tearing or skewing of the received copy. In practice, synchronous motors locked to the frequency of the 60-Hz ac line are usually used to drive both the drum and the lead screw on a machine. If it is not possible to use the ac line frequency as a standard, it is common practice to use an amplitude modulated facsimile subcarrier as the frequency standard for both the transmitting and receiving machines. The frequency of 2400 Hz is often used for the a-m subcarrier, as it is easily divided by 40 to produce 60 Hz ac to drive the synchronous motors, and it can be transmitted through normal audio-bandwidth channels. Another method used to ensure synchronization is the incorporation of a highly stable frequency standard inside each machine, with appropriate frequency dividers.

Phasing

While synchronization ensures that the received FAX picture is spatially consistant with the subject copy being transmitted, it is also important that the start of each scan line coincide with the edge of the paper on the receiving end. If this is not done, the possibility exists (in fact it is probable) that the received image will run off the edge of the paper. Thus, it is necessary for the transmitting machine to send a series of phasing pulses prior to sending the actual picture. The effect at the receiving end of the phasing pulses is to obstruct the rotation of the receiving drum bit by bit until it is exactly in step with the transmitting drum.

Standards

Standards vary greatly between services and between machines. Generally drum writing speeds are multiples of 60 lines per minute (lpm) with 60, 120, and 180 appearing commonly. A commonly used scan density is 96 lpi (lines per inch), although applications requiring greater resolution use greater densities. One measure of the compatibility of different machines is the index of cooperation. The index of cooperation is the product of the total length of one scan line and the number of scan lines per unit length. A facsimile signal may be received without height or width distortion on a receiving machine that is larger or smaller than the transmitting machine, as long as they have identical indices of cooperation (provided the drum speeds are also identical). If the drum speed of the transmitting machine is a multiple of the speed of the receiving drum, the received image will consist of a proportionate number of pictures, each with only part of the information contained in the original. For example, a drum at 60 lpm receives 4 pictures each containing one fourth of the information sent by a transmitting drum at 240 lpm.

The drum speed, scan density, type of recording material used at the receiver, and bandwidth limitation of the transmitted signal all affect the resolution obtainable from the system. With slow drum speeds (in the order of several minutes per picture) and very fine light beams, excellent-quality photographs can be transmitted in a communications-bandwidth channel.

CONVERSION OF TELEFAX TRANSCEIVERS TO AMATEUR SERVICE

Conversion of a telefax transceiver is easy to do. First, remove the cover and check the tubes in a tube tester. Check to see if you have a stylus. If necessary, replace the stylus with carbon-steel wire only. A wire brush is a common source of stylus wire.

Remove the exciter lamp, clean its opening, and set it aside in a safe place. These lamps are hard to obtain. Carefully remove the lamp telescope, then remove the lenses, and clean them. Be sure to replace the lenses in the same direction as they came out. Replace the telescope and exciter lamp. Plug in the 117-V line cord and push the white OUTGOING button to turn on the lamp. Focus the light spot on the drum by moving the telescope back and forth.

Remove the photo-tube telescope and clean both lenses, then reassemble. Turn on the lamp and focus the telescope image on the pinhole at the back of the telescope tube assembly. Put a paper with typed letters on the cylinder. Focus the edge of a letter on the pin hole. This is very important if you are to send sharp pictures.

Remove the bottom plate and solder a .01 μF disk capacitor from the junction of the 2000-ohm and 2700-ohm resistors in the cathode circuits of the 12AX7 tube to ground. This keeps rf out of the video amplifier. Clip one of the leads of the 51-ohm 2-watt resistor on the INCOMING push-button switch. The other two leads can also be clipped and the switch can be used to switch the line between your mic and the receiver's audio output.

Clip the wire coming from relay LR, the normally closed contact, and going to relay HR, the moving contact. Clip the wire on the rear of the OUTGOING push button, the normally open contact. Run a wire from this contact to the moving contact of relay HR just made available. See Fig. 1. These changes assure proper operation of the transmit-receive relay.

Remove the ACKNOWLEDGE push button, solder the leads together, and insulate them with spaghetti or tape. In the push-button hole, mount a spdt toggle switch. Disconnect the leads going to the contacts of relay LR (line relay). Run three wires from the spdt switch to the three leads at relay LR, replacing the relay function with the switch. Now, when you close the switch, the carriage mechanism for the drum will feed. If your transmitter is keyed with a push-to-talk switch, you may use a dpdt switch, with the second pole to key the PTT line. This will key the transmitter automatically at the start of the scan.

Carefully remove the line transformer and remount it on the rear apron of the chassis in a vertical position behind relay LR. In the original position, the "gray motor" on the chassis above the line transformer will induce hum into the video signal. Solder the shielded leads at the old line-transformer location, red to red and black to black. Run two shielded leads from the secondary of the line transformer through the nearby hole in the rear apron and to the line terminal strip. Hook a shielded lead to the line terminals of the line transformer for connection to your rig's mic jack and speaker leads.

It may be necessary to replace the stylus shielded lead. The old rubber-insulated shield may have become very leaky. Also it's a good idea to replace the lead from the 6V6 tube to the plate choke.

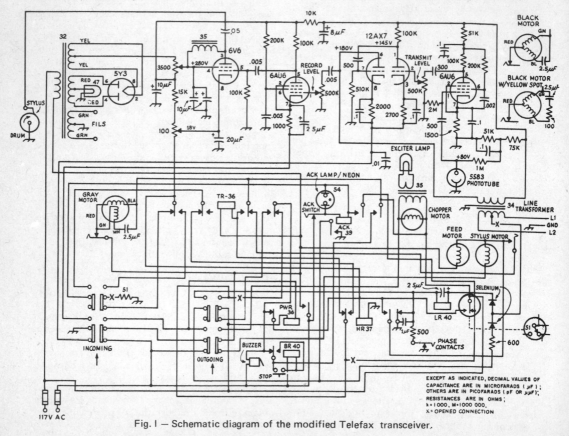

Fig. I — Schematic diagram of the modified Telefax transceiver.

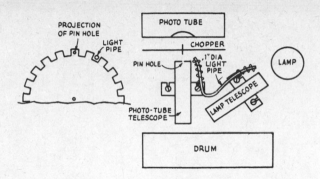

Fig. 2 — Addition of a fiber-optics light pipe for transmission of positive pictures.

Positive Pictures

Fig. 2 shows a modification for sending positive pictures. Mount a short piece of fiber-optics light pipe between the exciter lamp and the chopper wheel. The light pipe is easily held in place by wrapping it with No. 14 wire, placing the wire under the two telescope screws, as shown in Fig. 2. Carefully position the light pipe so it shines through a slot in the chopper wheel when the pin-hole light is cut off by the chopper. Connect an oscilloscope or ac voltmeter to the LINE leads and move the light pipe nearer to or farther from the exciter lamp until the scope or meter shows a null. Fig. 3 shows an experimentally derived circuit which will send sync pulses when in the OUTGOING mode before picture scanning begins. This circuit also receives sync pulses before scan begins to synchronize the drum angle.

An alternative method of conversion to positive picture transmission is presented in Fig. 4 (modification information from WA9RSB). It completely replaces the transmitting section of the FAX machine (chopper wheel and motor, photo-diode tube, and all components in the transmitting section) and will send several gray levels between black and white. The audio quality produced by this circuit is good. No output occurs on white copy. It should be noted that this circuit does not respond to writing with most felt-tip pens — pencils writing produces the best results. The new unit can be built from new parts for about $10. The phototransistor, a Motorola HEP P-001, represents about half the entire cost.

Fig. 4A is the diagram of the new transmit section. It consists of two major parts, an audio oscillator, Q1, set to about 2000 Hz by the value of resistor R1, and an amplifier, Q2, whose operating point is shifted by the phototransistor, Q3. Potentiometer R2 sets the nominal bias for Q2, and R3 is used to set the proper modulation level for the amateur transmitter. It is recommended the transmitting section be housed in its own small Mini-box and be well grounded to the chassis. After the original transmitting electronics have been removed, enough space will be available to

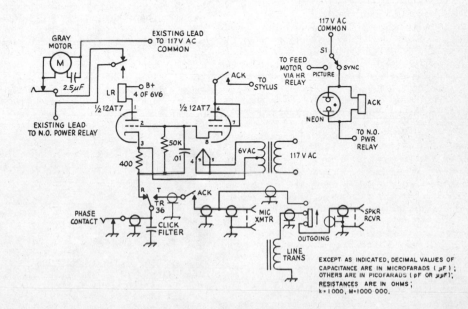

Fig. 3 — Circuit modification for sending or receiving sync information before picture scan begins. These modifications were originally described by W7QCV in *QST* for May, 1972.

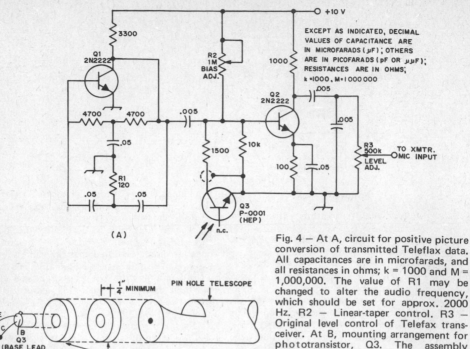

(A)

(B)

Fig. 4 — At A, circuit for positive picture conversion of transmitted Teleflax data. All capacitances are in microfarads, and all resistances in ohms; k = 1000 and M = 1,000,000. The value of R1 may be changed to alter the audio frequency, which should be set for approx. 2000 Hz. R2 — Linear-taper control. R3 — Original level control of Telefax transceiver. At B, mounting arrangement for phototransistor, Q3. The assembly should be secured with a suitable type of cement.

secure this box to the chassis. The maximum current required by this circuit is about 10 mA, and a simple power supply can be used.

A suggested manner to mount the phototransistor on the end of the pin-hole telescope is shown in Fig. 4B. Rubber feet, reamed out to the diameter of the phototransistor and glued together and to the telescope, as shown, work very well. The transistor should fit snugly into the end of the assembly. Note that the transistor must be at least 1/2 inch behind the pin hole. Shielded cable should be used from the transistor to the transmit section to minimize hum pickup.

Setup should be done in the following manner. Set R2 so that audio is present on the collector of transistor Q2. Adjust the value of R1, if necessary, to obtain the desired audio frequency (values in different models have ranged from 100 to 1000 ohms). Next, put a white sheet of paper on the drum and then adjust R2 *toward* B+ just to the point where the audio disappears. Finally, put black copy on the drum and adjust R3 for the desired modulation level for the transmitter. (If no audio output occurs for black copy, R2 has probably been adjusted in the wrong direction.)

It is most convenient to set the transmitter mic gain control for the normal voice level and then adjust the FAX gain control to the proper level. This should be done to about 90 percent as viewed on a scope. It is possible to set the level if one's relative output indicator normally responds to voice: note the peak deflection of the meter during voice operation and then set the FAX output to

obtain about the same deflection. While this will produce a usable output, it's still better to use a scope (either at the transmitter or on a receiver).

It may be of interest to some to note that the circuit constants shown in Fig. 4 were optimized for the gray-level response of the original FAX receiver using on-the-air tests. Because the phototransistor, Q3, is essentially a current source, its beta will to a certain extent affect the results obtained. Those so inclined may wish to alter the value of the collector resistor of Q3 *slightly* to "tune up" an individual circuit. The 1500-ohm value shown offered the best overall compromise. Smaller values (to 1000-ohms) will shift the linear

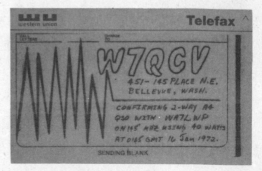

A "QSL" card sent via FAX. To be valid for an operating award, however it must bear an *original* (not a reproduced) signature of the sending operator.

Western Union Telefax transceiver. Machines of this type are available as surplus for less than $20. The drum accommodates a sheet of paper measuring approximately 4 1/2 X 6 1/2 inches.

The Telefax transceiver with cover removed. The shaft along which the drum traverses is visible at the left of the drum. The photo-optic assembly may be seen on the right-hand side of the chassis, just behind the drum. The lamp and its focusing lens system appear at the right, while the photo-electric cell is housed behind its lens system inside a light shield with appropriate opening.

portion of the light-response curve toward the light gray end and larger values (up to 2200 ohms) will shift it toward the dark gray end.

RECEPTION OF WEATHER SATELLITE FACSIMILE SIGNALS

One of the most intriguing uses of facsimile is in the reception of weather photographs from automatic picture transmission (APT) satellites. The information which follows illustrates some of the approaches that have been used successfully by amateurs to receive and record these photos.

The first three systems described are designed to be compatible with the 240 lpm transmissions from some of the earlier APT satellites. At present, the Essa-8 (137.62 MHz) satellite uses those standards. Additionally, the Applications Technology Satellites (ATS) 1 and 3 in geostationary orbits transmit weather facsimile data on 135.60 MHz using those same standards (ATS-1, transmitting between 0130-0215 GMT and 1400-1445 GMT daily, ATS-3 transmitting between 0730-0815 GMT and 2045-2130 GMT daily). Both Noaa-2 and Noaa-3 (transmitting on 137.50 MHz) plus future APT satellites use a 48 lpm standard for their photos. Additionally, they transmit continuous rather than individual photographs. The fourth section details the modification of surplus Telefax transceivers for the reception of 48 lpm satellite facsimile. In order to use the transmissions with gear designed for 240 lpm it is necessary only to modify the line printing rate to 48 lpm. Orbital information for APT satellites is transmitted by W1AW during the course of all normally scheduled bulletin transmissions. The techniques described here are indicative of the practical aspects of FAX to be found in any amateur application.

THE K2RNF SYSTEM

The simplicity of this ground station equipment is made possible by the slow-scan APT camera system and the high-power (5-watt) transmitter in the satellite. This combination gives enough signal-to-noise ratio for effective operation without the giant parabolic dish antennas usually associated with satellite signal reception.

With APT the satellite camera shutter is opened briefly, storing the picture in the vidicon camera tube. The picture is then transmitted by slow-scan television, completing the frame in 200 seconds. After 8 seconds for recycling, the operation is repeated. Pictures can be received as long as the satellite is within line of sight to the ground station. Usually, three pictures can be received on each pass.

The simple receiving and display system shown in Fig. 2 was assembled from readily available components, most of them from the junkbox. The crystal-controlled converter for 136.95 MHz was built along the lines of a regular two-meter converter. An outboard i-f for the station receiver was built to increase the bandwidth to 20 kHz and to add an fm discriminator. With this arrangement, the signals were strong enough to be received with a folded dipole antenna laid out on the roof, but there were some obvious nulls from local reflections as the satellite passed over. More work is definitely required here. A dipole in the clear would probably overcome much of the difficulty. The next series of weather satellites will transmit the APT pictures from a horizontal whip, which might seem to be an ideal match to a horizontally polarized rotary beam. However, as the satellite passes a line directly to the east and west of the station, the whip is seen from below one end and the received signal is vertically polarized. Some of

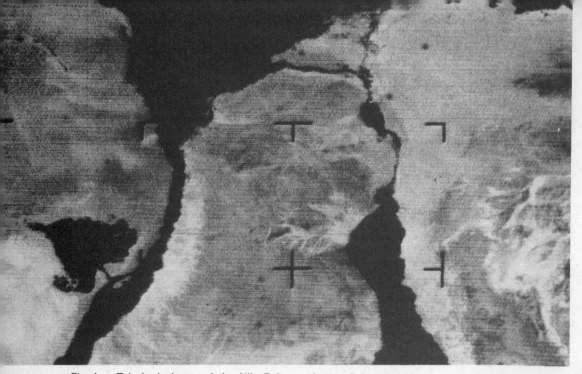

Fig. 1 — Televised picture of the Nile Delta received at Fairbanks, Alaska, during the Nimbus 1 flight using the Advanced Vidicon Camera System (AVCS). The Automatic Picture Transmission (APT) system described in the text gives approximately the same resolution but transmits the picture by slow scan. *(Photo courtesy of Goddard Space Flight Center.)*

the commercial stations get around this problem by using a circularly polarized antenna; others use separate receivers for the horizontal and vertical polarizations with diversity combining at the receiver outputs. The circular polarization appears to be less complex, but has a 3 dB loss compared to matched polarization. The extent of the improvement needed will depend on the picture quality desired, of course.

Receiver System

The rf section of the receiver is quite conventional. A low-noise 2-meter converter, tuned to 136.95 MHz, provides a simple front end. (Provision should also be made for future APT satellites, which will operate near 137.5 MHz.)

The 20-kHz bandwidth of the fm signal is wider than the usual amateur receiver band pass. An auxiliary i-f amplifier and an fm detector were built to give the proper characteristics at 455 kHz. The signal is taken from the mixer output of the receiver. Three stages of i-f amplification are used to provide sufficient limiting and to make up for the loss in gain resulting from the use of 47-KΩ swamping resistors on the primary and secondary of each i-f transformer.

The fm discriminator uses a J.W. Miller 12-C45 transformer and a 6AL5. This combination does not require modification for the 20-kHz bandwidth. The dc output of the discriminator is monitored during signal reception as a tuning indicator. With the i-f bandwidth matched to the signal, it is necessary to compensate for about ± 5 kHz of Doppler shift during a pass.

With the APT signals, the fm discriminator output is an amplitude-modulated 2400-Hz audio tone. This signal was recorded on a stereo tape recorder, with 60 Hz from the ac line used on the second channel for synchronization on playback. Although use of the tape recorder was not absolutely necessary, it provided a means for testing the picture-recording equipment when the satellite was not overhead (which was most of the time, of course).

Picture Recorder

The present recorder is built along the lines of a facsimile recorder, but it is operated in a darkroom instead of having a light-tight case. An 8 × 10 sheet of Royal-X Pan photographic film, wrapped on a rotating drum and secured by double-sided Scotch tape, is exposed to a signal-modulated argon lamp through a reverse 50X microscope. The microscope, working backwards, focuses a highly-demagnified image of the lamp on the film.

Recorder Drum

The drum rotates once for each line of the picture, giving the equivalent of the horizontal scan of a TV picture. A motor-driven lead screw slowly moves the drum and its mount in traverse to give the "vertical" scan.

Only readily available materials and hand tools were used to construct this recorder. After a number of unsuccessful tries, it was apparent that the design would have to accommodate considerable shaft misalignment and relatively poor bearings. The somewhat unconventional mechanical

Fig. 2 — Block diagram of the recording and photo-reproducing system used by K2RNF. A modified version which uses the 2400-Hz audio carrier and frequency dividers to obtain the 60-Hz power for operating the drum-rotation motor is described in the text. The special circuits for the modified arrangement, which requires only a monaural tape recorder, are given in Figs. 6 to 9, inclusive.

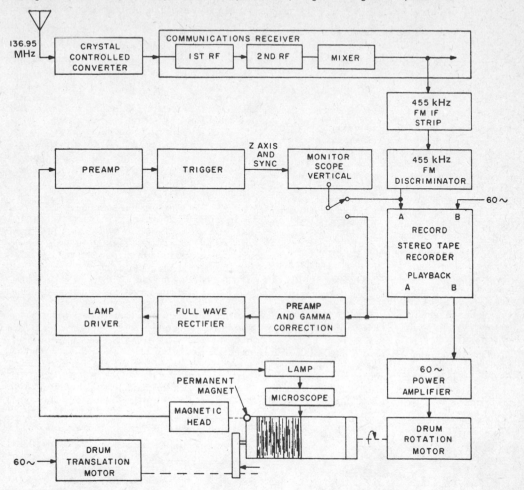

arrangement shown in Fig. 3 has been quite satisfactory, maintaining synchronization, steady traverse, and good focus without the need for delicate adjustment.

The drum itself is a kitchen rolling pin. The original shaft had nylon bearings running on a steel shaft. The left bearing is one of the originals, running on a section of the shaft material. The other is aluminum. All the bearings were made quite thin and slightly oversize to prevent binding due to misalignment of the holes. In the drum shaft coupling to the drive motor, shown in Fig. 4, a rubber band is used to absorb the minor bearing roughness which had previously caused the motor to slip sync occasionally. Direct coupling between the motor and rolling pin can not be used since the motor shaft bearings are quite precise and do not permit enough coupling misalignment.

The drum assembly traverses in a wooden track, driven by a 3/16-inch 24 threaded rod in a tapped plate. The track must be smooth to prevent

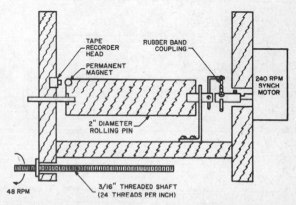

Fig. 3 — The drum and carriage assembly, showing the synchronizing system using a tape-recorder head and permanent magnet. The carriage is moved along a track by the lead screw for line-by-line scanning.

Fig. 4 — Detail of the rubber-band drive.

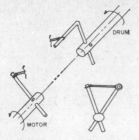

irregular movement, which results in line-pairing or worse. Talcum powder is sparingly used as a lubricant. The bearing for the traverse drive was made from a 3/16-inch lead anchor. It was threaded and locked onto the lead screw; it turns in a 1/4-inch panel bushing. The motor mount is adjustable to remove residual misalignments, which cause a bar pattern in the picture at a five-line pitch (the drum makes five revolutions for each turn of the lead screw.)

Motors and Lamp Driver

The motors are 5-watt Hurst synchronous, Type CA. These inexpensive motors have limited torque, but are adequate with proper care of the bearings. A 240 rpm model is used for drum rotation and a 48 rpm model is used for the traverse lead-screw drive. The layout of the unit is shown in Fig. 5.

The circuit used for driving the AR-3 argon bulb is shown in Fig. 6. Several more complex arrangements were tried, but this one worked quite well. At the beginning, provision was made for assurance that the bulb would fire at low signal

levels. However, this is apparently not a problem, since no threshold is observed down to currents less than 1% of full drive. The space between the AR-3 electrodes should be made vertical to avoid line-pairing when the position of the glow discharge shifts.

Film Exposure and Development

The overall linearity of the signal driver circuit was adjusted by the 1N1763 networks to give a fairly good gray scale match between the APT signal and the Royal-X Pan film. The APT signal characteristic provides equal signal level steps for each gray step. By setting the sync pulses to 7.5 volts peak-to-peak at test point A in Fig. 6, the networks correct the gamma to provide equal density steps on the film for equal signal amplitude steps. The film was developed as recommended by Kodak to achieve a gamma of 1.0 (10 minutes in HC-110 diluted 1:15).

Synchronization Techniques

In setting up the recorder at the beginning of a picture, it is necessary to synchronize the drum and the tape recorder. The drum motor is driven by a 60-Hz signal derived from the timing track, but the start of the picture must be synchronized with the edge of the film — otherwise, the negative will have to be cut to get the proper picture. To monitor the position of the drum (and the edge of the film) with respect to the incoming sync pulse, a tape recorder head (spare part for a portable transistorized tape recorder) and a permanent magnet are used. The magnet is fastened on the drum in such a position that it passes the recorder head, fixed on the frame, at the place where the film edge passes the modulated light source. The pulse from the recorder head is amplified and

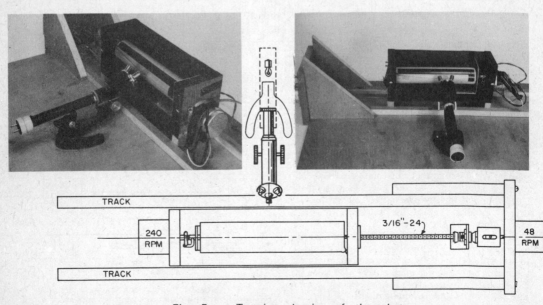

Fig. 5 — Top-view drawing of the photo-reproduction assembly. Photographs show the equipment from two different angles.

Fig. 6 — Lamp driver and preamplifier. Fixed resistors are 1/2 watt; fixed capacitors may be ceramic or paper except those with polarity indicated (electrolytic).

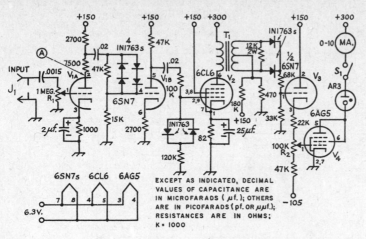

J₁—Phono jack.
R₁—Audio-taper control.
R₂—Linear-taper control.
S₁—S p s t toggle.
T₁—Driver transformer, 3:1 pri. to ½ sec., 30-ma. primary (Stancor A-4723).

EXCEPT AS INDICATED, DECIMAL VALUES OF CAPACITANCE ARE IN MICROFARADS (μf.); OTHERS ARE IN PICOFARADS (pf. OR μμf.); RESISTANCES ARE IN OHMS; K = 1000

Fig. 7 — Synchronizing-indicator circuit. Capacitor with polarity indicated is electrolytic; others may be paper or ceramic. Fixed resistors are 1/2 watt.

R1 — Linear-taper control.

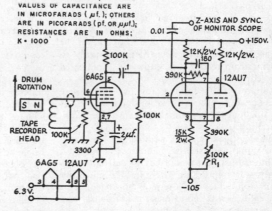

EXCEPT AS INDICATED, DECIMAL VALUES OF CAPACITANCE ARE IN MICROFARADS (μf.); OTHERS ARE IN PICOFARADS (pf. OR μμf.); RESISTANCES ARE IN OHMS; K = 1000

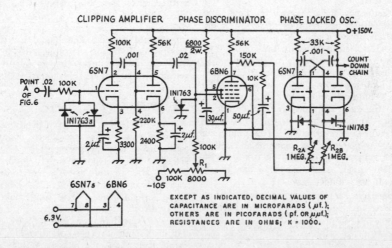

Fig. 8 — Phase-locked oscillator circuit. Capacitors with polarity indicated are electrolytic; others may be paper or ceramic. Fixed resistors are 1/2 watt.

R1 — Linear-taper control.
R2 — Dual control, linear taper.

Fig. 9 — Frequency divider, 2400 to 60 Hz. Capacitors are paper or ceramic; fixed resistors are 1/2 watt.

RI, R2 — Dual control, linear taper.

R3, R4 — Dual control, linear taper.

T1 — Small output transformer primary tuned by C1 to 60 Hz. Capacitance of C1 may need to be varied to obtain resonance; value given (1μF) is based on an inductance of about 7 henrys.

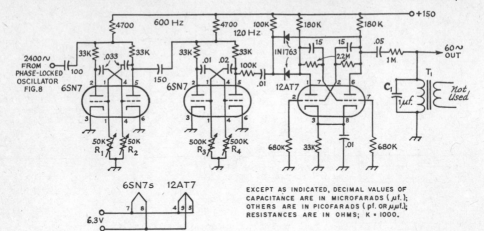

EXCEPT AS INDICATED, DECIMAL VALUES OF CAPACITANCE ARE IN MICROFARADS (μf.); OTHERS ARE IN PICOFARADS (pf. OR $\mu\mu$f.); RESISTANCES ARE IN OHMS; K = 1000.

shaped with the circuit shown in Fig. 7, then used to Z-axis modulate the monitor scope. This signal can also be used for scope sync. In operation the drum motor drive is interrupted momentarily to allow the drum to slip back into sync, as indicated on the scope.

Maintaining synchronism for the drum drive depends on the exact 15:1 relationship between the 60-Hz line and the horizontal line rate generated in the satellite.

A stable 60-Hz oscillator with vernier frequency control could be used to maintain the required sync, but adjustment would be difficult, although certainly not impossible. The 2400-Hz subcarrier frequency provides an alternate approach. This frequency is exactly 600 times the horizontal scan frequency, related by a count-down chain in the satellite.

A 40:1 frequency divider is used on the ground to derive the 60-Hz drum motor drive. Since the signal is often noisy, a phase-locked oscillator is used to provide a clean signal to the count-down chain. These circuits are shown in Figs. 8 and 9. The PLO circuit has given excellent results, holding synchronism during fades of several seconds. To achieve this holding ability, the oscillator was adjusted to free-run at the proper frequency with zero signal-to-noise ratio by observing the drift in synchronization after a signal fade. These fades are automatically available at the beginning and end of a pass. This adjustment is relatively simple with tape-recorded signals, since the tape can be re-played several times if necessary.

This approach has the further advantage of being operable with a single tape-recorder channel (monaural instead of stereo).

Conclusion

The choice of components was primarily determined by the availability of parts in the junk-box and the most inexpensive components obtainable.

The microscope is from Edmund Scientific Co. but almost any low power microscope should work as long as the image of the light source is about the same size as the line-to-line spacing on the film.

The photographic film negative size was determined by the circumference of the rolling pin. The traverse motor speed and lead screw threads per inch are set to give a picture that is approximately square. If a photographic enlarger is available, a smaller diameter drum and slower traverse might be used to get all three pictures for one pass on a single strip of film. The microscope would have to be higher power to accommodate the smaller line-to-line spacing, and somewhat more care in the mechanical construction would be required.

The electronics used for driving the AR-3 and in the synchronizing circuits are not particularly critical since they operate at mid-audio frequencies. The tube types already on hand determine the design in most cases; many of the tubes used were 20-year-old surplus. The liberal use of 1N1763's was primarily due to their low price. Their 500 mA 400-volt rating reduced the amount of calculation required to be sure of safe operation.

THE W4MKM SYSTEM

All of the circuitry of K2RNF's system (previous section) was assembled on a dismantled sideband chassis measuring 11 by 17 by 3 inches. The panel, a stiff power supply good for 300 volts at 200 MA, an auxiliary filament transformer, and a VR-105 arrangement for negative biasing voltage were left in place. Some tube sockets were relocated for better layout. The countdown chain for Fig. 9 was built on a 5 1/4 by 3 by 2-inch Minibox with its base bolted to the back of the panel well above the chassis, with tubes mounted horizontally to the rear, and with control knobs on the upper side for access. The isolation of this circuit proved advantageous. To the main chassis

APT SIGNAL DESCRIPTION

Carrier:	136.950 MHz
Modulation:	f m
Deviation:	± 10 kHz
Subcarrier:	2400 Hz
Modulation:	a-m
Polarity:	Max. amplitude sync. 80% amplitude max. white
Video:	0–1600 Hz
Line Rate:	4 per second
Frame Time:	208 seconds
Gamma:	Equal voltage increments per gray step
Orbit Parameters:	
Duration of Overhead Pass:	approximately 10 minutes, or about 3 frames
Sun synchronous, 80° retrograde.	

were added three VR-150s and a four-stage Class-A amplifier with a tube line up consisting of a half-12AT7 preamp., 6C4 driver, and 6550 output. The last three were given fixed grid bias, with 250 volts on plates and screen grids. The 6L6 was first tried as the output tube but the 6550 had to be added to take the drum motor load at 115 volts ac with a good sine wave. The impedance match was good at 2600 ohms, with the motor fed through five 1-μF 600-volt capacitors in parallel. The motor holds sync speed down to about 80 volts. The 1-volt peak-to-peak from the count-down is controlled at the 12AT7 grid to regulate the voltage output to the motor.

No great difficulty was encountered except that synchronization became restless at times. To cure this a separate small power supply was built with two VR-150s separately feeding Figs. 8 and 9. At K2RNF's suggestion the grid of the 6CL6, Fig. 6, was isolated by a 1000-ohm resistor with a 30-μF electrolytic behind it to ground the wide voltage fluctuations at the 6CL6 grid.

If it were being done over again, all four of K2RNF's circuits would be built in separate shielded boxes with a VR-150 on each box. Good isolation, however obtained, is important.

Drum Assembly

The drum and carriage assembly of Fig. 5 was built on a 13 by 29-inch piece of 3/4-inch marine plywood with black Formica applied to the upper surface with pressure cement. Two 3/4-inch square rails were cut from the base material and fastened to the base with screws to form the track. Formica pieces 3/4 by 1 inch were glued to the bottom and sides of the front and rear carriage legs to provide smooth bearing surfaces. All burrs were sanded smooth. The rolling pin was equipped with two 1/4-inch stub shafts of drill rod. After the shafts were cemented in with epoxy, the drum was mounted in 1/4-inch ball bearings in the end pieces

of the carriage. A small pulley was temporarily fixed to a shaft end and the drum was driven in its bearings for sanding to a smooth concentric finish of uniform diameter. A small planetary universal joint, made of thin sheet rubber of extreme flexibility, was used to couple the drum to the motor, which was mounted with adjusting screws for alignment. The 3/16-inch-24 transverse screw was carefully selected for straightness. It was coupled to the motor shaft with a short piece of 3/16-inch ID tubing cemented to the motor shaft and screw with epoxy. The screw was lined up true, with minimum wobble, just before the epoxy glue set. The drum magnet, about 3/16-inch square by 3/4-inch long, came from the corner of a cloth potholder. The pickup coil was made with a 1/4-inch stack of 1/4-inch U laminations cut from E's, with about 1200 turns of No. 42 enameled wire

It was found later that even a slight wobble in the screw caused banding in the picture, while a slight misalignment of the drum motor shaft caused the drum to oscillate with resultant wiggles in the picture, most apparent in the fiduciary marks. The black strip of tape shown on the drum in Fig. 5 is used to locate one edge of the film, which is fastened to the drum with double "stick-um" tape applied to the upper and lower back edges of the film. The lower edge is pressed down on the drum against the edge of the black tape guide and then wrapped around the drum, and the other edge pressed down to hold the film firmly on the drum. It would appear that overlapping to some degree is advantageous, depending, of course, on the size of film used. The guide tape must be located experimentally with respect to the magnet, depending also on the film size and direction of rotation.

The two black squares near one end of the drum in Fig. 5 are part of 15 equally spaced markings of uniform size around the drum. When viewed under a stroboscopic lamp with line AC voltage these marks stand perfectly still when the drum is rotating at 240 rpm or 4 revolutions per second, the speed synchronous with the frequency of 60 Hz divided from the satellite carrier frequency of 2400 Hz. The markings, although remaining relatively stationary, may oscillate to some degree. This is usually caused by slight binding of the drum motor shaft. In aligning the motor by means of the adjustment screws the disappearance of oscillations will coincide with very little or no noise from the motor gear train.

Receiver

While the electrical circuitry and facsimile were being built a single dipole cut for 137.5 MHz and fed with 52-ohm coax was erected about 15 feet above the roof. An Ameco 2-meter converter very similar to the 144-MHz converter described in the ARRL *Handbook* was used. No difficulty was experienced in peaking the converter for 137.5 MHz in and 43 MHz out for the i-f strip of a modified TV chassis to which a tunable oscillator was added.

The dipole brought in strong but rapidly fading

signals from Essa II – enough, however, to peak the converter and test out the whole rig for synchronization, lamp modulation and general stability. No attempt was made to print pictures at this stage.

Notes on Synchronization

In the matter of synchronization, K2RNF suggested two changes in Fig. 8 of his article to improve the operation of the locked-phase oscillator: the addition of two 1N1763 diodes, back to back, in parallel with the 220-kΩ resistor at pin 4 of the 6SN7 clipper tube, and a 68-kΩ resistor instead of the 150-kΩ resistor at the 6BN6 plate, pin 7.

The writer's experience in attaining reliable synchronization involved the following prodecures:

With a 7-volt peak-to-peak signal at Point A, Fig. 6, from a tape recording of a satellite signal with a 4-Hz pulse and 2400-Hz carrier, the vertical oscilloscope input was connected to the output of the oscillator, pin 5 of Fig. 8. R2 was adjusted until oscillations started and synchronized on the scope at 2400 Hz. The signal was removed and the frequency drifted. It was interesting to see the wave pull in to synchronization when the signal was again applied to Point A. R2 was carefully adjusted close to the sync point, and the dc voltage at pin 7 of the 6BN6 plate was measured on a VTVM. Rl, the 8000-ohm resistor in the 6BN6 grid circuit, was then adjusted to give the same voltage both with and without a signal at Point A. After this the scope pattern remained unchanged for an appreciable time after the signal was removed to simulate a short fade in the signal from a satellite.

With the oscillator performing well in locked phase condition the dual potentiometers R1-R2 in the countdown chain, Fig. 9, were adjusted to give a small 60-Hz output across the resonant tank, the capacitor of which (C1) was adjusted to give an output of about 1 volt peak-to-peak The 240-rpm drum motor was connected to the Class A amplifier, which was adjusted for 115 volts output. Rotating in response to the 60-Hz input, the drum showed the 15 equally spaced lines on the drum surface as standing perfectly still, indicating good synchronization with the signal at Point A.

At this point the resistances of the dual potentiometers of Figs. 8 and 9 were measured. A pair of matched 1/2-watt resistors corresponding to the measured resistances of R3 and R4 was substituted for those potentiometers, which seemed to be noncritical. R1 and R2 were replaced by a 10-kΩ dual pot with 6800Ω 5% 1/2-watt resistors in series with each leg.

The 500-kΩ pots were used to replace the 1-MΩ dual pot R2 of Fig. 8. Matched 470-kΩ 1/2-watt resistors were connected across the outer terminals of the 500-kΩ dual pot with no series resistors.

If after the above adjustments the synchronization is still unstable the trouble is probably due to the pulse getting into the countdown chain, most likely through the power-supply lines. This will explain why it is necessary to go to extremes to isolate the 150-volt lines to the various sections of the overall circuitry.

The Helical Antenna

The second stage of progress began with the building of the helix. A few details of the method of construction will be given. Dimensions were

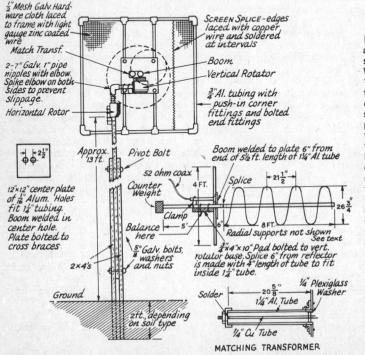

Fig. 10 — Sketch of the helical antenna built for weather-satellite reception by W4MKM. Dimensions are for 137.5 MHz. The tubing and fittings used in the frame were obtained from Sears. Rotator shafts are clamped tight to pipe nipples with U bolts; rotator leads and coax cable are fastened to the pole and looped at the top to clear the counterweight. The antenna end of the matching transformer is fastened in the hole in the center plate with screws and nuts, using four angle clamps held on the tube with short sheet-metal screws. After assembly the Plexiglas washer should be doped with epoxy for waterproofing. The aluminum end cap is made of sheet material fastened to the tube with sheet-metal screws, and is mounted after the inner conductor is soldered to the coax fitting. The rest of the antenna, exclusive of rotators, was about $20.

calculated for 137.5 MHz from data given by W1CER in his article on helical beams. The antenna is supported on a 2 x 4 pole mounted between two oak 2 x 4's, (Fig. 10) anchored in the ground. The anchoring bolt at the lower end of the pole is removed when the antenna is lowered for servicing by means of a rope tied to the end of the pole. The bolt is replaced to provide a convenient hitch for the hauling rope.

When the boom was ready for the helix wire it was supported horizontally at a convenient height. Starting 9 inches from the screen, rings were scratched around the boom tubing at intervals of 7 1/6 inch. Three notches 120 degrees apart were filed in the end of the tube, from which three lines were stretched taut and fastened to the screen so that they were parallel to the tube axis and 120 degrees apart all the way. At points of intersection between these lines and the circular spacing lines, 3/8-inch holes were drilled, with 1/8-inch holes at the opposite side of the tubing. These holes progress spirally at 120 degrees outward toward the end. Thirteen pieces of 3/8-inch doweling were cut to 14-inch length, and beveled slightly at both ends. A 1/4 by 1/8-inch deep slot was filed in one end and a 1/8-inch hole drilled about one inch deep in the center of the other end. The inside ends were anchored with 1/8-inch nails pushed in lightly.

In mounting the helix wire on the radials, a coil of about 35 feet of aluminum clothes line was worked out into a 30-inch diameter and one end hooked into the wire screen near the transformer terminal. The coil was then drawn out over the dowels and the wire loosely tied to the radial ends as the turns moved out. Then by working back and forth the helix was formed with uniform diameter and spacing and lashed firmly into the slots of the radial supports. The nails anchoring the radials in the boom and the wire lashings were doped with epoxy cement. The outer end of the helix was clipped at about 1/8 turn beyond four full turns, and the other end was curved down and inserted into the transformer inner tube. A small hole was drilled and tapped through both members. A small brass screw and nut tightened the joint, which was then taped with plastic adhesive tape. A counterweight of about two pounds was fastened to the rear end of the boom. The dowel radial supports were varnished with spar varnish and the assembly set aside in a warm dry place where the epoxy would cure before being exposed to the weather.

In mounting the boom on its pad the rotators were lowered and the completed antenna was hauled into position. (Before raising or lowering, the rear boom extension should be tied to the pole to hold the boom parallel with the pole; this avoids undue strain on the rotator gears.) The coax cable was connected to the transformer and dressed together with the rotator control cable to avoid interference with the boom end when traveling in a vertical position. Good braking is necessary on the vertical rotator. Channel Master rotators with updated automatic braking were used.

While the front-to-side ratio seems good, the front to back ratio is not very good. This could no doubt be improved by clipping the end and checking with a small signal from a remotely-located oscillator. In the present location this has not yet seemed necessary. The location is relatively free from man-made noises, but unfortunately is surrounded by tall trees with very little sky in the clear. Despite this the antenna works well in most directions. There is some fading from Nimbus II as it travels at a low angle from due south. This may be due to Doppler shift, as the receiver discriminator appears to be a little off center. There is no fading as the satellite recedes to the north where the forest is just as thick. This problem has yet to be explored.

Tracking is easily done visually since the antenna is only 25 feet from the shack and in plain view. K2RNF tracks successfully by watching the rotator indicator compass bearings. W4RNT has devised an ingenious device which tracks from a tape, punched for a predetermined orbital path. However, tracking is one of the least worries since most passes can be tracked with only four or five movements, and good pictures in certain directions have been made with no movement of the antenna for over three minutes.

Considering the fact that the helix is mounted directly under an ancient oak tree with a dozen or more tall oaks and pines within 50 yards in all directions, it would appear that man-made noises, especially automobile ignition noises, are the worst enemy to good reception and not intervening objects. Pictures have been made from signals 10 degrees above the horizon with trees running from directly overhead to a half mile in the direction of the satellite.

Receiver Changes

When the helical antenna was hooked up the receiver performed much better. In fact, quite a number of acceptable pictures were made from Essa II with this setup. However, the absence of limiting made it necessary to ride the tuner — a bothersome chore — while watching the antenna for tracking.

This led to a search for a receiver with double crystal control and good limiting qualities. Such a receiver was found. A Sensicon PA8616A-12 chassis was bought at very low cost from a surplus list. It came with a front-end crystal in an oven, which called for a converter crystal to deliver 49.540 MHz to the receiver. Two such crystals were obtained from International, for Essa II and Nimbus II. At the same time a small International transistor oscillator with interchangeable crystals for 136.95 and 137.5 MHz output was purchased. This little oscillator has earned its cost as a check on antenna, converter and receiver performance.

The Sensicon "A" chassis with its 18 good tubes also had a second i-f conversion crystal, two stages of limiting, a Permakay 8436A wide-band filter, a differential noise silencer, and a convenient control switch socket. The control switch was mounted on a small chassis with a 150-volt power supply and a 0-200 microammeter to indicate deviation. A high-impedance source was found ahead of the audio power tube for connection to

Fig. 11 — Lamp and lens mounting. Dimensions are for a lens having a focal length of 1 inch. Height of this assembly should be adjusted carefully to put the light spot exactly on the drum center line, and the

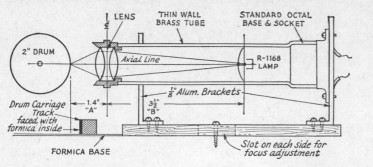

beam should be at right angles to the drum surface. For lenses of other focal length, dimension B should be three or more times the lens focal length.

Then

$$A = \frac{BF}{B - F}$$

where F is the focal length.

the mike input of the tape recorder. Receiver audio output was adjusted to a medium level and volume controlled at the recorder amplifier.

Lamp Change

After a period of time, a Sylvania modulation glow lamp, type R-1168, having a rated life of 150 hours with an average current of 15 mA was substituted for the AR-3 lamp. It was mounted in one end of a thin-wall brass tube with the lens fitted at the other end. The tube is supported on a sliding base for focusing.

The 800 picture lines on a 2-inch drum have apporximately 0.008-inch spacing. A light spot of

0.006-inch diameter was thought to be about right. The lens mounting dimensions are given in Fig. 11.

The thickness of the wooden base is such as to bring the light spot level with the drum center. Screws through the slots at each side are permanently tightened when the lens is in focus. The brass tube, a plumbing item, was found in a hardware store. One end is slightly larger than the main tube diameter and fits snugly over the R-1168 base. To avoid reflections from the glass tube end, the end is covered with black adhesive tape or paint except for a small circular aperture at the center. Diaphragm opening, not shown, is adjustable from $f/32$ to $f/1.9$. A 1-inch focal length

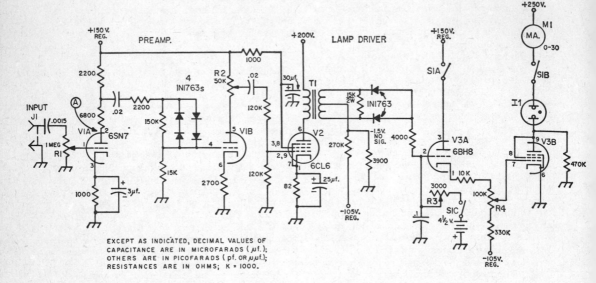

Fig. 12 — The W4MKM lamp driver and pre-amplifier for positive printing. This circuit is a modification of Fig. 6 in K2RNF's. The 6BH8 was substituted for the 6SN7-6AG5 combination in the original circuit because the pentode section of the 6BH8 has relatively high plate/screen current, desirable for the R-1168 lamp. Capacitors with polarity marked are electrolytic; others are ceramic or mica. Unless otherwise indicated, fixed resistors are 1/2-watt composition. The series resistance in the cathode circuit of V3A (shown as

330-kΩ above) should be adjusted to obtain proper control of V3B grid bias through R4.

I1 — Modulation glow lamp, Sylvania type R-1168.
J1 — Phone connector.
M1 — 0-30 dc milliammeter
R1 — Audio-taper control.
R2, R3, R4 — Linear-taper control.
S1 — 3-pole single-throw, any type.
T1 — Driver transformer, 3:1 primary to 1/2 secondary 30-mA primary (Stancor A-4723 or equivalent).

lens is convenient for compact design, but lenses with other focal lengths can be used. The lens speed should be at least $f/4$. The lens is focused wide open and then stopped down according to the sensitivity of the film in use.

A darkroom adjacent to the operating bench has proved to be most convenient. A room four feet square was constructed of Masonite at one end of the bench, which extends through it. Inside the room, the top of the bench was enclosed for a height of 24 inches, with a sliding panel in vertical grooves for access to the enclosure. The drum mechanism is located on the bench inside this inner darkroom, and control wires run through the main darkroom wall.

A safelight in the outer darkroom is kept on while loading and unloading the drum. After the drum has been loaded and its position checked, closing the sliding panel makes the inner enclosure light-tight.

Positive Printing

With the helix antenna, a good receiver and the R-1168 lamp in operation, many good pictures were captured so many, in fact, that the cost of about 70¢ per picture for film and paper became a matter of concern. It was decided to try for positive printing within the framework of K2RNF's circuitry.

First came the matter of finding a photographic paper with enough sensitivity to respond to the small amount of available light. Correspondence with the Eastman Kodak Co. brought sympathetic response with samples of exceptionally fast papers, but with the notation that the papers were not available except in prohibitive minimum quantities. Kodabromide Grade I was suggested as our best chance. Some Kodabromide F-1 sheets were obtained and printed as negatives. With lamp-current peaks of 20 mA some good negative prints were made.

The next step was that of inverting the lamp drive for positive printing. The diodes at the secondary of T1, Fig. 6, were reversed. Then came the cut-and-try process of adjusting the bias of the cathode-follower tube, its cathode resistance, and the other circuitry of Fig. 6 to give a good grey scale. The final circuit as modified for positive printing is given in Fig. 12 and the lamp current in relationship to signal voltage at point A is charted

in Fig. 13. All work was concentrated on optimum biasing for positive prints on Kodabromide Grade I paper. Fig. 12 shows the biasing arrangement as it is at present. Although there is no assurance that this is the final answer, scores of acceptable positive prints have been made from Nimbus II signals. Landmarks have shown up from the Pacific Coast of Southern Mexico to the eastern coast of Labrador. All of one season's hurricanes were captured, some with landmarks to orient them accurately. The photographic work has been speeded up to the point where a picture shot by Nimbus II over Cuba can be inspected in daylight while signals are still coming in from the same pass to the north. The paper is insensitive to an amber safe light, so the paper can be applied to the drum and all photographic work done with fair visibility. Finally, the cost has come down to about 10 cents a picture. Kodabromide F-1 paper with standard processing using Ektol developer, a stop solution, and hypo fixer make up the photographic procedure.

Since duplicates are seldom needed it is the writer's practice to print the picture as it is being received. Recordings are useful, however, for checking synchronization or for making duplicate pictures. For this, the tape recording heads must be frequently cleaned and the reel tensions kept within specifications However, even with the best of care the taped pictures are seldom as good as those printed directly from the satellite signals.

In Fig. 12, R3 is used to adjust the lamp current to near cutoff with 7.5 volts peak-to-peak at point A. R4 is used to adjust the maximum lamp current with no signal at point A.

Practice is required in adjusting the gain when pictures are printed directly, since adjustments during the transmission period usually result in banded areas. The signal level is more easily set with a tape recording, as a test run can first be made. In positive printing, experience is the best guide in setting R3 and R4 for the paper used. In addition to audible monitoring with a small speaker, the scope pattern at point A is observed, preferably on a calibrated scope. The writer has also monitored with a VTVM connected to point A, using a 14-volt peak-to-peak scale, but this gives only a rough idea of signal peaks because of meter damping Here, also, some experience is helpful. This problem has not been completely resolved.

Fig. 13 — Peak to peak ac voltage at Point A, Fig. 12 vs. current in I1. The curve was made by using a 2400-Hz audio voltage applied through J1. R4 was set for 20 mA lamp current with no signal, and R3 was set for 2.5 mA lamp current with 7 volts peak-to-peak at point A, in obtaining the solid curve. Dashed curves show effect of changing the setting of R3 with R4 left unchanged.

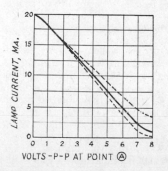

The 137.5-MHz circularly-polarized helical antenna built by W4MKM for reception of weather satellites. It is rotated in both azimuth and elevation.

CATHODE RAY TUBE DISPLAY UNIT
FOR SATELLITE WEATHER PICTURES

The picture-reproducing system described here permits use of an ordinary camera for recording the weather-pictures transmitted by the satellites. Relatively simple circuits are used, with horizontal synchronizing controlled by pulses included in the picture transmission. An oscilloscope-readout facsimile device allows use of standard photographic methods. The surplus advertisements were examined for a suitable scope tube, and a 5CP11 was located. The P11 phosphor is short-persistance, which is just right for photography.

Since there is no mechanical movement in the reproducing system it was unnecessary to provide 60-Hz power for driving a synchronous motor, and since the light for photography is provided by the CR tube an argon lamp was not needed. The picture-synchronizing system used here resembles, in principle, the synchronizing methods used in television reception.

The Horizontal Circuit

The horizontal sync circuit, Fig. 1, makes use of the 12.5-millisecond pulse transmitted at the beginning of each line. The output of the video demodulator (Fig. 4) is applied to one section of a 12AU7 where the video is removed and only a small percentage of the 12.5-ms sync pulse remains. This pulse is amplified by two more 12AU7 sections and is then applied to a differentiation network. The output from the network triggers the 6AU6 phantastron* sweep circuit shown in Fig. 2. The HEP-l58 diode is used as a gate to make the operation more stable, as this synchronizing system is amplitude-sensitive and therefore subject to interference from random noise pulses.

The phantastron generates a 250-millisecond ramp voltage which is adjusted for the proper period by means of the timing control. The diode-connected 12AU7 section, in combination with the 0B2 voltage-regulator tube, holds the ramp voltage to a 105-volt level. The ramp generator output is coupled to the push-pull deflection

amplifier through a 12AU7 section used as a cathode follower and the 12AV7 deflection amplifier/phase inverter permits centering the ramp voltage sweep on the CR tube screen. The sweep is from 16 volts positive to 16 volts negative, with the bucking circuit adjusting the zero crossing point for centering.

Vertical Sync

The vertical ramp generator is a Miller rundown circuit* driving a vertical amplifier. The rundown is started by removing the negative 105 volts dc from the grid network of the first tube section in Fig. 3 by opening the sweep/reset switch. This allows the 24-μF capacitor (which must be nonpolarized — paper, oil, etc. — and have very low leakage) to discharge through the network resistors.

The bucking circuit at the 12AV7 vertical-amplifier grid has the same function in the vertical system as in the horizontal sweep circuit described earlier.

CRT Circuit

The video signal input (modulated 2400-Hz tone from the receiver or a tape recording) goes to the 4-ohm winding of an output transformer, T1 in Fig. 4, to be stepped up to a level suitable for driving the cathode-ray tube grid. The output is converted to varying dc by a bridge rectifier and coupled to the CR tube through a 500-pF capacitor. The rectifier gives a positive signal for driving the CRT grid.

The signal can be monitored through a phone jack connected to the 4-ohm winding of T1 in series with a 47-ohm resistor.

Power Supplies

Two power supplies are used. One, shown in Fig. 5, furnishes the low voltages required: 350

---

* Millman and Taub, *Pulse and Digital Circuits*, pp. 221 and 217 (McGraw-Hill Book Co., New York).

Facsimile

A satellite weather picture reproduced by the system described in the text. This was transmitted by Nimbus II in a passage over the West Coast.

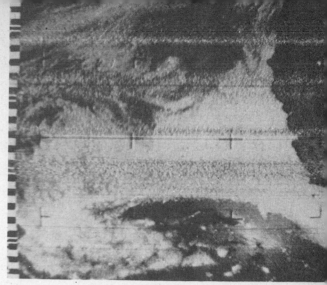

volts dc without voltage regulation, 220 volts dc electronically regulated, and −105 volts dc for bias, regulated by a VR tube, as well as heater power for all tubes except the 5CP11. The regulator circuit for the 220-volt output was taken from the *Handbook*.

The second supply develops the high voltage for the cathode-ray tube. Fig. 6 is the circuit of this supply. Note that there are two half-wave rectifier/filter circuits, each producing about 1800 volts dc, one positive and the other negative with respect to ground. Thus the total voltage applied to the CR-tube circuit is approximately 3600 volts. approximately 3600 volts.

Construction

With the exception of the power supplies, all circuits are built on a 17 x 12 x 2-inch chassis. The layout is shown in the photographs. The timing controls and bucking controls are mounted on the chassis near their respective vacuum tubes. The signal-input and monitor-speaker jacks are on the rear apron as are also the astigmatism control and power supply input connections.

All other controls are on the 9 × 12-inch front panel, along with the CR-tube bezel.

Separate cables are used to connect the power supplies to the scope unit in order to minimize magnetic interference. While it may be possible to operate the CR tube without the shield, there is always the problem of magnetic interference. Sometimes a scope shield complete with mounting hardware can be salvaged from a surplus radar indicator.

The brightness and focusing controls should be submounted on an insulated plate and their shafts should be isolated from the control knobs by insulated couplings, since these controls are at high voltage with respect to chassis.

Setup and Operation

To adjust the phantastron circuit, set the triggering control at zero resistance and couple an oscilloscope probe to the plate of the phantastron tube. Then turn the triggering control toward maximum resistance, and at some point the circuit should start generating a free running ramp voltage. Adjust the timing control for a repetition rate of 250 milliseconds (four sweeps per second),and then back off the triggering control toward minimum resistance until the circuit just stops running free.

At this point it is necessary to use an APT signal, which may be from a tape recording made earlier. With a signal from the video demodulator applied to the input in Fig. 1, the negative sync pulses coming out of the pulse amplifier will trigger the phantastron and the ramp will be locked at a rate of 250 milliseconds. Slight readjustments of the timing control probably will be needed for optimum operation.

In the vertical deflection circuit, the Miller rundown is initiated by opening the sweep/reset switch, with the test/use switch closed. Adjust the timing control for a 200-second ramp.

Opening the test/use switch removes the 24-µF timing capacitor from the circuit and allows the

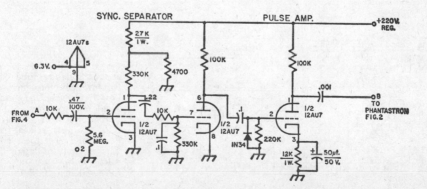

Fig. 1 — Line synchronizing circuit. Capacitances are in µF. Capacitors are paper, 600-volt, except as indicated; capacitors with polarity indicated are electrolytic. Resistances are in ohms (k = 1000); resistors are 1/2-watt except as indicated.

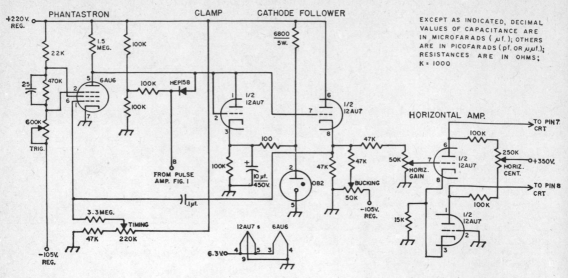

Fig. 2 — Horizontal sweep and deflection circuit. Capacitor with polarity indicated is electrolytic. Fixed resistors are 1/2-watt except as indicated. Variable resistors are composition controls, linear taper.

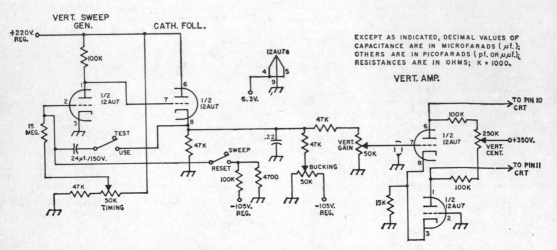

Fig. 3 — Vertical sweep and deflection circuit. The vertical sweep is started manually for each frame. Switches are spdt toggles; variable resistors are composition controls, linear taper.

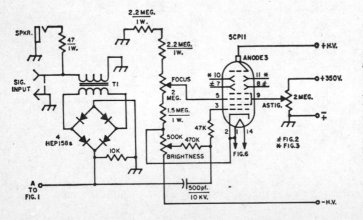

Fig. 4 — Video demodulator and cathode-ray tube circuit. Resistances are in ohms (k=1000); except as indicated, fixed resistors are 1/2-watt. Variable resistors are composition controls, linear taper. Focus and brightness control must be well insulated. T1 is a 5000/4-ohm output transformer (Knight 54B 1403).

Fig. 5 — Low-voltage power supply. Capacitors with polarity indicated are electrolytic. Resistances are in ohms (k=1000); except as indicated, fixed resistors are 1/2-watt. Variable resistor is a composition control, linear taper.

L1 — 8 henrys, 85 mA (Knight 54B 1485).
J1 — Chassis-mounting ac socket, female.
T2 — 125 volts, 50 mA; 6.3 volts, 2A (Knight 54B 1411).
T3 — 700 volts ct, 90 mA; 5 volts, 3 amp.; 6.3 volts, 3.5A. (Knight 54B 1429).

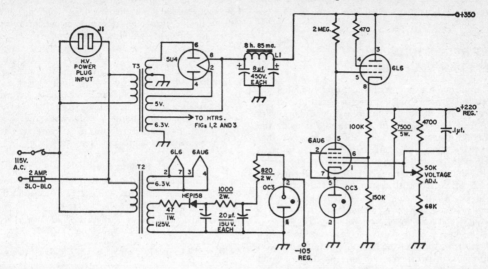

operator to adjust the vertical gain (Fig. 3) for proper deflection.

The bucking controls of both horizontal and vertical sections are adjusted to produce a signal that swings from positive through zero to negative polarity with equal-amplitude maximum voltages of both polarities. The voltage excursions can be measured with a dc coupled scope connected at the high ends of the gain controls.

The astigmatism control, Fig. 4, should be adjusted in conjunction with the focus control to give a sharp trace.

Adjust the signal input amplitude and the brightness control for a suitable picture; this probably will require some experimentation. The first line of the picture is at the top of the CRT face, with the horizontal sweep starting at the left.

Adjustment of the synchronizing and deflection circuits, if carried out as described above, can be done without applying high voltage to the CR tube. Extreme care should be used when the high voltage is on, and a metal enclosure grounded to the chassis should be used in regular operation.

Photography

The camera presently used here is a 35-mm Praktica with a Zeiss $f/2$ 58 mm lens. A 10-mm extension was used to allow the distance to the CRT face to be 10.5 inches.

The lens iris is set at $f/8$, and at the beginning of a picture sweep the shutter is opened by a cable release and locked. The monitor speaker is a great

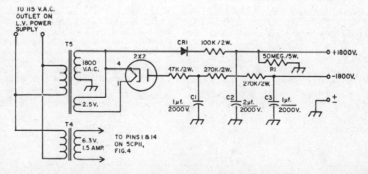

Fig. 6 — High-voltage supply for cathode-ray tube. Resistances are in ohms (k=1000); resistors are composition.
C1, C2, C3 — Paper or oil-filled.
CR1 — Selenium, 6500 volts PRV (International Rectifier 61-8969).

R1 — Five 10-megohm, 1-watt composition resistors in series.
T4 — 6.3 volts, 1.2 A; 5000-volt insulation (Knight 54B 3715).
T5 — 1800 volts, 2 mA; 2.5 volts, 1.8 A (Knight 54B 3727).

help at this time. At the end of the 200-second vertical sweep interval the shutter is closed. The pictures are taken in a darkened room, using tape recordings of the satellite passes as the signal source.

There is no reason why a Polaroid camera could not be used, perhaps with the use of a close-up lens kit.

APT RECEPTION WITH TELEFAX RECEIVERS

Considerable interest in adapting the plentiful Western Union Telefax unit for satellite pictures has seemed evident. The following details were supplied by W6WMI, on a method for using the Telefax machine to record the 48 lpm weather photos generated by current weather satellites, as well as those still in the planning stages at present.

The reception of the satellite signal, approx. 137.5 MHz, is the first step. Here the articles by K2RNF, W4MKM, and 2-meter information in *The Radio Amateur's VHF Manual* are the starting point. Hand-held dipoles operated in the shack or the backyard with a little experience will often outperform some of the complex antennas now in use, so keep it simple, at least at first. A good converter is a must, and remember, the receiver must be fm and have a 20-kHz bandwidth or more.

The second hurdle in the project is the construction of a standard-frequency generator putting out exactly 16 Hz. This is best done by dividing down from a 1.6-MHz crystal oscillator with five decade counters. The oscillator must be exactly on frequency or skewing of the picture will result. Use of compression type crystals which can be adjusted by either loading with a pencil or solder, or by grinding with kitchen cleanser such as Ajax, is desirable. An alternate arrangement is to use a circuit with provisions for trimming the crystal frequency. The need for the 16-Hz frequency will become evident shortly.

Driving the drum at the correct speed is the third problem. The drum of the desk FAX, when driven by 60-Hz line voltage, turns at 180 rpm, which is near four times the satellite's 48 lines per inch. An exact multiple of four would be 192 rpm. In order to speed up the drum from 180 to 192 rpm we just feed in a higher frequency of ac. To find the correct frequency we use simple ratio and proportion of $60/180 = x/192$. Solving for x we get 64 Hz, or four times 16. Restating all this, if we record 16 Hz on the left channel of our stereo tape recorder and the picture information on the right simultaneously at 1-7/8 ips, and then play back at

7-1/2 ips, we will multiply both the outputs by four. The 64-Hz output should be fed into the voice coil of a reversed output transformer. The 5000-ohm winding is tuned to resonance to help shape the 64-Hz output to a sine wave. This output is fed into the input of a 15-watt amplifier to feed 130 volts under load into the drum motor. This will turn the motor at 192 rpm in synchronism with the video at 192 lines per minute which is being fed into the stylus through the Telefax amplifiers. The only changes necessary on the Telefax are those to make it functional for amateur facsimile, and the addition of a dpdt switch to transfer the motor, including its capacitor, from the ac mains to the new line from the 64-Hz amplifier. Since the pictures which are now produced are negatives, some means of inversion is necessary, such as a dc inverter.

Bibliography

Source material and more extended discussions of topics covered in this chapter can be found in the references given below.

Anderson, "Amateur Reception of Weather-Satellite Picture Transmissions," *QST*, Nov., 1965.

DeMaw, "The Basic Helical Beam," *QST*, November. 1965.

King, "Conversion of Telefax Transceivers to Amateur Service," *QST*, May, 1972.

McKnight, "Evolution of an Amateur Weather-Satellite Picture Station," *QST*, April 1968.

Spillane, "Cathode-Ray Display Unit for Satellite Weather Pictures," *QST*, June, 1969.

Winkler, "Facsimile Transceiver for Weather-Satellite Pictures," *QST*, May 1974, Technical Correspondence.

Supplementary information about facsimile may be found by consulting the following literature:

Costigan, *FAX – The Principles and Practice of Facsimile Communications,* Chilton Book Co., Philadelphia, 1971.

Stong, *The Amateur Scientist,* Scientific American Magazine, Feb., 1974, p. 114-120.

Vermillion, *A Guide to Construction of Inexpensive Automatic Picture-transmission Ground Stations,* NASA SP-50800, Greenbelt, Md., 1969.

Detailed information about the APT program may be obtained by writing to: APT Coordinator, National Oceanic and Atmospheric Administration, National Environmental Satellite Service, Washington, DC 20233. A bibliography of *QST* articles pertaining to amateur reception of weather satellite picture transmissions is available upon request from ARRL, as is a list of possible sources of surplus FAX equipment and supplies for the amateur.

Radioteletype

Since the earliest days, communications has been an important aspect of everyday life. Early communications involved smoke signals and signaling drums. Later came the written word, with message runners and eventually the famed "Pony Express." Then the telegraph was invented, and the first major breakthrough in high-speed long-distance communication had been achieved.

In 1906 the first American teletypewriter was invented, and a company to market it was formed by the inventer, Charles Krum, and financier Joy Morton (of the Chicago Morton Salt Company fame). Called the "Morkrum Co.," the young firm had pretty rough sledding until 1915, when the Associated Press decided to use the Morkrum equipment.

A German immigrant, Edward Kleinschmidt, independently was manufacturing a machine bearing his name about the same time. In 1925 these two companies were merged, and the combined company was purchased in 1930 by Western Electric, the manufacturing branch of Bell Telephone Company. At this time the company was known as the Teletype Corporation.

At this point it seems appropriate to describe a teleprinter, in the event that you don't know what we are talking about! A teleprinter is a typewriter that has additional parts which change the mechanical motion of the typist's fingers into electrical pulses for transmission on radio or wire circuits. At the receiving end these pulses are again changed back into mechanical motion and the message is printed automatically on the special typewriter. You have probably seen such a device at the local newspaper office, on television news shows, or in a modified form at the stockbroker's office. All teleprinters are commonly called "Teletype machines," since the Teletype Corporation was so well known in the teleprinter field. However, the word "Teletype" is a registered trademark of the Teletype Corporation, and when using the word it should always be capitalized — otherwise, to be technically correct, one should refer to such a machine as a "teleprinter."

Radioteletype (abbreviated RTTY) is, therefore, a form of telegraphic communication employing typewriter-like machines for (1) generating a coded set of electrical impulses when a typewriter key corresponding to the desired letter or symbol is pressed, and (2) converting a received set of such impulses into the corresponding printed character. The message to be sent is typed out in much the same way that it would be written on a typewriter, but the printing is done at the distant receiving point. The teletypewriter at the sending point may also print the same material.

Amateur RTTY

In this country, amateur RTTY started about 1946. Both on the East Coast and on the West Coast, groups commenced using the equipment on both 2 meters and 80 meters. On the lower frequencies, MAB (make-and-break) keying, which resembles normal cw, was used. The pulse length on a teleprinter machine is quite short, and it was soon found that ordinary MAB was not nearly as satisfactory as leaving the transmitter running continuously and shifting the carrier in frequency to correspond to key up or key down. This was allowed on 11 meters, and as a result, some of the important contributions were first made on that band. On vhf, the amateur regulations allowed (and continue to) use of a carrier with audio tones. This

Merrill Swan, W6AEE, one of the pioneers of amateur RTTY, is shown here engaging in the art of "picture swapping," discussed later in this section. His machine is a Teletype Corp. Model 28ASR.

made very simple equipment possible and offered great immunity to large amounts of frequency drift in the receiver or transmitter. The method is called afsk (audio frequency shift keying) and gives excellent results where it is permitted.

In 1953, the FCC modified its rules to permit fsk (frequency shift keying) on lower frequencies, using shifts of 850 Hz ± 50 Hz. However, many commercial stations using RTTY had found that certain problems could be minimized by use of shifts more narrow than 850 Hz. In fact, if you were to listen to commercial frequencies, you would find shifts ranging from 70 Hz on up to 850. Certain "standards" such as 70, 85, 170, 240, and 425 are common. Amateurs also wanted the opportunity to experiment with these narrower shifts, and in March 1956 it became possible to use "any shift up to 900." This has been an aid to experimentation and has relieved the need for accurately calibrated systems.

TELEPRINTER EQUIPMENT

There are two general types of machines, the page printer and the tape printer. The former prints on a paper roll about the same width as a business letterhead. The latter prints on paper tape, usually gummed on the reverse side so it may be cut to letter-size width and pasted on a sheet of paper in a series of lines. The page printer is the more common type in the equipment available to amateurs.

The operating speed of most machines is such that characters are sent at the rate of either 60, 67, 75 or 100 wpm, depending on the gearing ratio of a particular machine. Current FCC regulations allow amateurs the use of any of these four speeds. Interchangeable gears permit most machines to operate at these speeds. Ordinary teletypewriters are of the start-stop variety, in which the pulse-forming mechanism (motor driven) is at rest until a typewriter key is depressed. At this time it begins operating, forms the proper pulse sequence, and then comes to rest again before the next key is depressed to form the succeeding character. The receiving mechanism operates in similar fashion, being set into operation by the first pulse of the sequence from the transmitter. Thus, although the actual transmission speed cannot exceed about 60 wpm (or whatever maximum speed the machine is geared for), it can be considerably slower, depending on the typing speed of the operator.

It is also possible to transmit by using perforated tape. This has the advantage that the complete message may be typed out in advance of actual transmission, at any convenient speed; when transmitted, however, it is sent at the machine's normal maximum speed. A special tape reader, called a transmitter-distributor, and tape perforator are required for this process. A reperforator is a device that may be connected to the conventional teletypewriter for punching tape when the machine is operated in the regular way. It may thus be used either for an original message or for "taping" an incoming message for later retransmission.

The teleprinter machines used for RTTY are far too complex mechanically for home construction, and if purchased new would be highly expensive. However, used teletypewriters in good mechanical condition are available at quite reasonable prices. These are machines retired from commercial service but capable of entirely satisfactory operation in amateur work. They may be obtained from several sources on condition that they will be used purely for amateur purposes and will not be resold for commercial use.

Some dealers and amateurs around the country make it known by advertising that they handle parts or may be a source for machines and accessory equipment. *QST's* Ham-Ads and other publications often show good buys in equipment as amateurs move about, obtain newer equipment, or change interests.

Periodic publications are available which are devoted exclusively to amateur RTTY. Such publications carry timely technical articles and operating information, as well as classified ads. It is a little-known fact that any individual or firm can purchase directly from the Teletype Corporation. However, the high cost of the equipment has kept amateurs in general from doing so. At the present time, though, a low-cost line of equipment is being manufactured which can be purchased at prices the amateur can consider. This is the "32" line; more on it later.

During World War II, the government built a large manufacturing plant for Kleinschmidt, and again we have two major sources of teleprinter equipment in this country. The Kleinschmidt equipment is used mainly by the military services,

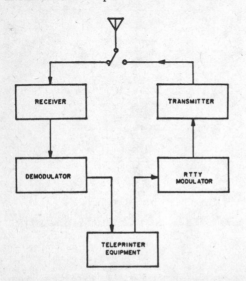

Block diagram showing the basic setup required for amateur RTTY operation.

and turns up occasionally in amateur hands via MARS (Military Affiliate Radio System) stations.

The Bell Telephone Company normally destroys antiquated equipment when it is replaced with new and more costly units. Several societies have been formed in various states by interested personnel, and Bell often allows these societies to have the discarded equipment for junk-weight prices — often as low as $25 for a teleprinter. These machines are normally in "as is" condition, but since they are taken out of active service, usually have been well cared for and need little or no maintenance. Many machines have been made available to MARS members, and this is a source not to be overlooked.

Very few machines have been made available through Western Union. There are two minor differences in the Western Union machines that might be interesting to mention. First, the bell rings (to attract attention) when the Figures "J" key is struck rather than when the Figures "S" key is struck (the latter is more common). Also, the stop pulse is 22 milliseconds instead of 31 milliseconds (more on that in a subsequent section) and thus they operate at about 65 words per minute instead of 60. However, these machines use the same 420-rpm motor-driven shaft speed and are perfect copy on any normal machine. (The European speed, which is 66.6 wpm, is not to be confused with the Western Union machines.) So do not hesitate to get a 65-wpm Western Union machine should one be available at a cost you consider reasonable.

TYPES OF MACHINES

There are four basic types of machines the amateur normally will be interested in obtaining:

1) Page printers, such as the Models 15, 26, 28 and 32, which print the message on a continuous roll of paper fed over the platen in much the same way that a sheet of paper goes through a regular typewriter.

2) Tape readers, called "TDs" (for *Transmitter Distributor*). These machines generate the transmitting pulses by scanning a punched tape, which is perforated in advance of transmission.

3) Reperforators and typing-reperforators, such as the Model 14, for making punched tape either from a local keyboard or the incoming signal. The typing-reperforator also prints the message on the tape, using the regular characters of the alphabet.

4) Composite machines that include the page printer, a tape reader, and a perforator to cut tape from the keyboard for later playback. Examples include the Models 19, 28ASR, and 32ASR.

Model 15 Page Printer

About 250,000 Model 15s were made before production was stopped. This machine is one of the most easy to obtain and was intended for continuous 24-hour duty. The Model 15 is so rugged that with a little care and routine lubrication it could well outlast the average amateur. It is heavy, fairly large, and somewhat noisy, but does an excellent job.

Model 26 Page Printer

The Model 26 was built during WW II and critical metals were held to a minimum in its construction. It was intended for light or occasional duty of 3-4 hours per day, maximum. A great number of these showed up around military installations, and once they were very popular in amateur circles. Experienced RTTY enthusiasts prefer newer machines these days, and there is little demand for Model 26 equipment. If these machines can be located, they are usually available for little or no cost. The keyboard is the easiest to use of any of the older machines. The 26s are quiet and make a good teleprinter for amateur use; however, parts are difficult to obtain and they were never intended for heavy duty. A major disadvantage might be the necessity for the table that accompanies the unit, since the roll of paper is stored inside the table rather than inside the printer, as in the Model 15.

The Model 15 page printer with table. This type of machine is in use in a great many amateur RTTY stations.

Model 28KSR Page Printer

The Model 28 equipment is an entire series within a series. The 28KSR (*K*eyboard *S*end-*R*eceive) is a modern version of the Model 15, and has certain automatic equipment available which makes it quite versatile. These units have a marvelous keyboard with very light touch, resembling that of an electric typewriter. They are capable of speeds up to 100 words per minute with the correct gears. These machines are currently popular among amateurs.

Model 14 tape reader (TD) showing tape from a typing reperforator.

Tape Readers

The "TD" that the amateur will most often find will be the Model 14. These units have their own independent motor and clutch for advancing the tape from a remote position. Some of the units intended for the military had nonsynchronous motors that were governor controlled. If you have a choice, avoid the governor-controlled motor. It needs to be set against a special 87.6-Hz tuning fork that may be hard to get, and arcing at the brushes often causes rf interference with weak signals. Most of these machines have been converted to 60-Hz synchronous motors.

Model 19

This is a composite set that includes a Model 15 page printer, a tape perforator that punches holes in the tape from the keyboard (but not from an incoming station, and it does not print on the tape), a counter showing how many characters have been punched in the tape so the operator

The Model 32 page printer is the newest type that can be obtained directly from the manufacturer at a price that is reasonably attractive to the amateur.

Model 32 Page Printer

The Model 32 comes as a page printer called the 32 KSR, or as the 32ASR composite set. The KSR has a light touch but the key travel is fairly long, and as the keys are plastic for low cost they sound a little like the keyboard on a toy piano. These machines are being used by amateurs today, and they are most attractive. Cost is quite reasonable, they are very lightweight, and rather quiet. Although not intended for heavy duty, a new machine should provide years of excellent service. Parts are very easily obtained and very low in cost. The Model 32 sells for under $450 new from the Teletype Corporation.

A Model 19 composite unit (right), and Model 14 typing reperforator (left).

knows when to start a new line, a large power supply to operate the punch magnet, a tape reader to play the tape, and a metal desk for all these things to be placed upon. These units are quite sought after, since they represent rather a complete station in themselves. The keyboard is quite stiff, even when not pulling tape, since it continues to operate the mechanical levers that would otherwise operate the tape punch.

Model 28ASR

The 28ASR is a modern Model 19 with many additional features. With the integral "stunt box," nearly unlimited functions can be inserted at the operator's desire — for example, automatic "non-overline" control (prevents printing over a line already typed), automatic carriage return (prevents "pile-ups" at the end of the line should a carriage return signal be missed), ringing a bell if somebody types your call letters, or suppressing all printing until somebody calls you specifically. A great variety of accessories is available, including a tape reader having a pivoted sensing unit that can "walk up" to the last letter on the tape, making the usual 4- or 5-inch tape loop unnecessary. Some MARS stations occasionally have access to these units, considered by most RTTY enthusiasts to be the ultimate in teleprinter equipment.

Model 32ASR

This is a new line of equipment which can be purchased directly from the Teletype Corporation. The 32ASR is not as versatile as the 19 or the 28ASR, since the keyboard cannot be used to punch tape while receiving an incoming signal. However, it does include a tape punch and a tape reader, and has all the usual advantages that go with the ability to make and play tape. These machines are similar to the 32KSR in appearance, are lightweight, and are modestly priced at $580 new, including stand and a box to catch the chad that is knocked out of the tape by the punch. Many options are available, so one should request the communications type (rather than Bell Telephone or Western Union type), with automatic carriage return and automatic nonoverline. With these features, you can walk away from the machine and regardless of the quality of the signal received, you will not pile up letters at the end of a line nor print over a previous line accidentally.

Model 14 Reperforators

There are numerous Model 14 types, including a strip printer that prints on a narrow 3/8-inch tape. As even a short conversation uses a lot of tape the page printer is much more economical, so the Model 14 strip printers for the most part sell for very little. They have little use in the normal installation and are often used for parts.

Many of these machines use standard Bell Telephone characters and the operator would wish to change over to "communications" type. This can be done if the owner is skilled with a soldering iron. The necessary conversion kits are easily obtained. Many 15s and 19s need this conversion

also. If not converted, there will be fractions above certain letters, such as the C, V, B, and F.

There are 14RO (Receive Only) reperforators that punch holes in tape directly from an incoming signal. Don't turn one of these down merely because it has no keyboard. It can be remotely used from an extra keyboard or directly from the page-printer keyboard.

The more usual type is the Model 14 typing reperforator. These may or may not have a keyboard, but while punching holes they also print on the tape, so you can read what will be sent when the tape is played.

The most advanced version of the 14 "reperfs" would include a cover with tape reel, and end-of-line indicator which turns on a small light to tell the operator to commence a new line, a back-up so the tape may be moved to eliminate an error (part of the back-up system is a second lever that allows the ribbon to be raised to view the tape), a keyboard, and sometimes a solenoid-controlled tape feed-out (which is seldom used by amateurs).

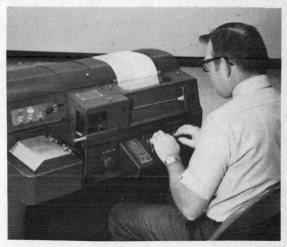

An amateur RTTY installation using a Teletype Corp. Model 28ASR teleprinter. This model contains the keyboard, page printer, and facilities for making and sending perforated tapes.

When buying, one would do well to inquire whether the motor is synchronous or governor controlled. The changeover to synchronous is not difficult, and involves obtaining an 1800-rpm synchronous motor (around $10) and a set of gears (around $7) to match. Also inquire about the other features mentioned, to know what you're getting.

Other Equipment

Of course, a lot of other machines have been built by the Teletype Corporation, but those mentioned are best suited for amateur use. These are all capable of running the prescribed speed and all have the necessary "5-unit" code to be discussed in a later section. The Model 33, for instance, is similar in appearance to the Model 32 but uses the newer "8-unit" code and has a four-row keyboard instead of the typical three-row keyboard. The Model 35 uses the "8-unit" code and is the heavy-duty version intended for continuous operation.

Very few Kleinschmidt units have appeared on the amateur scene, and when they do it is normally

The HAL Communications RVD-1002 RTTY Video Display Unit and RKB-1 TTY Keyboard (right), a part of a solid-state RTTY system. Sent or received information is displayed on a TV monitor (left).

through a MARS station. If one is advertised, write the owner for descriptive material.

Solid-State RTTY Systems

Modern integrated-circuit technology has made possible the design of teleprinter systems which are completely solid state, with the characters displayed by means of a cathode-ray tube. With such a system, gone is the oily smell, gone is the noise, and gone is what some might consider an unsightly monstronsity of the mechanical systems.

One of the first of such solid-state systems was introduced to the market by HAL Communications Corporation. The complete system consists of three units: a video unit, a keyboard, and a display monitor. The video-unit output of the HAL system is compatible with U.S. commercial TV standards, i.e., 525 lines interlaced and 30 frames per second. Thus, the monitor may be one that is commercially made for closed-circuit TV, or an ordinary TV receiver modified slightly to accept video information directly.

TELEPRINTER HARDWARE

Teletype Codes and Speeds

In order to transmit information electrically, codes have been devised to convert the alphabet into electrical pulses. Around 1832, Morse proposed the code that has since been known simply as "Morse Code." It involved dots and dashes which were obtained by holding a key down and releasing it. This is called a "binary" (meaning two states) code. The Teletype codes that we are concerned with also are binary.

Either of two systems can be used: (1) "neutral" keying, where there is current in the line with the key down and no current when the key is up; and (2) "polar" keying, where there is a change in the polarity of the current with keying — during key down the current flows in one direction in the line and with key up the direction is reversed, without change in the current amplitude.

Both systems are used in the process of setting up an amateur station. We shall discuss this aspect in greater detail later when looking at receiving demodulators (converters) and frequency-shift keyers for transmitters.

The system now known as Continental Morse is based on the dot: one dash equal to the length of 3 dots, one dot length between elements of the same letter, 3 dot lengths between letters of the same word, and 7 dot lengths between words. It has been shown that the *average* length of letters is 9 dots, but the *actual* length ranges from 4 dots for the letter E (counting the space between letters) to the equivalent of 22 dots for the number Ø. Such a system is called an "uneven length code." As one can easily imagine, it is very difficult to construct an automatic reader to work efficiently on such a variety of characters.

To overcome this, the "5-unit" code was devised. Five consecutive pulses in a binary system

(where any pulse may be either "plus" or "minus") give 32 possible combinations ($2^5 = 32$). Since all pulses occupy the same length of time, this is called an "even length" code.

With such a code some form of timing is necessary so that each of the impulses may be properly received, identified and interpreted at the receiving station. The early machines required great precision in the adjustment of the motor speed at both ends in order to remain in synchronization. The "start-stop" system now in use provides the necessary timing, although recently some systems have reverted to the synchronous method. (These systems are of little interest to the amateurs, since the FCC rules clearly state that a normal start-stop system must be used.)

The fact that the 5-unit code has only 32 characters available has posed a hardship on the alphabets of some countries, and in any event has limited flexibility. Many other codes are in service using more units than five. For example, the stock ticker and the teletypesetter machines each have their own separate 6-unit codes. In the U.S. an 8-unit code is in common use with computer-terminal equipment, called the USA Standard Code for Information Interchange, and abbreviated USASCII, or just ASCII. (See appendix.) However, the FCC rules for amateurs spell out use of a machine using the 5-unit code.

The five units or elements of the TTY code are sent in sequence. Each element has two possible states, either "mark" or "space," which are indicated by different types of electrical impulses (i.e., mark might be indicated by a negative voltage and space by a positive voltage). The letter code as it appears on perforated tape is shown in Fig. 1, where the black dots indicate marking pulses. Figures and arbitrary signs — punctuation, etc. — use the same set of code impulses as the alphabet,

Fig. 1 — Teleprinter letter code as it appears on perforated tape. Start and stop elements do not appear on the tape. Elements are numbered from top to bottom, and dots indicate marking pulses. Numerals, punctuation signs, and other arbitrary symbols are secured by carriage shift. There are no lower-case letters on a teletypewriter. Where blanks appear in the above chart in the "FIGS" line, characters may differ on different machines.

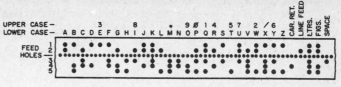

and are selected by shifting the carriage as described below.

In regular teleprinter practice, a "start" pulse is added in front of the 5 units of information and a "stop" pulse is added at the end, making a total of 7 pulses. This is called a "start-stop 5-unit code." For the 60-word-per-minute speed, normal pulses are 22 milliseconds in duration. The stop pulse is 31 ms, which is 1.41 times as long as a regular information pulse. Thus we have a total time of 163 ms for each character typed, as shown in Fig. 1. This gives a total of 7.41 pulses per character in the American system. This has at times been erroneously referred to as a "7.41-unit" code. It is not. The 7.41 correctly defined is merely the character interval expressed in units of normal pulse length.

The length of the stop pulse helps to control the ease with which the machine stays in correct synchronization should a noise burst or other interference cause it to miss a correct start pulse. In various systems this stop is of different length. In the Western Union system, it is only a regular 1-unit length of 22 ms. In the International system, it is actually 1.50 times longer than normal. In certain military applications where special cryptographic codes are used, a 2-unit (44 ms) stop pulse is employed; in these systems correct synchronization of the sending and receiving machines is essential because if one letter is missed, the entire transmission must be repeated.

In speaking of the speed of the system, it does not tell the correct story to talk only in terms of words per minute. Instead, engineers have introduced the term "baud." A baud is a unit of keying rate and the baud rate is found by dividing the shortest pulse length into unity. In this case, $1/.022 = 45.45$ — usually rounded off to 45.5 bauds. This is the system required for use by American amateurs for 60-wpm operation. The International system uses pulse lengths of only 20 ms with a stop pulse of 30 ms. This is a "50-baud" system and may also be used by American amateurs under present FCC regulations.

Western Union machines also use a 45.5-baud system, although their stop pulse is only 22 ms rather than the more usual 31.

Printing Speeds

Fig. 2 shows the construction of a typical character. You will note the stop pulse is 31 ms long, so this system uses a total time of 163 ms to complete a character. If we divide one character's time into one minute we get the total number of characters possible in that minute. Since there are 60 seconds in one minute,

$$\frac{60}{0.163} = 368 \text{ characters per minute}$$

This is more often called "368 opm" (for "operations per minute").

One word is usually thought of as 5 letters plus one space, to total 6 characters. Thus

$$\frac{368}{6} = 61.3 \text{ wpm}$$

This is normally rounded off to be called a "60 wpm" machine.

Table I lists various speeds used throughout the world. You will notice that all speeds use the standard 5-unit code. Although the International machines go 66.6 wpm they are not compatible with the American Western Union machines which go 65 wpm. The normal 61.3-wpm machines are compatible, since they both use 45.5 bauds.

With a 60-wpm machine, all *characters* are sent at the rate of 60 wpm, but the actual transmission speed achieved depends on the typing speed of the operator, when using the keyboard direct. With punched-tape transmission it is possible to operate at the normal speed continuously.

Since this is a start-stop system, the actual shaft speed of the motor is faster than the 368 opm. In fact, with the 1-unit stop pulse used by Western Union, one gets 390 opm. The shaft speed actually is made greater than that figure to allow for correct synchronization.

Fig. 2 — For 60-wpm operation, the standard 5-unit code consists of six 22-millisecond intervals followed by 31 ms long, occupying a total time of 163 ms. The first and last intervals are "start" and "stop" pulses, respectively. The drawing above shows the mark and space intervals for the letter "Y".

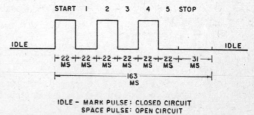

IDLE — MARK PULSE: CLOSED CIRCUIT
SPACE PULSE: OPEN CIRCUIT

TABLE I — Some of the Teleprinter Speeds in Current Use

WPM	Bauds	Signal Length	Unit Code	Stop Pulse	OPM	Character Interval	Shaft Speed
65	45.5	22 ms	5	1.0 (22 ms)	390[3]	7.0	420 rpm
62.5	45.5	22 ms	5	1.27 (28 ms)	375	7.27	420 rpm
61.3	45.5	22 ms	5	1.42 (31 ms)	368[1]	7.42	420 rpm
57.2	45.5	22 ms	5	1.96 (43 ms)	342[4]	7.96	420 rpm
66.6	50.0	20 ms	5	1.5 (30 ms)	400[2]	7.5	461.5 rpm
62.5	50.0	20 ms	5	2.0 (40 ms)	375	8.0	461.5 rpm
75	56.9	18 ms	5	1.42 (25 ms)	460	7.42	525 rpm
100	74.2	13.5 ms	5	1.42 (19 ms)	600	7.42	685 rpm

[1] Standard 60-wpm American system used by amateurs.
[2] Standard International system.
[3] Standard Western Union system in U.S.A.
[4] Often used by U.S. government agencies for crypto transmissions.
[EDITOR'S NOTE: In some instances the figures above are mathematically inconsistent to a minor degree. They are the ones actually used in the industry, however.]

Motors

There are two types of motors available: synchronous for regular 60-Hz house circuits, and governor motors which may be set independently of the incoming ac frequency — and, in fact, run from 117-V dc if needed. These latter motors are set by use of a special 87.6-Hz tuning fork, and are to be avoided since one must obtain the fork, make periodic checks for speed accuracy, put up with replacement of carbon brushes, accept the rf interference — which invariably destroys weak incoming signals — and put up with frequent nearby television interference caused by the brushes arcing.

With either type of motor, gears are used to turn the shaft of the printer and keyboard at 420 rpm (for 60 wpm). This is correctly synchronized down to the 368 opm by clutches. Thus very accurate speed control is maintained with the sending station.

Synchronous motors are obtainable for around $10 used, but since they run at 1800 rpm and the governor motors run at 2100 rpm, different gears must be used when replacing a governor motor. When buying any Teletype equipment, attempt to learn whether it has a synchronous motor. Nevertheless, if the price is low enough, even equipment with governor motors obviously would be worthwhile for purchase.

How the Keyboard Works

When you hit a letter on a regular typewriter no electrical pulses are generated — the letter struck is directly connected to the type bar which then strikes the paper. On a teleprinter it doesn't work this way. It may be difficult at first to realize that the printer and keyboard are actually two entirely separate devices operated from a common motor. The two wires coming from the "keyboard distributor" (device generating the appropriate electrical pulses) can be hooked in the same circuit as the actuating magnets on the printer, in which case the combination operates much like a normal typewriter. However, this *need not be*. For example, you can keep the printer on an incoming signal and concurrently use the keyboard on a different circuit to operate a tape punch. This feature is one of the most difficult for a newcomer to assimilate, as at first it seems quite impossible that one could use the keyboard for other purposes while the printer is running from an incoming signal!

It has already been stated that in a 5-unit system it is possible to have only 32 characters. As there are 26 letters in the alphabet, this leaves only 6 more that can be used. Or so it would appear. Since there are more numbers than 6, something has to be done.

As a result, we "shift" into upper case for many of these remaining functions, such as numbers and

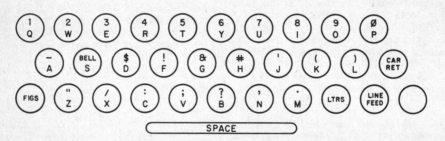

Fig. 3 — Communications-type keyboard. The keyboard resembles that for a regular typewriter, but has only three rows instead of four. All printed letters are capitalized, there being no lower case letters used in RTTY. The characters which appear above letters of the alphabet are typed when the carriage is in the shifted or Figures position.

all punctuation. A newcomer's typical reaction is that it seems strange you can't get at least a period or comma without all this extra work. This is readily explained by the keyboard arrangement. See Fig. 3.

26 keys for the letters in the alphabet
1 key for space between words
1 key for carriage return
1 key for line feed
1 key for up-shift ("Figures" key)
1 key for down-shift ("Letters" key)
1 blank key (seldom used)
total — 32 keys

And that is why *all* punctuation must be done after up-shift to the "Figures" position. Unlike a normal typewriter, where you merely let go of the shift when you are finished, you must tell the teleprinter to come back down. The "Letters" key provides this information. (The "Letters" key is also used to remove mistakes when preparing tape. More on that later.)

Types of Keyboards

In the United States we use four basic keyboard configurations. In each, the identical placement is used for lower-case letters. Only the upper-case ("Figures") symbols are varied, as shown in Table II.

The four are:

1) *Bell System business keyboard.* This system is used by most business firms, and is quickly identified by having fractions such as 1/2, 3/4, etc., over certain keys. Many of the machines made available to amateurs have this type of keyboard. Conversion to communications type is possible.

2) *Weather type.* Many of the upper-case symbols pertain to cloud coverage, wind direction, and other specialized symbols. Again, these can be converted to communications type.

3) *Western Union.* This keyboard fairly closely approximates the American communications keyboard except that the bell sounds from upper-case "S," as in all Bell System machines. If you have a machine of this nature it will also run at 65 wpm (390 opm).

4) *Communications type.* This is the "standard" amateur keyboard and is shown in Fig. 3.

The FCC stipulates that we should use a keyboard conforming to CCIT No. 2 insofar as letters, numerals and slant bar go. You can use anything you want for the remaining "Figures" case. The "standard" American communications keyboard shown in Fig. 3 meets this requirement.

Many machines when obtained do not have the "slant zero" (∅) which the FCC regulations stipulate. Many owners of these machines use the letter O rather than going into upper case for regular zero, as it appears to them to be the same and is "easier." However, the change to the proper symbol is not difficult.

Unshift on Space

Commercial stations frequently send groups that include many numbers. They want to stay in upper case throughout these number groups. However, a machine of this type is a nuisance to an amateur, because if a false "Figures" symbol is received, the machine will go into upper case and print those symbols rather than the letters it should print. It will stay this way until the local operator somehow gets the machine back into lower case or else, finally, a "Letters" character comes along which accomplishes the same thing.

Most Teletype machines are equipped with a mechanical lever which can be changed to give "unshift on space," so that each time a space bar is touched (or the equivalent function received) between words it automatically returns the carriage to lower case, if it happens to be in upper. Then one would not remain accidentally in upper case for more than one word.

Wiring

There are so many different types of machines available that publishing wiring diagrams would be pointless. Usually a classified ad for an instruction book for the particular machine in question will provide the information.

Many machines taken out of service have had the electrical wiring altered over the years for a particular subscriber. Often the machines come with a red jack and black jack dangling from wires about three feet long. Usually the red jack is for the printer and the black jack is for the keyboard.

However, there are only six wires that need interest you:

Table II — Various Keyboards

Lower Case	Upper Case			
	American Communications	Western Union	CCIT No. 2	Bell Systems (TWX)
A	-	-		
B	?	?	?	5/8
C	:	:	:	1/8
D	$	$	Note 4	$
E	3	3	3	3
F	!		Note 1	1/4
G	&	&	Note 1	&
H	#	#	Note 1	#
I	8	8	8	8
J	'	Bell	Bell	'
K	(	(	(	1/2
L	)	)	)	3/4
M	.	.	.	
N	,	,	,	7/8
O	9	9	9	9
P	∅	0	∅	0
Q	1	1	1	1
R	4	4	4	4
S	Bell	'	'	Bell
T	5	5	5	5
U	7	7	7	7
V	;	!	–	3/8
W	2	2	2	2
X	/	/	/	/
Y	6	6	6	6
Z	"	.	+	"

Carriage Return (Note 2)
Line Feed (Note 2)
Letters (Note 3)
Figures
Space
Blank

[1] Available as wished by each government.
[2] For page printers.
[3] Also used for erasure of errors.
[4] To operate the answer-back unit.

2 for the selector magnets on the printer

2 for the keyboard contacts

2 for the motor, which are intended for 117 volts ac.

Actually, all electrical wiring and all terminal strips not connected directly to the above six wires can be removed. This greatly simplifies later maintenance when needed. However, most amateurs just locate the needed connections and never bother to clean out the superfluous wiring. One might use a 2-foot piece of "Ham-M" rotor cable, which is 8-conductor, having two heavier than the rest. Attach an octal plug to one end with its protective cap; the two heavy wires attach to the motor, two others go to the selector magnets and two more to the keyboard contacts. This leaves two extra for other uses, such as remote transmitter control from the printer. This adapter dangles from the machine a few inches. Then extension cords having octal plugs on them can readily be used so the machine can be placed at any convenient point in the room, and all machines are readily interchangeable. Such a system may or may not appeal to the newcomer, but it is one example of a versatile system.

Polar Relays

Polar relays were used in original land-line equipment as isolating devices. Many early amateur converters were designed to utilize the polar relay. However, for a number of years such relays have not been used by either the advanced amateur or most commercial operators. Since they are mechanical they are a constant source of difficulty; they are hard to maintain in optimum condition, being affected by temperature changes as well as by humidity, and wear. They also generate high-frequency rf hash because of arcing at the contacts while in transit, and require "bias" voltages which make it difficult to keep the relay properly balanced for mark and space operation. The newer mercury-wetted types, which have only one coil (no "bias" winding) and through capillary action "make-before-break," are much better, but the use of any keying relays is discouraged.

Mark and Space

The earlier Morse writing machines used a pen attached to a mechanical arm. On dots and dashes the pen would make a mark on the paper in ink. Between the marks would be spaces where the pen wrote nothing. This soon became known as "mark" and "space", and we keep the same terminology for RTTY. "Mark" is the condition in which the circuit to the printer is closed and current keeps the selector magnets closed. "Space" occurs when this circuit is opened momentarily and the selector magnet releases. "Marking" is equivalent to "idle"; the motor runs, but otherwise the machine is quiet.

The Local Loop

A "loop" is nothing more than a closed circuit in which current circulates. A "local loop" is one in which the entire circuit and voltage source is located in the immediate vicinity of the particular machine. It is used for machine adjustment or test purposes, primarily. Other "loops" are those for receiving and for transmitting.

Fig. 4 shows a typical local loop. The large dropping resistor allows high voltage to be used initially to close the selector magnets quickly and yet keep the maximum current in the circuit from exceeding a particular amount − that is, 60 mA.

Selector Magnet Current

There are two identical selector magnets. They have about 100 ohms dc resistance and may be hooked in series or in parallel. In either case, each coil should have 30 mA current through it − thus the choice of 30 mA or 60 mA "loops." (You will hear conflicting reports about running 20 mA rather than 30. Even the Teletype Corporation hates to say which of these two is correct. They prefer the 30-mA designation, but Bell Telephone has been using the 20-mA value in certain series circuits.)

At any rate, with the magnets in parallel the total resistance is 50 ohms. Thus if we use 60 mA the voltage drop across the magnets is only 3 volts. However, because of the inductance of the selector-magnet coils such a low voltage would not close the selector magnets quickly enough. Since the ability of the machine to copy signals which have been distorted in transmission rests on the portion of the 22-ms pulse that is available for sampling, we try to get the selector magnets closed as quickly as possible when a current pulse is received. To effect this, rather high voltages are employed in the loop circuit. Some military circuits use up to 300 volts, but a more typical voltage is 120 volts dc. Voltages considerably less than this can be used, but with some loss in protection against distorted signals.

When operation is at a fixed value of high voltage with a current-limiting resistor, the current can build up considerably faster in a parallel circuit than in a series circuit using the same coils, because the inductance is much smaller. This becomes particularly important when using transistor keyers rather than vacuum tubes, because the available voltage is lower. The 60-mA loops are also better when several machines are used in series at the same time, and also when the transmitter is keyed directly from a printer rather than from a separate keyboard.

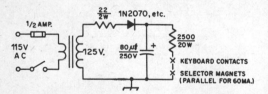

Fig. 4 − Local loop circuit. This can be used for checking machine operation or typing practice. The transformer should deliver 50-60 mA at 125 volts (Stancor type PA-8421 or equivalent).

Holding Magnets

The older machines built prior to World War II had "pulling" magnets, which are characterized by a spring, with thumb screw adjustment, connected to the armature of the magnet. The newer types are "holding" magnets and have no such spring. One should try to get the "holding" magnets if possible, as there are no adjustments to be concerned with. The letter "H" is usually stamped on the range-adjustment plate, which is graduated from 0-120 points.

Range Selector

During transmission over long distances, telegraph signals may become distorted quite badly; thus mark or space pulses may be considerably shortened or lengthened from their correct values. It is essential that the receiving system be capable of receiving and interpreting these signals without error. To accomplish this, the receiving distributor is arranged so that it is sensitive for the reception of the selecting impulse only for a very short time at the middle of each impulse. The exact location of this sensitive period is adjustable in each receiving distributor so that it may have maximum tolerance for receiving distorted signals.

This adjustment is called the "range selector," and it is assumed that the operator will occasionally check the accuracy of the setting. You can check the adjustment quite easily. The selector has a movable arm which is locked with a thumb screw and moves in an arc over a 0-120 scale. With one hand, quickly type the letters "RY" alternately while adjusting this arm with the other hand. As you approach 10-15 points the machine will no longer print accurately. Remember this setting. Advance the arm toward the other end of the scale while still typing "RY." At around 100 points the machine will "lock up" and stop printing. Remember this last setting that produced good print, and then place the arm midway between these two settings. The easy way is to add the two settings together, divide by 2 and set for that point. A total range of 80 or more points indicates an excellent system and a machine in good adjustment. With this setting, one can get good copy on at least ±40 percent distortion.

If the incoming signal has really horrible distortion it is possible that an improvement could be obtained by deliberately misadjusting the range-selector arm. Such a method is discouraged. Some receiving converters can make this correction either automatically or manually.

Actually, the sending station should be told that his signal is badly distorted — sooner or later somebody else will tell him, and certainly if your own signal were poor you would appreciate being notified to that effect.

Receiving International Speeds

Since the International machines normally run at 50 bauds, the pulses are 20 ms rather than 22 ms. This means that the stop pulse for each character comes some 12 ms too soon for American printers. By deliberately setting the range selector to sample the initial part of the first pulse instead of the middle, it is possible to copy an International station if conditions are good and the signal is not distorted. However, such a system is strictly a compromise approach and will give second-rate results. If you really want to copy 50-baud International transmission, a much better solution is to use a "regenerative repeater." These repeaters have an adjustable control for allowing copy of such signals without making any adjustment on your own printer. Regenerative repeaters are sold at the present time on the surplus market.

Answer-Back

The newer machines have an automatic "answer-back" feature that can be triggered by the operator who pushes an appropriate key; or they can be triggered automatically from the other end, usually by hitting an upper-case "C" key on the Bell System machines ("D" on Western Union). Amateurs disconnect the automatic feature so an erroneous upper-case "C" will not trip it off.

Automatic Carriage Return

The Models 28 and 32 have optional automatic carriage return. If the sender neglected to send a carriage-return signal, or it was mutilated in transmission, copy would normally "pile up" at the end of the line and lose the information. The "auto cr" feature eliminates this by automatically returning the carriage and turning up a new line when the end of the line is reached. Kits are available to convert the 15, 19 or 26 machines to this feature. It is most worthwhile. The 14, of course, has no need for it.

Nonoverline

Many times a false carriage-return signal is received, allowing the printer to print on top of the information it has just typed. This wipes out both the old and the new copy, and of course is most frustrating. It can easily be prevented by a minor modification of the printer.

If the normal carriage-return function is disconnected entirely, nothing happens when a carriage return signal is received. The carriage-return lever then can be connected to the line-feed mechanism so that when a line-feed signal is received, it trips both the line feed and the carriage return. This system has been used quite successfully. Combined with auto carriage return, it prevents loss of information caused either by accidental carriage returns or the absence of carriage returns. This then gives a machine that allows one to not be present and yet get all the information. It is particularly beneficial during tests on weak signals.

The Teletype Corporation can supply Model 32 machines (new) with automatic carriage return and nonoverline features. After once using a machine so equipped, you would never be satisfied with an "ordinary" printer again.

Removing Errors

When using tape equipment, errors can be removed by backing up the tape the appropriate number of spaces and then striking the "Letters" key over the incorrect letter or letters. This punches all five holes in the tape and you then continue as though you had never made an error. When the machine comes to this point in the tape, it does not print anything on the page at all. Thus perfect copy can be transmitted even though the operator has made several actual errors.

If you hit a wrong key while sending with the keyboard, it is customary to space, type several "XXXXX" keys, and then continue. This indicates that the word preceding the XXXXXs should be disregarded.

RYRYRYRY

This combination is used for a test, as the "R" key contains the 2nd and 4th pulses, and the "Y" key contains the 1st, 3rd and 5th pulses. Thus all pulses are checked alternately. The "Letters" key contains all five pulses but no printing is done, so the RYRYRYRYs are used for testing.

Typing

Sooner or later you are going to be faced with the fact that to operate on RTTY you must use your fingers. A few operators have had prior experience with typewriters and had already mastered touch typing, but the majority of fellows know little or nothing about regular typewriters. In fact, it seems to be the case that quite a number of amateurs have hesitated to get on RTTY merely because they have no typing ability. This in itself is no problem — everybody has to start sometime, so don't think you represent an unusual case. What *is* strange, however, is that so very little progress has been made by many of the fellows already on RTTY.

The touch system is not at all difficult to learn, but involves doing it — like learning cw, it is not something you are born with. Although the majority of amateurs follow the "hunt-and-peck" method, using only two or three fingers, there is no reason to be satisfied with such a system. You will never enjoy RTTY as you could if you spent even a few minutes attempting to learn the correct use of all nine fingers. (Yes, all *nine* — the left thumb normally is never used at all.)

The RTTY keyboard is much easier to learn than a regular typewriter. We suggest training yourself to send "THE QUICK BROWN FOX JUMPED OVER THE LAZY DOGS BACK" without looking at your fingers or the keyboard, before actually putting a station on the air.

Table III is a chart for the placement of the fingers. The left little finger is placed on the "A"

key as an anchor and the right little finger is placed on the "Carriage Return" key as an anchor. You will notice the left index finger and the right index finger each have six letters to use and the other fingers have only three each. The right thumb does all the spacing between words.

With this chart it should not take long for you to type at least as fast as you would with only two fingers via "hunt and peck," and in short order you should quickly exceed that speed. Hook up a local loop to the printer and just sit down and teach yourself the touch system. All it takes is practice!

PREPARING A TELEPRINTER FOR USE

As mentioned earlier, teleprinter machines are available to amateurs on a low-cost basis from several sources. Once you get your machine, the first step is to check the speed for which it is geared. Information from Table IV will be of help here. If gears for a different speed are required, they are available from several sources.

The next step will be to prepare the machine for "local-loop" operation. A power supply capable of delivering approximately 130 volts dc at about 100 mA will be required for the Model 15, and about 500 mA for the Model 19. Some machines come with a power supply and many also have some sort of table with them. The machines are all very heavy, but fortunately they can be broken down into several component parts in a matter of two or three minutes.

It will now be necessary to locate the keyboard and selector magnet circuits. This is very easy, as the two keyboard contacts usually are brought out through a cord to a black telephone-type plug and the selector magnet is brought out through a cord to a red plug. These plug into jacks in the back of the table. The wiring to these jacks should be located and a pair of wires from each brought out to a barrier-type terminal strip with about a dozen terminals.

Next, connect the positive and negative dc power-supply output leads to a pair of terminals on the terminal strip. Connect one or more resistors to other unused terminals on this strip to provide about 1000 to 2000-ohms resistance at about 30-watts. Now by means of jumpers tie all of the above circuits into a series circuit. This will include the dc power supply output, the resistors, the keyboard and the selector magnet. The extra terminals will provide for easy insertion of the TU or fsk polar relay, or TD unit, into this series loop circuit. An example of such a connection is shown in Fig. 1.

Table III

Fingers →	Left Hand					Right Hand			
	5	4	3	2	2	3	4	5
Top Row	Q	W	E	R T	Y U	I	O	P
Middle Row	A	S	D	F G	H J	K	L	CAR. RET.
Bottom Row	Z	X	C	V B	N M	LTRS	LINE FEED	BLANK

TABLE IV — Teletype Gear and Pinion Numbers

EQUIPMENT	OPM	WPM	GEAR	TEETH	PINION	TEETH
Model 14 typing	368	60	78509	30	78510	7
reperf, sync	460	75	88945	24	94267	7
motor (1800	600	100	110877	42	110876	16
rpm)						
Model 14 typing	368	60	110651	53	110650	10
reperf, governed	460	75	122042	34	122041	8
motor (2100	600	100	111265	39	111264	12
rpm)						
Model 14 TD,	368	60	80165	44	80166	9
felt clutch,	396	67	114455		114454	
sync motor	460	75	82479	39	82480	10
(1800 rpm)	460	75	91284	47	91285	12
	600	100	110284		110883	
Model 14 TD,	368	60	77036	40	77034	7
felt clutch,	390	65	91505	54	91504	10
governed motor,	460	75	82477	41	82478	9
(2100 rpm)	460	75	91282	32	91283	7
Model 14 TD,	368	60	135036	44	80166	9
steel clutch,	390	65	136583	60	136582	13
sync motor	396	67	135065	50	116767	11
(1800 rpm)	460	75	136525	47	91285	12
	600	100	135035	36	110883	12
Model 14 TD,	368	60	135067	53	91131	13
steel clutch,						
50-Hz sync						
motor (1500						
rpm)						
Model 14 TD,	368	60	135068	40	77034	7
steel clutch,	396	67	135066	53	123711	10
governed motor	460	75	135064	32	91283	7
(2100 rpm)	600	100	135061	35	77025	10
Model 15 and	368	60	74913	30	74912	7
19 printers,	460	75	91287		91286	
sync motor	600	100	110870		110869	
(1800 rpm)						
Model 15 and	368	60	84019	25	84018	7
19 printers,						
50-Hz sync						
motor (1500 rpm)						
Model 15 and	368	60	74151	35	74505	7
19 printers,						
governed motor						
(2100 rpm)						
Model 28 printer,	368	60	151131		151130	
fiber gear series,	396	67	152764		152765	
sync motor	460	75	151133		151132	
	600	100	151135		151134	
Model 28 printer,	36	60	159279		159278	
nylon gear series,	460	75	159282		159281	
sync motor	600	100	159285		159284	

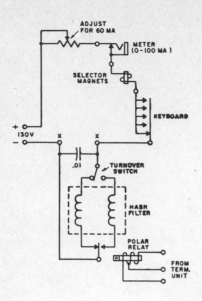

Use an ohmmeter to check the resistance of the selector magnet at the terminal strip. If the resistance is 180 ohms this will indicate that the dual coils are connected in series, and it will now be necessary to adjust the resistor values so that a current of 20 mA will flow in the loop circuit. If the resistance of the selector magnet is 45 ohms, the coils are in parallel and the loop current will have to be adjusted for 60 mA. This latter is the more typical condition. It is easy, however, to provide for the current you prefer.

Now that the machine is set up to operate on its local loop circuit, it is necessary to provide for receiving and transmitting teleprinter signals via radio. For receiving, it will be necessary to provide a "converter" or "terminal unit." There are many circuits available for TU construction, a few being presented in a later section.

TRANSMITTING RTTY

To be used in radio communication, the pulses (dc) generated by the teletypewriter must be utilized in some way to key a radio transmitter so they may be sent in proper sequence and usable form to a distant point. At the receiving end the incoming signal must be converted into dc pulses suitable for operating the printer. These functions, shown in block form in the introductory pages of this chapter, are performed by electronic units known respectively as the frequency-shift keyer or RTTY modulator and receiving converter or RTTY demodulator.

The radio transmitter and receiver are quite conventional in design. Practically all the special features needed can be incorporated in the keyer and converter, so that most ordinary amateur equipment is suitable for RTTY with little or no modification.

Transmission Methods

It is quite possible to transmit teleprinter signals by ordinary "on-off" or "make-break" keying such as is used in regular hand-keyed cw transmission. In practice, however, frequency-shift keying is preferred because it gives definite signals on both mark and space, which is an advantage in printer operation. Also, since fsk can be received by methods similar to those used for fm reception, there is considerable discrimination against noise, both natural and manmade, distributed uniformly across the receiver's passband, when the received signal is not too weak. Both factors make for increased reliability in printer operation.

Frequency-Shift Keying

On the vhf bands where A2 transmission is permitted, audio frequency-shift keying (afsk) is generally used. In this case the rf carrier is transmitted continuously, the pulses being trans-

mitted by frequency-shifted tone modulation. The audio frequencies used at one time were more-or-less standardized at 2125 and 2975 Hz, the shift being 850 Hz. (These frequencies are the 5th and 7th harmonics, respectively, of 425 Hz, which is half the shift frequency, and thus are convenient for calibration and alignment purposes.) With the recent trend to use 170-Hz shift almost exclusively, tones of 2125 and 2295 are employed. With afsk, the lower audio frequency is customarily used for mark and the higher for space.

Below 50 MHz, F1 or fsk emission must be used. The carrier is on continuously, but its frequency is shifted to represent marks and spaces. General practice with fsk is to use a frequency shift of 170 Hz, although FCC regulations permit the use of any value of frequency shift up to 900 Hz. The nominal transmitter frequency is the mark condition and the frequency is shifted 170 Hz (or whatever shift may have been chosen) lower for the space signal.

RTTY with SSB Transmitters

A number of amateurs operating RTTY in the hf bands, below 30 MHz, are using audio tones fed into the microphone input of an ssb transmitter. With properly designed and constructed equipment which is correctly adjusted, this provides a satisfactory method of obtaining emission which cannot be distinguished from F1 at the receiver. The user should make certain, however, that audio distortion, carrier, and unwanted sidebands are not present to the degree of causing interference in receiving equipment of good engineering design. The user should also make certain that *the equipment is capable of withstanding the higher-than-normal average power involved.* The RTTY signal is transmitted with a 100-percent duty cycle, i.e., the average-to-peak power ratio is 1, while ordinary speech waveforms generally have duty cycles in the order of 25 percent or less. Many ssb transmitters, such as those using sweep-tube final amplifiers, are designed only for low-duty-cycle use. Power supply components, such as the plate-voltage transformer, may also be rated for light-duty use only. As a general rule when using ssb equipment for RTTY operation, the dc input power to the final PA stage should be no more than twice the plate dissipation rating of the PA tube or tubes.

FREQUENCY-SHIFT KEYERS

The keyboard contacts of the teletypewriter actuate a direct-current circuit that operates the printer magnets. In the "resting" condition the contacts are closed (mark). In operation the contacts open for "space." Because of the presence of dc voltage across the open keyboard contacts in such an arrangement, they cannot normally be used directly to frequency-shift key another circuit. Isolation in the form of a keying relay or electronic switching is ordinarily used.

Hf transmitters can roughly be divided into two basic groups, those intended primarily for single-sideband operation, and those usually referred to as "a-m and cw" types. As far as the RTTY enthusiast is concerned, the difference is principally in the type of VFO used. The ssb transmitter normally uses a "heterodyne" VFO and the cw/a-m types normally use a "multiplying" VFO.

Transmitters with heterodyne VFO units are invariably much more simple to use on RTTY, and usually offer superior stability. Transmitters using frequency-multiplication VFO units pose inherent problems for RTTY, and are seldom comparable to the heterodyne type in stability, especially at the higher frequencies.

Frequency-shift keying in amateur RTTY can be accomplished in a number of ways. For example, if a small capacitor — say, 10 pF — is connected from the cathode of the usual VFO to ground, the frequency will be lowered a small amount, usually about one kilohertz. The capacitor may be switched in and out of the circuit by means of diode switching to obtain frequency-shift keying. Another way to obtain fsk would be to connect a voltage-variable-capacitance diode in the VFO circuit and switch the dc bias levels applied to this diode. Practical circuits are shown in a later section.

The Heterodyning VFO

In the heterodyne VFO system a basic VFO range is beat against different fixed frequencies to obtain the various amateur bands. The neophyte can recognize this type of unit by its tuning dial, since all bands have the same bandspread. In the more advanced types the dial calibration is the same for all bands and the dial runs in the same direction on all bands. A transmitter having such a system is usually the easiest to use on RTTY, as it adapts quickly and satisfactorily to fsk.

Some ssb transmitters use heterodyne VFOs that convert up for one group of bands and convert down for the remainder. On this type of trans-

mitter there are dual dial calibrations, identical except that they run in opposite directions. Such units present minor difficulties in adapting to RTTY, but should not discourage the owner.

In a transmitter of this latter type, where the cw portion of the band is at one end of the dial for 80 meters, and at the other end for 20 meters, two problems exist: (1) the shift will be normal on 20 with a normal circuit, but will be upside down on 80 if there is no provision for inverting the shift; (2) the fact that the 80- and 20-meter frequencies are so far apart on the VFO dial will cause a substantial variation in the shift — if set for 850 Hz on 20, the same keying unit would provide perhaps only 750-Hz shift on 80. Conversely, if set correctly for 850-Hz shift on 80, it would then be in excess of the legal limit of 900 Hz on 20.

In this case the best solution is to incorporate two little keyers in the VFO instead of one. The first would be set for normal operation on 20 meters at 850-Hz shift, and the second would then be set for inverse operation on 80 meters, also adjusted for 850-Hz shift. The operator would then merely select the correct keyer for the band in use.

The Multiplying VFO

The older a-m/cw transmitters normally use VFOs that have one, or at the most, two basic ranges, and then use harmonics for the higher bands. These units are quickly recognized by their elaborate dials having a different set of figures for each band to be used. The bandspread on each band is thus different. The bandspread on 10 meters normally is a fraction of that on 40 meters, for example.

When using this type of transmitter, a shift set correctly for 850 Hz on 40 meters would become 1700 Hz on 20, 2550 Hz on 15, and 3400 Hz on 10. At the same time it will be obvious to the reader that drift becomes a much more serious problem on the higher bands.

Transmitters with multiplying VFOs therefore need some method by which the shift can be radically changed as the transmitter is switched from band to band. Separate pre-set keyers for each band offer one solution.

It can be stated that at this time little or no RTTY activity exists on 10 meters, little or no activity on 15, and very little activity on 40. Thus a keyer for 80 meters and another for 20 will provide the average station with adequate capability for at least 90 percent of the time.

Frequency-Shift Circuits

It was pointed out earlier that addition of a small amount of capacitance will lower the frequency of a VFO. The problem then becomes how to add this capacitance when needed and take it away when not. Various switching circuits have been used in the past, even including small relays inside the VFO, but the semiconductor diode is now universally used. The diode does not require filament voltage or special sockets, is very small, and has excellent life expectancy. The cost, is negligible.

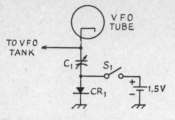

Fig. 2 — Basic diode circuit for frequency-shifting a VFO. The amount of shift can be varied by varying C1.

In the elementary circuit of Fig. 2, when the switch S1 is closed the diode CR1 conducts and grounds C1, thus lowering the frequency of the VFO. The circuit has been much simplified, as normally an rf choke would be used to keep rf off the leads to the switch. Also, in this case, the diode would pull approximately 25 mA, which would damage many germanium diodes. It illustrates the principle, however.

When the switch is open, the frequency is not exactly the same as when C1 is disconnected completely from the oscillator cathode. This is caused by the fact that the diode is slightly conducting as a result of rectification of the rf voltage appearing on C1. The effective resistance of the diode is quite high in comparison to its resistance when the switching voltage is applied, but must not be completely overlooked. This rectification makes it difficult to set the correct shift, since with different settings of C1 the frequency changes at a different rate for both key up and key down. (The fsk system, which will be shown later, circumvents this by applying reverse bias to attain complete cutoff while the key is open.)

As it is customary to lower the transmitted frequency for space, substituting the RTTY keyboard for the switch in Fig. 2 would result in upside-down keying (also called reverse keying) because the keyboard is normally closed for mark. The circuit shown in Fig. 3 will give correct keying. The 220-ohm resistor not only limits the current through the diode to about 4 mA, which is quite satisfactory, but also keeps the battery from being

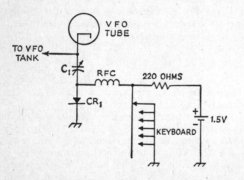

Fig. 3 — Using the keyboard to transmit a "right-side-up" RTTY signal.

short-circuited during mark. However, such a circuit is not recommended for various reasons, the principal one being that insufficient voltage is placed on the keyboard to keep the contacts clear of the oil film that builds up. The rotating mechanism of the Teletype machine throws off small oil droplets which invariably get on the keyboard contacts.

Shift-Pot Circuits

If a multiplying VFO is used, some means must be provided for quickly and easily changing the shift when the transmitter is moved from band to band. Simple "shift-pot" fsk circuits have been generally used.

Fig. 4 shows a suitable shift-pot circuit. It works on the "partial conduction" method, the shift being changed in a rather uniform and linear manner as the potentiometer setting is varied.

A typical voltage-*vs*-frequency characteristic is shown in Fig. 5. Changing the dc voltage on the diode changes its ability to conduct and hence the shift is varied. However, since the dc voltage on the diode, rather than the adjustment of C1, now controls the basic frequency shift, it should be

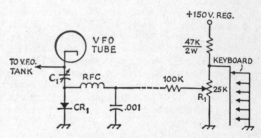

Fig. 4 — The "shift-pot" circuit. Frequency shift depends on the voltage applied to the diode through R1 and the 100-kΩ limiting resistor. The part of the circuit to the left of the dotted connection should be installed close to the VFO tube; that to the right can be in any convenient location. R1 is a linear composition control.

obvious that exceptional voltage stability is required in such a circuit. This in turn means that the keyboard must be separated from the printer's selector magnets. To get "local copy," then, it becomes necessary to tune the receiver to the transmitter's frequency and copy the signal as though it were coming in from another station. This has the advantage of demonstrating that the transmitter is working normally, since if you can copy your own signal with your own receiver-demodulator combination, you can assume the station at the other end is getting a suitable signal. However, it places an awkward restriction on versatility.

The primary disadvantage of the shift-pot circuit is that each time the band is changed, the shift usually must be varied, since this type of circuit is

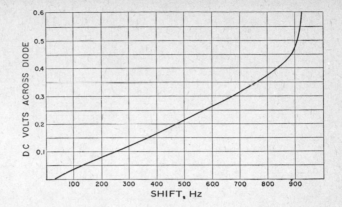

Fig. 5 — A representative frequency-shift vs voltage characteristic of a diode (1N270) in a circuit such as Fig. 4 operating on 3.5 MHz, when C1 is appropriately adjusted.

most normally used with transmitters having multiplying VFO units. Few amateurs have adequate means for accurately setting the shift to 170 Hz, so any system which would allow convenient selection of a preset shift has much merit. The circuit shown in Fig. 6 offers this selection.

Use of Keying Relays

In an effort to overcome the disadvantage of separating the keyboard from the printer magnets, many stations have used relays to key the transmitter. This solves one problem but substitutes others which are probably of more concern, such as distortion, keying transients, rf generation by arcing contacts (hash), need for bias voltages if polar relays are used, and so on. If the scheme presented in the next section is used, keying relays will be unnecessary.

Saturated Diodes

Once sufficient voltage has been placed on the diode to make it conduct completely (about 0.6 volt in the illustration shown in Fig. 4), the shift becomes primarily a function of the value of the capacitor used. Circuits using the saturated diode have many inherent advantages for multiplying VFOs, even though they were developed primarily for use on ssb or other transmitters where the shift need not be changed at frequent intervals.

In the diagram of Fig. 7 the fsk system is combined with the receiving demodulator, the 6W6G being the keyer tube in the demodulator. The keyboard and the printer remain together, meaning that "local copy" need not be received from the receiver-demodulator combination. When the switch, S1, on the grid of the keyer tube is closed, the tube draws current and the printer can then respond normally to its own keyboard. This switch also provides a standby condition so the printer motor need not be turned off while the receiver is being tuned. A fringe benefit is that the receiver can be operated while transmitting without affecting the printer as the operator is typing.

The circuit develops dc voltage of one polarity for mark and a reversed polarity for space. This is accomplished by the unique method of providing the ground return for the loop supply that drives the keyer tube. Resistor R3 is the heart of this system. When the keyboard distributor is closed,

current flowing through R3 (approximately 60 mA) causes a voltage drop in R3 which is of negative polarity with respect to chassis ground. The voltage drop across R2, in series with R1 across the loop supply, is positive with respect to chassis. The *difference* between these two voltage drops is applied to the diode keyer circuit through R4, a current-limiting resistor, and since the drop across R3 is greater than that across R2, the net voltage on the diode is negative. When the keyboard circuit is opened by the distributor, current ceases to flow through R3 and the positive voltage across R2 is applied to the diode keyer. With these reversing voltages, the polarity of the diode as wired in the keyer controls whether it conducts on space (normal) or on mark (non standard). Some transmitters require both methods.

This system is readily adapted to nearly any existing transmitter in a matter of moments, with no permanent changes in the transmitter itself. The components of the basic keyer, also shown in Fig. 7, can be mounted on a small terminal strip with any convenient length of wire (dotted section) to the basic fsk driver. The keyer should be connected to the VFO tube by a short length of wire hooked around its cathode pin. That is the only transmitter connection needed. The terminal strip is then attached to some screw or bolt in the vicinity of the VFO tube, to provide both mechanical mounting and a chassis ground. Once the little keyer is constructed, it can normally be installed in the

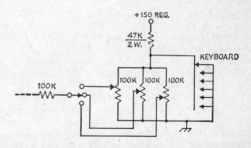

Fig. 6 — Substituting this circuit for the part to the right of the dotted connection in Fig. 4 will permit selection of three pre-set values of frequency shift. Any desired number of pots can be used provided the total resistance of all in parallel is kept in the 25-k to 50-kΩ region.

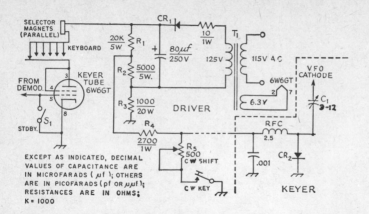

narrow-shift feature, the adjusting pot, R5, can be set for a 100-Hz shift for hand keying. This causes the printer to lock up automatically, and at the same time indicates to the other operator that it is Morse and not RTTY code being sent. Few ordinary fsk systems using shift pots can or do offer such a simple and effective auxiliary system for cw identification.

Fig. 7 — Fsk driver and keyer circuits. The keyer, shown boxed at the right by dashed lines, should be as close as possible to the VFO tube. The driver section can be installed anywhere; dotted connection between the driver and keyer can be any desired length, preferably of shielded wire (a common ground connection between the two units is assumed). In some transmitters, more than one keyer section may be required for use on different bands or in different VFO ranges, with suitable switching added from the driver section.
C1 — 1.5—7pF ceramic trimmer.
CR1 — Silicon diode, minimum ratings 100 mA, 400 PRV.
CR2 — Germanium diode, 1N270 or similar .
R5 — 500-ohm linear control.
S1 — Spst toggle (or integral with transmitter control switch; see text).
T1 — Power transformer; 125 volts, 50 mA; 6.3 volts, 2 A.

transmitter in a minute or so, with no permanent connection or alteration of any type.

Should the keying be upside-down, the diode can be reversed and then normal operation will result. For certain ssb transmitters, such as the Hallicrafters HT-37 and HT-32, two such keyers should be constructed and placed in the VFO area. The diodes in the two keyers should be connected in opposite polarity so one will conduct on space and the other will conduct on mark. A switch can then select the correct keyer for the band in use.

Narrow-Shift CW Identification

The circuit of Fig. 7 includes a cw key for narrow shift identification. The FCC regulations require that RTTY transmissions be identified either by cw or by voice, and because voice modulation is not permitted in the RTTY segments of amateur bands below 30 MHz, the required identification must be sent by cw. Many stations use types of cw identification that cause the machine at the receiving station to run wild unless the operator can quickly activate the standby or mute switch on the demodulator. Some of the methods in use even "sound like" RTTY, and the receiving operator is not sure whether he should allow the printer to operate or not. With the

Selecting Components

It is suggested that you do not substitute other parts for those specified in the fsk driver section, since these have been carefully selected to give optimum results. The circuit was designed for 60 mA (parallel selector magnets) operation.

However, there is considerable latitude in the selection of components for the keyers. Suggested are 1N270 diodes, high-speed computer switching diodes that are quite easy to obtain and quite cheap compared with some. They give excellent results, but nearly any type of germanium diode will give satisfactory results. Even silicon diodes will no doubt work adequately. The only requirement is that they should be able to conduct at least 10 mA and have the ability to withstand at least 50 volts reverse bias.

The size and type of the trimmer capacitor, C1, will vary with the reader's preference and type of equipment. For 170-Hz shift, usually a 1.5-7-pF trimmer is best. For 850-Hz shift, a 3-12-pF capacitor is quite satisfactory. The rf choke can be quite miniature, since only 4-5 mA of current at the most will be passed.

To summarize, the fsk system presented here offers the following features:

1) Once the shift is correctly set, it will hold for that part of the VFO dial indefinitely.

2) With reversing voltages, the effect on the VFO dial calibration after installation is minimum — usually less than 1 kHz change.

3) It is much easier to set to the correct shift, since the back bias keeps the change in frequency to a minimum during nonconduction.

4) Optimum keying is achieved because reversing the voltages forces the diode to switch instantly from cutoff to full saturation.

5) The keyboard and printer are kept together without resorting to a keying relay for local copy.

6) "Retransmit" is automatically offered; the transmitter can be keyed directly from an incoming signal, if desired.

7) Conduction on either mark or space can be selected merely by reversing the polarity of the diode.

8) The keyer unit uses very few parts and can be mounted easily and quickly in nearly any VFO, with no modifications or alterations.

Fig. 8 — Crystal-oscillator frequency-shift circuit for use with fsk driver (Fig. 7). Resistors are 1/2-watt; fixed capacitors are disk ceramic except SM indicates silver mica. Values are suitable for 3.5- and 7-MHz crystals.
C2 — 50-pF air trimmer.
C3 — 150-pF variable.
CR4 — Germanium diode; 1N270 or similar.
S2 — Spst toggle.
Y1 — Crystal at desired frequency, HC-6/U type (*not* FT-243).

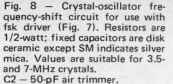
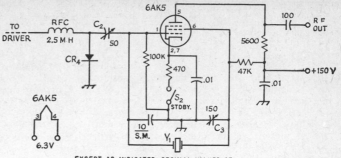

EXCEPT AS INDICATED, DECIMAL VALUES OF CAPACITANCE ARE IN MICROFARADS (μf.); OTHERS ARE IN PICOFARADS (pf OR μμf); RESISTANCES ARE IN OHMS; K = 1000.

Adding Keyers

Although a shift pot readily can be added if needed, by putting a 1-megohm pot in series with the fsk line to the keyer or keyers involved, this is not particularly recommended. Normally, one would instead add an extra keyer pre-set for the required shift.

CRYSTAL-SHIFT FSK

Another method of fsk that provides outstanding results is crystal shift. In the past, some shift-pot circuits that have been added to crystal oscillators have given such poor results that many of the advanced enthusiasts still shy away from crystal shift. The fsk driver shown in Fig. 7 provides excellent results when used in conjunction with the circuit shown in Fig. 8.

In this case the standby switch, S2, would be operated simultaneously with the external control switch that puts the transmitter on the air. If S2 were not automatically thrown, the crystal oscillator would run continuously, blocking the incoming signal from the receiver.

By carefully juggling the two variable capacitors, C2 and C3, any legal shift can be preset within the part of the crystal's activity range that provides equal output voltages for both mark and space. This circuit was developed primarily for the fsk driver system of Fig. 7 by W8SDZ from work previously done by W6NRM. Other circuits were tried but rejected in favor of the one shown.

The advantages of crystal shift are numerous and should not be overlooked. Once the shift is set, it will hold indefinitely. Warm-up time is virtually nonexistent. For any type of day-to-day recurrent operation such as autostart, no other system can compare for reliability. Drift is inappreciable, and this feature alone is reason enough for its use by those owning older transmitters. It does, of course, have the limitation of holding the operator to one frequency. However, RTTY operating practice is such that most operators normally use approximately the same frequency day after day, anyway. Two or three crystals would be more than adequate for the typical operator.

Crystal shift can also be used in ssb transmitters in various ways. The advantage is a constant fsk shift regardless of the setting of the VFO dial. However, with some transmitters there is the disadvantage that mark and space must be turned upside down on certain bands. In general, the amateur will find it difficult to attempt to shift an existing crystal oscillator in an ssb transmitter, as compared with applying the very simple keyer shown in Fig. 7 to the transmitter's VFO.

Setting the Frequency Shift

To ensure that the transmitted signal will match receivers having demodulators using sharp filters at the standard audio tones of 2125 and 2295 Hz, the frequency shift should be set to 170 Hz with as much accuracy as possible. A calibrated audio generator is probably the most readily available source of a 170-Hz tone for comparison.

Using the audio generator for setting the keying shift is a simple matter. First tune the signal from the VFO (or crystal oscillator) to zero beat in the receiver with the keying circuit open. Then close the keyer circuit and compare the beat tone with the 170-Hz tone from the audio generator. Adjust the fsk shift control so that the beat tone and the af generator tone are the same, then open the keyer circuit and make sure that the oscillator signal is still in zero beat. If it is not, a little back-and-forth jockeying of the frequency control will eventually result in a frequency difference that matches the audio generator tone.

The prime disadvantage of this technique is that exact zero beat is difficult to obtain, especially with receivers having narrow i-f response and a BFO that is offset in frequency from the i-f passband. Suitable adjustment can sometimes be made by matching the pitch of tones known to be separated by 170 Hz, such as those of a received signal of accurate shift setting. As a last resort, notes of a piano can be used for reasonably close adjustment by matching tones. Use A and C of the second octave above middle C (880 and 1047 Hz, respectively).

AUDIO FREQUENCY-SHIFT KEYING FOR RTTY

Audio-shift keying, which is introduced into the microphone jack of a transmitter, was first used on the vhf bands, where many types of emission not permitted on the lower frequencies are legal. It was almost a necessity, since the carrier stability on those bands with older a-m transmitters was not of the order needed for carrier frequency-shift keying. Use of audio fsk with carrier offers an inherent tuning advantage — if the second or third station in a group is a few hertz (or even a kilohertz or two) off frequency, it will not matter. Thus, afsk with carrier compares to fsk (of the carrier itself) in the way that tuning an a-m signal compares with tuning ssb: inexpensive equipment and novice operators can normally get excellent results.

It was natural, then, for owners of expensive ssb transmitters to adapt some of the afsk keyers to the microphone input circuits of their transmitters, rather than dig into the vfo or pto circuits. The system does appeal to many who have no desire to alter or modify expensive equipment in any way.

However, there may be unexpected consequences from such a move. When afsk is used for RTTY with an ssb transmitter the *carrier suppression becomes important, and the unwanted sideband suppression becomes a significant item.* You are using, on cw frequencies, a type of system that differs from normal carrier transmission, and distortion products that would cause "flat-topping" and "splatter" change the picture completely.

It should be obvious to anyone only vaguely familiar with ssb transmitter theory that even if the carrier is suppressed, there is *some* carrier still transmitted. Even if the unwanted sideband is suppressed, there is *some* sideband still transmitted. Even the best transmitters with excellent means to suppress the carrier and the unwanted sideband will have *some* of them remaining. If signal conditions are good, these undesired frequencies might easily interfere with adjacent-channel reception. An exact statement regarding this very thing was published by the FCC in Docket 15267, released July 7, 1964,

"Amateur licensees contemplating the use of audio tones via single-sideband suppressed carrier transmitters for the generation of A1 and/or F1 emissions are cautioned that any radiation of the carrier or suppressed sideband frequencies at an intensity sufficient to cause interference in receiving equipment of good engineering design constitutes spurious radiation in violation of Section 97.73."

It might be supposed that this applies principally to the quality of the ssb transmitter and that the afsk unit itself could be assumed to be flawless. However, such is not likely to be the case. Many inexpensive and simple afsk units have been designed, and hardly a month goes by but that some amateur publication prints a description of

such a device — intended mostly for use in connection with ssb transmitters. K3NIO ran exhaustive tests on many of these, using laboratory facilities available to but a few amateurs, and found that none of the units tested would meet the FCC minimum specifications when used with ssb transmitters. Many of them were incapable of generating an acceptable-looking audio sine wave, and all had undesirable keying transients when RTTY keying was applied. All units tested exhibited audio harmonic generation, with no means provided to suppress these undesired harmonics. All used *LC* switching, which was the reason for the keying transients.

Various authors have proposed the use of two oscillators with some form of switching between them as a possible solution. The signal generated by this method is not really fsk but rather what might be called "double a-m." Again, undesirable keying transients are generated that would not occur with a suitably designed frequency-shift oscillator. The subject is mentioned at this time simply to counter suggestions which have been made that such a system probably would solve the usual problems of the normal afsk unit, where only one frequency-shifted oscillator is used.

On the vhf bands, where either a-m or fm transmitters are used for RTTY purposes, audio tones are fed into the microphone input to transmit the RTTY signal. The mark tone, usually 2125 Hz, is changed from 2125 to 2295 for space as the keyboard contacts open and close, thus transmitting a frequency-shifted audio signal. The receiver at the other end feeds these audio tones into a **demodulator** (sometimes called a "TU" or "converter") which changes the tones into dc pulses that operate the teleprinter.

On the bands between 3.5 and 30 MHz, the audio tones from a good afsk unit could be fed to the audio input of a top-notch ssb transmitter. In general, ssb transmitters using mechanical filters have excellent sideband suppression, particularly when the tones of 2125 and 2295 Hz are used.

Perhaps most transmitters using mechanical filters or crystal lattice filters would be acceptable when teamed with an appropriate afsk unit. The phasing type of ssb transmitter would most likely give marginal results unless perfectly adjusted for carrier and sideband suppression. Phasing rigs seldom hold these critical adjustments over long periods of time.

High-Powered Transmitters

The use of ssb has introduced powerful linear amplifiers which can easily run the legal input of 1000 watts. Owners of such amplifiers are cautioned against their indiscriminate use on RTTY, since many of them cannot be run with continuous carrier at their ssb ratings. It should also be pointed out that should afsk generators be used with ssb exciters, the linear amplifier will greatly increase the seriousness of any minor problems caused by such an arrangement, so if the signal was marginal before, it might be entirely unacceptable after being boosted to one kilowatt.

For normal operation, the use of powerful amplifiers, of course, adds strength to a signal and helps the operator maintain satisfactory contacts. However, individuals contemplating purchase of an amplifier for RTTY purposes would do well first to inquire of the manufacturer as to its suitability for continuous-carrier operation.

Use of Transceivers for RTTY

A large number of transceivers are now being sold, principally for ssb use. Some of these will not operate in the cw bands, but most will. Many of them are not suited for use with RTTY from a number of standpoints, the most important of which would be their inability to operate with continuous carrier for any length of time.

Another problem in some transceivers is the audio sidetone which is available in the cw position so the operator can hear his keying. For RTTY, this usually must be disconnected; otherwise, it can become most distracting.

The major remaining problem concerns the fact that in a transceiver the receiver and transmitter are locked to the same oscillator frequency. For carrier-shift RTTY this becomes a major difficulty, since it is customary to tune the transmitter so that an audio tone of 2125 mark will result when received. Thus on a transceiver some means of changing the transmitter frequency by an amount equal to the mark value of the demodulator is required. Fig. 9 shows one circuit that should at last make RTTY transceiver operation satisfactory. Another standard keyer is added to the cathode of the VFO or PTO. This keyer is operated by the transmit switch and gets its voltage from any power supply in the demodulator or transmitter other than the regular fsk supply. Then when the transmit switch is operated, it (1) puts the transmitter on the air, (2) mutes the keyer-tube grid so the operator can type, and (3) automatically shifts the carrier frequency off to one side the necessary amount for correct transmission. The switch shown in Fig. 9 would be arranged to be either open for transmit or closed for transmit, whichever gives correct operation with the particular transmitter used; in one case it will lower the transmitter frequency from that of the receiver and in the other case it will raise it.

This circuit, when used in connection with the fsk system shown in Fig. 7, will provide an accurate, simple and inexpensive means of achieving excellent results from transceive equipment without resorting to afsk with its inherent problems.

In general, it can be said that transceivers probably will be somewhat unsatisfactory in RTTY service unless the considerations outlined above have been met.

Oscillator Transients and Harmonics

Afsk circuits published in the past for 850-Hz shift have generally used *LC* oscillators, usually

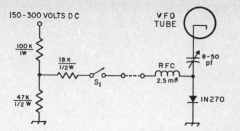

Fig. 9 - Carrier-shift circuit for establishing mark frequency in an ssb transceiver. This is used in conjunction with the keyer. S1 is operated simultaneously with the transmit switch as described in the text, and may be integral with the transmit-receive switch.

with one 88-mH toroid and a .033-μF capacitor across it for 2975 Hz and an additional .03 or .033 μF capacitor to go to 2125 for mark. Since adding capacitance to the *LC* circuit lowers the audio frequency, and since the mark tone is used as the reference, you can see the problem in trying to achieve any shift other than 850 with this type of circuit. It is also a problem to get narrow-shift cw identification that will come out "right side up." The greatest problem, though, arises from rapidly changing the frequency of a resonant *LC* circuit. Unless some provision is made to shape the keying waveform, by slowing up the transition from one frequency to the other, there can be key clicks that occupy more than the necessary keying bandwidth. Also, these oscillators have strong harmonics, particularly the even harmonics, while few, if any, simple afsk units use any type of low-pass filter to eliminate them. Although the transmitter itself will probably pass only the 2125 tone, the harmonics at 4250, 6375, and so on can adversely affect the audio and sideband stages.

The fact that the typical afsk circuit is simple and inexpensive is hardly justification for putting a mediocre system on a relatively expensive piece of equipment, when for only a few dollars more you could have additional benefits and do it right at the same time.

Requirements for Good AFSK

A few requirements are "musts" if you are talking about a decent afsk unit, and some other features are in the "nice-to-have" category.

In the "must" department, we would want:

1) No keying transients on going from mark to space.

2) Negligible harmonic content to create distortion in the transmitter.

3) Proper output level for the transmitter to be used.

In the "nice-to-have" department, we could add several things, but let's try these:

1) 170 shift as well as 850 shift.

2) Perhaps one or two positions for other shifts to experiment with.

3) Narrow-shift cw identification.

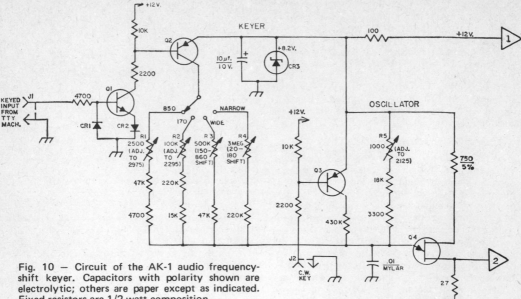

Fig. 10 — Circuit of the AK-1 audio frequency-shift keyer. Capacitors with polarity shown are electrolytic; others are paper except as indicated. Fixed resistors are 1/2-watt composition.

CR1, CR2 — Silicon; type not critical (1N4816 used).
CR3 — 8.2-volt Zener, 1 watt (1N4738).
J1-J4, incl. — Phono jacks.
Q1, Q5, Q6, Q7 — Silicon, npn; Motorola MPS-3394 or equivalent.
Q2, Q3 — Silicon, pnp; Motorola MPS-3702 or equivalent.
Q4 — Unijunction; 2N4871 or equivalent.
R1, R2, R5 — Linear taper.
R6 — For output level setting; see text.
S1 — Rotary, 1 section, 1 pole, 4 positions used.
S2 — Spst toggle.

4) Output to match either carbon or high-impedance mic outputs.

5) An input that will readily adapt to numerous different arrangements to suit the user.

In addition to such operating features, it would be advantageous to make the unit solid-state, for low power consumption and small size, as well as to allow use of an easily duplicated printed circuit board. From these requirements, Irv Hoff, W6FFC and formerly K8DKC, designed the unit described in the section which follows. The instrument was originally presented in *QST* for February, 1969.

THE MAINLINE AK-1

The heart of the AK-1, Fig. 10, is a unijunction transistor pulse generator. The circuit is essentially an *RC* oscillator, so decreasing *R* will increase the frequency. You can easily change to any shift you like merely by adding resistance in parallel (or by switching in different resistors) while keeping the mark frequency the same.

The pulse generator runs at 4250 pulses per second for the mark frequency. These pulses are fed into a flip-flop which changes state for each pulse, thus not only dividing by two to get 2125

cycles per second, but also providing symmetrical square waves from the short pulses.

Square waves theoretically have only odd-harmonic content, so the frequencies generated by this system are 2125, 6375, 10,625, 14,875, and so on. The flip-flop is followed by a 5-pole Butterworth low-pass filter that cuts off a little above 3000 Hz. This filter effectively removes all harmonics, changing the square wave into a sine wave.

The output of the low-pass filter goes directly to the ssb mic input, which always operates at a very low signal-voltage level. It also goes to an emitter-follower stage that will supply a relatively hefty 0.5 volt (peak audio) signal to a low impedance, for vhf transmitters using carbon microphones.

Since there is no inductor in the oscillator section, keying transients are minimized when the signal is changed from mark to space. Observations with a Tektronix 531 scope bear this out.

The input circuit of the AK-1 will operate from any system that gives a positive voltage for space.

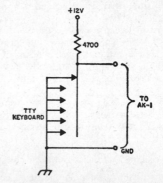

Fig. 11 — Teletype machine keyboard connections.

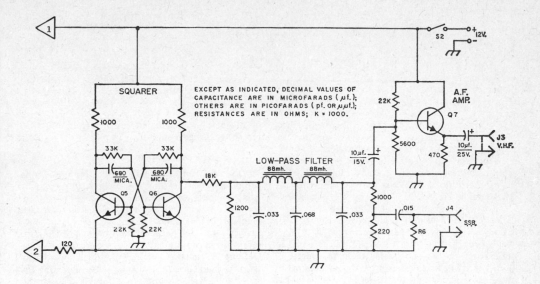

It is immaterial whether there is no voltage or a negative voltage for mark. This system adapts to most systems already in use for driving an fsk unit in the transmitter. It adapts immediately to the Mainline TT/L unit described in a later section. Most other demodulators do not include an fsk driving system, and in such case the operator probably has devised one – such as a "shift pot" system – himself. The AK-1 may also be driven directly from the keyboard as shown in Fig. 11.

Only when receiving on lower sideband do the audio tones come out properly. Consequently, when transmitting in the lower sideband position, the tones are transmitted normally, and mark will remain "stationary" regardless of what shift is in use. Plan to do all your transmitting and all your listening in the lower sideband position for normal operation.

Some transmitters will not pass 2975 as well as they pass 2125 Hz (we are not talking about the units that won't pass 2975 *at all* – supposedly the owner has changed the BFO crystal so that 2975 will be passed); that is, 2975 may not be passed at the same level as 2125. For instance, the audio circuits in the HT-32A attenuate the space tone of 2975 some 3 dB. To compensate for this audio roll-off, a simple high-boost circuit consisting of a .015-μF capacitor and a resistor, R6, was added. If your transmitter has less output on space than on mark, try various values of resistors at this point. For the HT-32A the required value is about 4700 ohms. You may not need any resistor at all.

The shift for cw identification may be set for about 110 Hz (FCC requires at least 100 Hz for narrow-shift cw for this purpose.) The nice thing about this arrangement on the AK-1 is that the cw identification shift is always the same regardless of the shift selected by the switch. Take the "side-arm" off the key so it will not short out and cause the shift to change inadvertently.

Constructing the Unit

There is tremendous flexibility in the choice of most of the parts. The unijunction transistor (Motorola 2N4871) was selected for its low cost, but many others may be used. Q1, Q5, Q6 and Q7 can be literally any npn type of silicon transistor (do not use germanium transistors). The pots can be the Centralab "Fastach II front" units, as these are modest in cost and various types of short shafts may be obtained. In the unit picured, Fig. 12, flush screwdriver shafts were used. You may prefer a

Fig. 12 – External connections are on the rear chassis wall. Aside from these and the controls lined up on the front wall, all components are mounted on a 5-1/2 X 3-inch etched board supported by brackets from the side walls of the chassis. The audio low-pass filter is at the left in this view. The unijunction oscillator and the keying circuits occupy the right-hand section of the board.

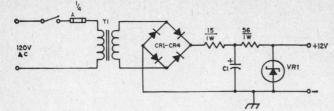

Fig. 13 — Power-supply circuit. Resistances are in ohms; resistors are 1-watt composition.
C1 — Electrolytic, 1000 μF or more, 15-25 volts.
CR1-CR4, incl. — Silicon, 200 mA, 50 PIV.
T1 — Any transformer having 12- to 12.6-volt secondary, 100 mA or more.
VR1 — Zener; 12 volts, 1 watt.

short shaft that can be turned with the fingers. The output connectors on the rear are inexpensive phone jacks that mount in a one-quarter-inch hole.

The use of a printed-circuit board greatly simplifies the construction of any project and this is no exception. The board in the instrument photographed measures about 3 by 5-1/2 inches.

For ease of adjustment, the pots for 2125, 2295 and 2975 were selected to give about 60-70 Hz total variation at the frequencies specified. As a result, you may need to hand-pick the resistors in series with the pots to enable them to operate at mid-range. The values shown on the schematic are those used in the unit photographed. The 500-kΩ and 3-MΩ pots should have right-hand log taper to give linear variations between various shifts you may want to use. If you wish, you can leave out the positions on the switch you do not feel you need, thus saving some money on the pots and resistors. If you never have any use at all for wide shift, you can dispense with the switch entirely, and with the 2975-Hz pot plus the other two. Their associated resistors can also be left off. You can easily enough add any or all of those things later if you wish.

One additional comment: Bypass each connector leaving the chassis with a .01- or .005-μF capacitor to guard against rf getting into the unit. This is not shown on the schematic.

Power Supply

Fig. 13 shows a suitable power supply if you need one. Depending upon what 12-volt transformer you use, you may need to change the value of the 56-ohm resistor to get a current of 10-20 mA in the Zener regulator.

Adjustment and Use

You can connect a pair of headphones (or an audio counter) to the vhf output and compare what you hear with a standard 2125 tone from an accurate audio oscillator, musical instrument, tape recorder, tone standard or whatever you have available for the purpose. The other pots may be set by first causing the keyboard to go to space. Holding down the "break" key will accomplish this. As mark does not change while adjusting the space tone, this is a simple and quick adjustment.

The unit is designed to work from a 12-volt supply and draws about 50 mA. With the voltage changed from 8 to 16, the output frequency changed only one hertz. There will be perhaps 10-15 Hz warm-up drift the first few seconds after you turn the power supply on. In a two-month period, the 850-Hz shift was never found to be off more than 1 Hz, after warm-up, regardless of room temperature.

In using the AK-1 make certain that you do not overdrive the transmitter with too much audio. This is easily checked by reducing the microphone gain control until the output drops noticeably. This will be the gain-control setting which you should never exceed. If you're tempted to ignore this admonishment and run the audio too high, trying to get that last ounce of power from the machine, all we can do is tell you that this is not the way it's done.

An additional 30 to 40 dB of carrier suppression can be achieved by moving the BFO frequency 1 kHz to transmit 2125- and 2975-Hz tones.

RECEIVING RADIOTELETYPE

A teleprinter operates from on-off dc pulses. The closed-circuit ("on") condition is called "mark" and the open-circuit ("off") condition is called "space." Ordinary Morse code is similar in many respects.

When a receiver with BFO on is tuned to a cw signal a tone is heard in the headset or speaker during key-down ("on") and noise is heard during key-up ("off"). The relationship between these two conditions is called the "signal-to-noise" (S/N) ratio. In ordinary cw it is customary to use relatively low rf gain to optimize this relationship and make it easier for the operator to distinguish between the signal and the undesired noise.

Frequency-Shift Keying

If the transmitter is kept on the air at all times and keyed by switching back and forth between two slightly separated frequencies, the signal-to-noise ratio can be greatly improved. The improvement is of little benefit in aural reception, but if automatic means are used to interpret the signal, this frequency-shift keying (called fsk) offers distinct advantages. In fact, fsk still remains one of the most practical methods that can be used for automatic reception of signals.

The fsk system is a standard method of transmitting not only RTTY but high-speed commercial Morse as well. Various frequency shifts are in common use, and for many years 850-Hz shift was the "standard" for radio amateurs. However, many enthusiasts found marked improvement in reception on crowded frequencies using 170-Hz shift, and the use of wide (850-Hz) shift has all but disappeared. Among other advantages, narrow shift allows using the highest selectivity that the receiver offers — usually 500-Hz bandwidth — for maximum rejection of unwanted signals.

Since the transmitter stays on the air continuously but shifts between two different frequencies, the over-all effect is that of two cw stations 170 Hz apart. The frequency in the no-typing or closed-circuit condition is called "mark" and is an "on-off" frequency when keyed. The other frequency is the open-circuit condition or "space," and is exactly the opposite of mark, or "off-on."

It can be seen, then, that either mark or space actually contains all the information transmitted. Indeed, certain advanced types of receiving equipment make particular use of this very feature.

Receiving the RTTY Signal

Three items are needed to print messages from radioteletype signals:

1) A good communications receiver.
2) An fsk demodulator (often called a "converter").
3) A teleprinter.

The receiver separates the particular station desired from others; the fsk demodulator changes the incoming signal into on-off dc pulses; and the teleprinter changes these electrical pulses into mechanical motion to print the message.

The Receiver

In general, any receiver usually considered adequate for single-sideband reception will do well on RTTY. The receiver is used for the same purpose as in receiving a cw signal — that is, to change the incoming radio frequency into an audio frequency that can be used, in this case, by the RTTY demodulator rather than by the human ear. A product detector (as used for ssb) is preferred over the diode detector found in older a-m and cw receivers, as it not only provides an improved signal-to-noise ratio as a general rule, but also simplifies the use of agc in the receiver, which at times can be helpful.

Since the mark and space signals are separated by only 170 Hz, it would be nice to have a selectivity position on the receiver of about 250 Hz. Most receivers do not offer exactly this bandwidth, but some manufacturers offer i-f filters of 400-Hz bandwidth or so. The optimum bandwidth of the receiver would be about 1000 Hz for wide-shift reception.

The cw operator usually adjusts his receiver to give approximately a 1000-Hz audio tone for copying code. In a carry-over from commercial practice, however, amateur RTTY demodulators usually are designed for a tone of 2125 Hz for mark, and space then becomes 2295 Hz. The BFO in the receiver must be properly set so these audio tones will result.

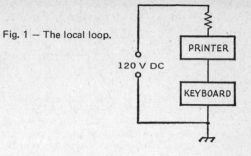

Fig. 1 — The local loop.

120 V DC

Frequency stability is quite necessary in RTTY, particularly when using narrow shift. Late-model receivers intended primarily for ssb reception are usually much more stable than their predecessors, and are set on lower sideband to receive normal RTTY.

The Demodulator

There are many different types of demodulators, just as there are many types of boats or automobiles or airplanes. While thinking of airplanes we can point out that there are two basic types in use — the propeller plane and the jet plane using no propeller. Then there are combinations where jet engines drive propellers, or — in some earlier military types such as the B-36 — where both propeller engines and additional jet engines are used.

In RTTY, we now have our new "jet-type" demodulators as well as the older "propeller-type" units. The latter still have some advantages and will not disappear immediately. The "propeller-type" are based on fm principles and the "jet-type" are based on a-m principles. Certain features of both types are similar, and in fact, only recently has it been found that even the older types can benefit immensely from the application of some of the newer a-m principles.

However, let us start by referring to the most simple demodulator that one could build. We mentioned that the teleprinter needs on-off dc pulses. Look at Fig. 1. In this case, the keyboard is nothing more than a switch that opens or closes the circuit. We could replace it with any type of device that would also open and close the circuit, such as a relay or a vacuum tube operated as a switch.

Now look at Fig. 2. If the grid is saturated with a positive voltage, the tube will conduct and act as a short-circuit. Actually there will be some voltage

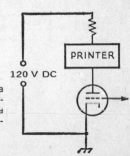

120 V DC

Fig. 2 — Loop using a keyer tube for operating the printer from a properly processed incoming signal.

Fig. 3 — A simple RTTY demodulator, converter, or terminal unit (all three terms are used). This circuit discards the mark portion of the fsk signal and uses only the space signal.

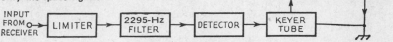

drop across the tube, so it acts more like a low-value resistor, but the magnets in the printer will be closed. Alternatively, if a sufficiently large negative voltage is applied to the grid, the tube will stop conducting and act instead as an open-circuit. The printer magnets will then open.

This tube then is called a "keyer tube." A typical keyer tube requires a bias voltage of about +15 to +20 volts for saturation of the grid and perhaps −30 to −40 volts for complete cutoff. Many older circuits use a relay instead of a keyer tube, but these introduce problems which make their continued use unsatisfactory.

Fig. 3 shows a block diagram of a simple demodulator for RTTY use. In this case a limiter is used to keep the audio voltage constant and thus overcome the undesirable effects that could occur when the output of the receiver changes with fading signals. This simple demodulator completely ignores the mark tone at 2125, and concentrates instead on just the space tone of 2295 Hz. The filter provides audio selectivity for this purpose. This space tone is then fed to the "detector" stage, which is essentially a rectifier that converts the audio into a dc pulse for the printer.

In this simple demodulator positive bias voltage is kept on the grid so that the printer will remain in mark. When a space signal is passed through the circuit, it puts a negative voltage on the grid that is strong enough to override the fixed positive bias, and the magnet circuit opens. Proper adjustment of the positive bias will produce reasonably satisfactory results, and in addition to having a very simple demodulator that works, one gets the further advantage of having a printer that will not operate at all until the space signal is received.

This very simple single-filter demodulator might work well under ideal circumstances such as one would normally find in 2- or 6-meter vhf work. However, on the lower frequencies such ideal circumstances rarely exist. It is not at all uncommon for the mark or space frequencies to fade independently ("selective fading") or for static bursts, poor signal-to-noise ratio, random noise,

impulse noise, or cw stations near the frequency to interfere with proper demodulation of the signal. For these reasons it is customary to take advantage of the fact that both mark and space are transmitted alternately. A slightly more sophisticated demodulator, then, uses filters for both tones — one eventually providing the positive voltage for the mark condition and the other providing the negative voltage for the space condition.

To get a sharper change from positive to negative at the keyer tube grid, some circuits use neon bulbs as trigger devices. Other units use special tube circuits which are much more sensitive to smaller variations in voltages.

Improving the Simple Demodulator

Continuing our analogy to airplanes, these simple units so far described would perhaps be the small, inexpensive and simple "training" planes. They work pretty well for fair-weather flying, but would quickly bog down when the going gets rough. For all-weather flying, additional "instruments" are needed to add the versatility and performance required. Fig. 4 shows an advanced demodulator based on the above simple principles.

The input band-pass filter in this case would be about 250 Hz wide. Its purpose is merely to restrict the input to the demodulator to the frequencies of interest. Since many receivers used for ssb have only 2.1- or 2.5-kHz i-f selectivity, it is apparent they will pass signals which have no bearing on the RTTY signal and may often disrupt what would otherwise be perfect copy. Also, since all receivers have *some* hum in the audio output, an additional benefit of the band-pass input filter is that it prevents this hum from reaching the RTTY demodulator. The additional improvement is substantial in weak-signal detection where the receiver has not been readjusted by the operator. Contrary to what some authors would have one believe, a narrow filter in the receiver will *not* satisfactorily replace a good audio band-pass input filter. Use of *both* would be optimum.

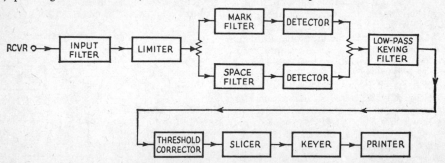

Fig. 4 — An advanced type of RTTY demodulator capable of printing accurately under difficult reception conditions.

The limiter again keeps the signal at essentially constant output. As long as the receiver is correctly tuned, the output voltage of the mark detector will be the same as the space voltage from the space detector. Consequently, it is usual for the one detector to be arranged for positve (+) output and the other for negative (−) output. The low-pass filter eliminates the rectified audio "ripple" from the desired dc pulse.

As long as the receiver is correctly tuned for placing the mark and space signals properly in their respective filters, the output from the low-pass filter should vary uniformly from mark to space. However, such ideal circumstances seldom last for long. If the transmitter drifts and the local operator does not make an appropriate correction, the voltage for mark might become greater than that for space. If no means are provided to correct automatically for this difference, "distortion" commences. Although the average printer can handle large amounts of distortion adequately, eventually a point is reached where the system no longer will print faithfully.

The threshold corrector, the circuit of which will be described in a later section, is an ingenious device which restores the balance between mark and space automatically. It was developed out of necessity for a different type of reception ("a-m" where no limiters are used), but we now find that it offers many advantages to high-performance fm demodulators as well. With such a device, simple drift or mistuning offers no problems to normal printing although, if carried to extremes, eventually a point is reached where good printing ceases.

The output of the threshold corrector provides a plus-and-minus signal to the "slicer" stage. A "slicer" can be called by other names just as well, and perhaps the term "trigger" would explain its action. The slicer is designed so that a small positive voltage will completely saturate the tube and it will conduct heavily. A small negative voltage will completely cut off the tube and no conduction results. The output of the slicer will be a fixed voltage for mark and an opposite but fixed voltage for space. These voltages could be used directly to key the printer on and off, but the slicer tube cannot draw the current necessary to operate the selector magnets (60 mA for parallel hookup). In fact, only a few low-cost receiving-type tubes *can* handle that type of current. Thus the slicer becomes a "buffer" stage and an additional keyer stage is used for direct control of the printer or printers.

Selective Fading

As has just been mentioned, simple circuitry is quite adequate when afsk is employed at vhf. A given signal is usually of almost unchanging amplitude, and the two audio tones at the receiver output are essentially of unchanging strength at all times. Simple circuitry will also provide quite satisfactory operation in the hf bands under good signal conditions. However, operation under interference and fading conditions in these bands demands more than simple circuitry, if reliable

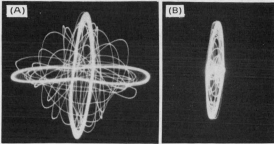

Fig. 5 — Oscilloscope presentations of a received radioteletype signal. For these displays the mark frequency is displayed on the horizontal axis and the space frequency on the vertical axis. The photo in A shows a signal during normal reception, while the photo in B shows a signal during selective fading where the mark frequency is momentarily absent.

copy from the received signal is to be made.

Shown in Fig. 5A is an oscilloscope presentation of a frequency-shift-keyed RTTY signal. In this photo, the teleprinter mark frequency is displayed on the horizontal axis and the space frequency on the vertical axis. Although only one frequency is present at a given instant, the persistence of the cathode ray tube display permits the simultaneous observation of both frequencies, which are 850 hertz apart. The two signals are of equal amplitude, and appear as ellipses because moderately-broad-response frequency filters yielding incomplete channel isolation were used in deriving the display. (Some of the mark-frequency signal appears in the space channel, and vice versa.) The smaller amplitude signals visible outside the ellipses appear because it is not possible (nor is it desirable) to shift the transmitter instantaneously from one carrier frequency to the other. These smaller signals represent the transitional frequency sweep.

When fsk is used in the high-frequency bands and sky-wave signals are received, the effect we call selective fading takes place. As these photographs of received signal displays indicate, radio frequencies only 850 Hz apart will fade quite differently from one another under some conditions. As alternate carrier frequencies are transmitted, the temporary loss of one audio tone at the demodulator input often results when one radio frequency momentarily fades nearly into the background noise level, while the other of the two frequencies may remain quite strong.

Fig. 5B shows an oscilloscope presentation of a received fsk signal during selective fading. The mark-frequency signal (horizontal axis) is essentially absent, having faded almost into the noise level. The space-frequency signal (vertical axis) is many times stronger, having faded only slightly. Similar fading, although normally not so severe, sometimes occurs under unusual conditions with 170-Hz shift.

The selective fade period for a single frequency may last from a few thousandths of a second to several seconds, depending on band conditions, and may occur at quite frequent intervals, several times a second. Generally, fading will affect first one frequency, which will momentarily return, and will then affect the other frequency, which will also momentarily return. After some interval of time, the cycle may tend to repeat itself. Of course fading is a random occurrence, and the pattern may not be repetitive in nature.

Simple demodulators requiring the alternate presence of both tones for proper operation will not provide reliable operation during such fading. The copy will appear as a meaningless jumble of letters during the fade period, or perhaps the printer will print nothing, depending on the circuitry of the demodulator. If such fading occurs often, so much copy may be lost that one might not even be certain what the transmitting station is discussing.

With properly designed circuitry, normal operation of the demodulator will continue during such a fade. Such circuitry permits the demodulator to operate automatically from either audio tone alone, as if it were on-off keyed, and combines the operation from both tones when no fading occurs.

OVER-ALL DESIGN CONSIDERATIONS FOR RTTY DEMODULATORS

The general requirements for reception of RTTY signals were discussed in broad terms in the preceding text, and a number of demodulator configurations were described in block-circuit form. It is now time to look at the individual sections of these circuits more closely, to see what performance characteristics are needed for optimum use of the incoming RTTY signal, particularly with reference to the advance-type demodulator.

These performance characteristics are determined by the nature of the signal, along with the noise and interference that is inevitably associated with it in amateur work. For example, the bandwidth of the RTTY signal is a major factor, so it is necessary first to look at this aspect.

Keying Bandwidth

A constant carrier with no modulation (such as a key-down cw signal) is basically a single frequency. It has no bandwidth, since a single frequency is not a band. But as soon as the cw key is activated, this no longer is true. The signal now becomes pulse modulated, and the bandwidth is closely related to the speed with which the keying is done; high-speed cw is a wider signal than slow-speed cw.

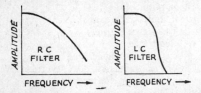

Fig. 6 — Comparison of roll-off characteristics of resistance-capacitance and inductance-capacitance low-pass filters.

Ordinary cw consists of on-off pulses, constituting a form of amplitude-modulated (a-m) transmission. If the pulses are essentially square-wave, the modulation theoretically has an infinite number of harmonics, all odd multiples of the basic keying rate. It can be shown mathematically and practically that as far as 60-wpm RTTY is concerned, this *basic* keying rate is 22.5 Hz. Since the keyed signal has sidebands on either side of the carrier, the total bandwidth of the basic keying rate becomes 45 Hz.

Post-Detection Filters

The RTTY detection process changes the signal into separate dc pulses (usually plus and minus) for mark and space. The rectified audio component is still present in the detector output and so are all types of random noise and beat notes that sneaked through the channel filters and the limiter. Thus a minimum-bandwidth low-pass keying filter following the detector (or detectors) will provide a maximum improvement in the signal-to-noise ratio. A simple RC filter, as is used in many amateur demodulators, will effectively eliminate the audio component, but the skirt selectivity is too poor to do a really adequate job. Look at Fig. 6, which compares the skirts of RC and LC low-pass filters. No attempt is made here to show precise frequencies, but the relative ability to restrict the bandwidth is demonstrated.

Such an LC filter would theoretically be designed for a cutoff frequency of 22.5 Hz, the basic keying rate, but practical limitations dictate that these filters should be a little wider, about 28 Hz for the types most commonly used for 60-wpm operation.

In a very interesting paper on filters for keyed pulses, Dr. Nyquist[1] suggested many years ago that the cosine curve would be an ideal waveform for filter response. Several types of filters approximate this cosine roll-off, but one that is simple, inexpensive and easy to design is the 3-pole Butterworth type. A newer type of filter, called the "linear phase," is perhaps better from an all-around standpoint, but to do the same job takes more components than the 3-pole Butterworth.

The Slicer

As explained earlier, the "slicer" in the advanced demodulator circuit, Fig. 4, is designed to swing between saturation (heavy conduction) and complete cutoff with a relatively small variation in the input-signal amplitude. The range of the input-voltage variation which continues to operate the slicer satisfactorily is called the "dynamic range" of the slicer stage. In a demodulator such as shown in Fig. 4, the limiter keeps these voltage changes from varying to any great extent (drift, of course, will cause *some* change). Consequently, the dynamic range of a demodulator using limiters need not be very great — perhaps 20 dB is more than adequate. However, if the demodulator is to be used to copy many different shifts other than

[1] Nyquist, "Certain Topics in Telegraphic Transmission Theory," *A.I.E.E. Transactions*, Vol. 47, April, 1928.

Fig. 7 — Pre-limiter and post-limiter filters. The combination provides higher performance than one set of filters alone, in either position.

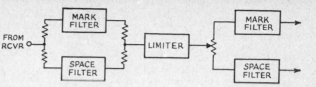

850 Hz, and no provisions are made to change the filter response accordingly, additional dynamic range is needed. This is discussed later in connection with linear discriminators.

Since the printer requires on-off dc pulses, the ability of the slicer to change quickly from complete conduction to complete cutoff has a direct influence on the ability of the printer to copy correctly. The slicer then becomes a high-performance type of circuit, and it is customary to use well-regulated voltage for its operation.

Mark and Space Filters

Since the transmitted fsk signal is a form of frequency modulation, we can treat it as fm in the demodulator. It should be pointed out at this time that the signal can be handled either as fm, as we are about to describe, or, with different techniques, as an a-m signal where no limiters are used.

If the signal is strong enough to "capture" the limiter used in fm demodulators, the limiter output is essentially of constant amplitude. If the mark and space signals introduced to the demodulator from the receiver are of equal voltage, rather narrow pre-limiter filters could be used without introducing prohibitive distortion due to timing error from the rise time of the narrow filters. However, in this unlikely case, there would really be little reason for using a limiter in the first place.

When mark and space are unequal, which is usually the case, then the limiter causes problems with narrow filters. If minimum-bandwidth filters (approximately 55-60 Hz for 3-pole Butterworth types) are used, the timing error because of the relative levels into the limiter becomes prohibitive if one of the two signals fades to an appreciable extent with respect to the other, which is often the case.

The answer to this problem is to use filters that are wide enough so that the timing error will be no greater than perhaps 25% under the worst case of fading, in which case the distortion introduced will fall within the ability of the machine to print satisfactorily. K3NIO[2] estimates that pre-limiter filters should be about four times the basic keying rate or, in the case of a 60-wpm system, about 200 Hz. This only pertains to the pre-limiter filters.

Two such filters could be used ahead of the limiter as well as behind, as in Fig. 7. The post-limiter filters, however, are not subjected to the limiter's peculiarities, and can have any bandwidth from the minimum up. It is customary to make them fairly broad, to alleviate the critical problem of exact, precise tuning needed with quite narrow systems, as well as to save the expense involved in meeting the more stringent requirements.

[2] Poor, "Filters for RTTY," *RTTY*, May, 1964.

When dealing with fm systems, optimum operation probably would result from two prelimiter filters about 200 Hz or so wide each, plus two quite narrow post-limiter filters. However, such a system is rarely if ever used, because of the cost involved, the advent of newer techniques using a-m principles, and — perhaps the best reason of all — the limitations it imposes for the amateur in particular. These limitations principally are caused by drift and incorrect shift (problems the ordinary RTTY amateur has yet to concern himself about).

Instead of using two pre-limiter filters, it is more customary to use a single filter of perhaps 1.0 kHz or so width. This filter allows any frequency falling within its limits to reach the limiter, in which case various shifts, 850 and less, can be satisfactorily received. Such a filter has the further advantage of being much cheaper than the two previously described, as well.

We can point out that many fm demodulators use *no* pre-limiter filter, but in this case receiver hum plus nearby signals that the i-f of the receiver may not be narrow enough to eliminate will cause degradation of the desired signal. This results because the limiter accepts the entire output of the receiver indiscriminately. Consequently, some form of pre-limiter filtering — usually a band-pass filter — should be used for best results.

The channel filters following the limiter can be either narrow or broad. This depends on several factors, such as cost, the range of shift the unit is expected to copy and, not to be overlooked, the type of indicator to be used to tune the demodulator. The better the filter with respect to skirt selectivity, the easier it will be to get a sharply defined tuning pattern with most indicators. Continuing our airplane analogy, a fighter plane is more expensive, more complex, and requires greater operating skill than, say, a small family plane. For its purpose, its performance will be unmatched, but for the average circumstance its limitations would dictate another type unit. So goes our analogy.

Thus few amateur fm demodulators use either pre-limiter or post-limiter channnel filters. They normally use a pre-limiter band-pass filter of 1.0 kHz or so bandwidth, and a simple but very effective post-limiter circuit called a "linear discriminator," which is discussed a little later. This linear discriminator can easily be constructed for under $10.

The Limiter

We have mentioned that the limiter puts out a signal of constant amplitude. This is not to say that the limiter can in any way separate the signal from the noise that may be passed along with it by the receiver. As is well known, the strongest signal presented to a limiter "captures" it. As long as this strongest signal is the desired one, all is well. But if that signal fades momentarily into the noise, the output of the limiter is then that of random noise – which the limiter tries to elevate to the same level at which the signal *had* been. However, if the mark and space filters following the limiter are of equal bandwidth, the output of the low-pass filter following the detectors will be only a fraction of the voltage level during normal peak-signal output. This is because the positive noise output from the mark detector will tend to offset and equalize the negative output from the space detector, since on noise both outputs are present simultaneously. The low-frequency cutoff of the low-pass filter tends further to eliminate peak noise variations.

When an interfering signal stronger than the desired one is presented to the limiter (perhaps a near-frequency cw station is heard in the receiver output) the limiter is captured by this stronger signal and it tends to suppress the desired signal. Thus an interfering stronger signal that gets into the fm demodulator ruins all reception. This signal can possibly be "notched out" in the receiver and then normal reception continues.

If the desired signal is stronger than any others on the frequency it will effectively suppress those other weaker signals and good copy results, even though interfering signals may be audible in the receiver output. Thus the limiter capture effect can be either good or bad, depending on the strength of the desired signal in relation to other signals and noise.

The Linear Discriminator

A linear discriminator (a good fm term, but it need not be confusing) puts out equal plus-and-

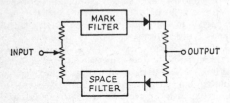

Fig. 8 – Simple discriminator circuit in elementary form.

minus voltages as one goes farther out on each side of a center frequency at which the output is zero. Fig. 8 is a very simple diagram of a typical circuit.

If the mark and space filters are tuned to be 850 Hz apart, are made fairly broad, and have simple construction giving wide skirt selectivity, the output voltage with respect to frequency might look something like Fig. 9. The discriminator curve in this figure can be considered to be linear if the voltage changes rather uniformly as you go farther to the left or right of the center frequency, which would be zero output volts.

If the peak linear response for an 850-Hz shift is ±50 volts, the voltage for 170-Hz shift should be

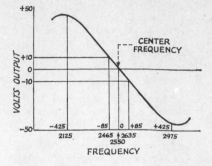

Fig. 9 – Linear-discriminator characteristic, showing difference in output voltage with wide (850-Hz) and narrow (170-Hz) frequency shift. This type of demodulator will respond to any shift within the limits of the linear part of the curve, but with reduced output as the frequency shift becomes smaller.

±10 volts. If the dynamic range of the slicer is such that the stage will continue to operate normally on less than ±10 volts, this system offers the ability to copy a wide range of shifts without changing filters. In fact, if the dynamic range of the slicer stage is great enough, shifts of only a few hertz could be copied, provided the equipment did not drift and a suitable means of tuning the receiver were employed. With such a system 4-Hz shift has been copied successfully, but this is of no practical concern.

It should be realized that with a discriminator characteristic such as shown in Fig. 9, the maximum signal-to-noise ratio exists when the shift is 850 Hz. However, as long as the incoming signal is stronger than the noise level this is of no importance. For best linear-discriminator circuits, very low-Q coils are used. These provide broad peak response and, at the same time, the slope of their skirt selectivity is so gentle that they make ideal filters for this purpose. TV width coils for horizontal oscillator circuits work extremely well for the purpose.

Maximum signal-to-noise ratio can never be achieved with discriminator filters that are 200-250 Hz broad. Of course, with any decent signal strength one does not need *maximum* S/N ratio.

The Limiterless Demodulator

Many unusual things can happen to the fsk RTTY signal on its way from the transmitter to the receiver. One of these phenomena is selective fading. In this instance the mark and space signals fade at independent rates, and it is entirely possible that one of the two tones will fade completely into the noise level for a short time, as shown in photos of the preceding section. Simple demodulators cannot always handle this type of circumstance, and many errors result until both the mark and space are again stronger than the noise level. The circuit in Fig. 4 does an excellent job of automatically copying right along, since there is a threshold corrector to take care of this very type of problem. However, the limiter tends to amplify the noise, and without an optimum low-pass filter the threshold corrector might not be able to work properly.

If the limiter is not used, the minimum-bandwidth channel filters of 45 Hz can be used. However, the practical minimum bandwidth for the filter designs normally used would be about 55-60 Hz. These, then, *do* offer minimum bandwidth and in certain circumstances (particularly when there is QRM from nearby stations) they offer a radical improvement in copy. However, they also bring up additional problems. For one thing, filters of this type are not easy to make at home. At the same time, even the least amount of drift produces quite a bit of distortion from these high-performance filters; small amounts of drift quickly change the output voltage from the filters and the signal can be lost before the receiving operator notices that he should retune. If the shift of the transmitting station is not exactly 170 Hz (and it seldom is), such sharp filters just will not work in normal circuits. Finally, one is seldom certain that the receiver is properly tuned. No limiting can be used, and the tuning indicator is only a rough guide. Therefore, the signal could have drifted or just faded. In any event, the tuning ratio of most receivers makes minute corrections of only 10-15 Hz rather difficult.

It was mentioned earlier that the mark and space frequencies are actually the equivalent of two independent transmitters each putting out the same information in complimentary form. With no limiter we are now using what is known as "a-m" detection. Because of selective fading, the outputs of the detectors often vary radically from moment to moment, depending on whether mark or space is being received at the time. In fm demodulators, this fading is handled by the limiter, but in a-m units, a special circuit called a "threshold corrector" is used. This circuit essentially provides the following (slicer) stage with voltages that vary uniformly from mark to space. It accomplishes this in a most unique manner, using storage capacitors to provide equalization of the voltages at its output. Thus, the slicer receives equal information for both mark and space, although this information may vary in overall amplitude. For example, at one moment you might have perhaps ±60 volts for mark and space and at another moment you might have only say ±6 volts. It is the job of the threshold corrector to provide this symmetrical output voltage regardless of the independent fading (or absence of one signal completely) at the input. It is this ability that allows the advanced a-m demodulator to work in such a superior manner under weak-signal conditions, particularly where one signal may temporarily fade completely into the noise level for short periods. It is also this feature that allows the a-m demodulator to give satisfactory copy when deliberately copying only one channel, such as mark only, during interference.

Several types of threshold correctors have been developed in recent years, but nearly all of these have had associated problems which make their use in amateur demodulators (where machine-speed sending is seldom used) unsatisfactory. A U.S. patent (No. 2,999,925, assigned to Page Communication Engineers, Inc.) contains a circuit that overcomes all the disadvantages of previous threshold correctors in such an ingenious way that it rather obsoletes those earlier efforts. This circuit, called a "decision threshold computer" ("DTC"), automatically keeps the decision point presented to the slicer at the correct point on the waveform. The DTC circuit finally makes a-m detection superior to the best fm demodulators, in a majority of instances. However, the DTC also can be used in conjuction with a good fm demodulator, and will improve its performance similarly. Thus it can be said that any type of converter not using the DTC is not getting the maximum performance as we now know it. The DTC circuit is included in the TT/L-2 demodulator, presented in a later section.

Since the output of a-m detectors can vary quite widely with no limiting, the dynamic range of this type of unit must be exceptional. A minimum of 40 dB is required, and more would be better.

Since many other phenomena exist in radio propagation, such as flutter fading and back scatter, to name two, advanced enthusiasts are still experimenting with a-m vs. fm concepts. So far, it appears that if the DTC is incorporated in both types, the fm unit will be quite satisfactory in a majority of instances. There is a lot of overlapping, but one thing seems evident – a deluxe demodulator should offer the possibility of having both types of reception available. The a-m type is far superior to the fm type if strong nearby stations become a problem. On the other hand, the fm type will allow the greatest latitude in off-shift copy and drift for normal use where the signal strength is moderate or better, and where little interference exists. Fm types also adapt readily to automatic copy where the operator can leave the room and yet continue to get satisfactory results.

Filters for the a-m type can be anything from minimum (55-60 Hz) bandwidth to something more broad. For normal amateur use, a bandwidth of around 150 Hz would probably offer the most advantage a majority of the time. Filters of this type are easier to build and less costly than the more narrow ones.

We have discussed only types of demodulators using the audio output of the receiver. In passing we should mention that many military types use i-f connections to the receiver. However, many receivers do not offer the specific i-f values needed, and in any case, this type offers certain other difficulties to the average enthusiast – for instance, trying to make a channel filter of only 100 Hz bandwidth at 455 kHz, much less at 3.395 MHz or higher, is neither simple nor inexpensive.

Many military demodulators have become available through MARS organizations and surplus facilities. One must admit they do work, but they were not designed to be operated in the presence of interfering signals or other adverse conditions which are peculiar to the hf amateur bands.

HIGH-PERFORMANCE RTTY FILTERS

Material for this section was contributed by Irv Hoff, and originally appeared in *QST* for August and September, 1966.

In a day when rapid progress is being made in all technological fields, radioteletype has its share of advances. Limiterless a-m (sometimes called "two-tone") reception has been developed to a level where it offers reliable copy under conditions where conventional demodulators using a limiter fail badly. Even fm reception using limiters has been substantially improved. Automatic-threshold computers now enable single demodulators to give diversity reception with fewer errors and better copy than old-style dual-diversity units using separate antennas and receivers.

The selection and proper use of filters for the RTTY demodulator offers the greatest potential improvement that can be made, since in all but a few isolated cases quite elementary filters are being used. When conditions are less than optimum — static, impulse noises, deep selective fading, in particular, adjacent-channel interference such as cw — simple filters, with or without the limiter, can do very little. At a time like this most operators just throw up their hands and quit for the day. It takes more complex filters to separate the desired signal from the surrounding noise. Such filters are rather expensive when purchased commercially.

This section will show how filters comparable in quality to commercial units costing $40 and more each can be made at a cost of less than $6. Yet they can be constructed easily, with surprising precision. Since these filter systems are so inexpensive, the operator can construct several of them easily and then choose quickly the one that suits the prevailing conditions the best. As with a good receiver, varying the filter selectivity will often mean the difference between good copy and no copy.

How Narrow Can We Go?

Since the RTTY signal is a pulse-modulated fsk carrier, it does exhibit a certain bandwidth. The modulating signal consists of a fundamental frequency determined by the pulse rate, with harmonics determined by the pulse shape. The fundamental audio frequency for 22-ms pulses will be approximately 22.5 Hz. While the filters for mark and space could be as narrow as 45 Hz and still retain the essential keyed information of a 60-wpm RTTY signal, you wouldn't *want* a filter *that* narrow. Such narrow filters can readily introduce distortion if the signal is not centered properly in the passband. However, the biggest objection is that the transmitted signal may not be exactly the right shift to fit the specific filters. An associated problem, nearly as serious, is the stability of the transmitter and receiver; obviously the closer the filter gets to minimum bandwidth the more critical the tuning becomes. So you don't get something without being inconvenienced elsewhere. For this reason the broadest filter system that conditions warrant is normally used.

Filters of 65-90 Hz bandwidth perhaps fall in the "minimum bandwidth" category. A most interesting technical paper was published on this subject by Vic Poor, K3NIO[1], and many of his ideas have been used in the development of the filters described here. Anyone interested in following up this subject should make an effort to read K3NIO's excellent article.

What Filter?

In general, the broadest filter that is compatible with band conditions would be a safe bet. If there was never any interference from a nearby station, the more simple filters would do an excellent job most of the time. Their broad bandwidths would give good reception on shifts which only vaguely resembled "normal," and would tolerate large amounts of drift in the incoming signal. However, this Utopia just does not exist, not even on "clear" commercial channels.

Unfortunately, on frequencies which must be shared with all comers — a situation peculiar to amateur radio — conditions change, and at an entirely unpredictable rate. What may have been a clear frequency for the past hour or so could in the next moment be clobbered by a strong interfering signal. In this situation the enthusiast who has some means of quickly changing to a different technique has a tremendous advantage over his less versatile counterpart.

The 88-MH Toroid

Earlier designs used TV width coils for several good reasons: first, they can be obtained at any radio-supply house; second, they are adjustable and thus can be tuned to the proper frequency; third, they are easy to install; and fourth, they present a nearly ideal bandwidth for general reception from extremely narrow to more-than-legal shifts.

However, the 88-mH toroids have been quite popular with amateurs who build RTTY equipment, as they are relatively easy to obtain (check the listings in the Ham-Ads in any *QST* issue) and are quite inexpensive when compared with any other suitable inductor — as little as 50 cents each when purchased in groups of five or more.

The 88-mH toroid has a quite high Q which makes it ideal for use in some types of filters, but in a simple single-tuned filter the Q could be too high to be satisfactory. For instance, the Q of a TV coil, when adjusted to resonate at 2125 Hz with a 0.15-μF capacitor, would be about 7, while the 88-mH toroid at this frequency (resonated with .064 μF) would have a Q of nearly 120, if isolated properly. The bandwidth with the TV coil would be about 300 Hz, but with the 88-mH toroid would be only about 19 Hz — much too sharp to make a good RTTY filter. However, it is this

[1] Poor, "Filters for RTTY," *RTTY*, May, 1964.

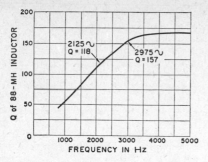

Fig. 1 — Q vs frequency for an 88-mH toroid, Western Electric type 632.

property of the toroid that makes it a good tuning indicator under certain conditions, and the Mainline TT/O Semi-Counter (described in a later section) takes advantage of the high Q to determine frequencies quite accurately for tuning filters or for checking shifts. Fig. 1 shows Q vs. frequency for a representative 88-mH toroid.

Ralph Leland, W8DLT, was kind enough to supply the data below, obtained from the manufacturer's (Western Electric) manual:

New Coil	Super-seded Coil	Inductance	DC Resistance	1000-Hz Resistance
632	622	88 mH	9.0 ohms	9.8 ohms
638		44 mH	5.1	5.5
	628	44 mH	4.7	5.1
639		22 mH	2.6	2.8
	629	22 mH	2.5	2.7

The resistance values include 7-1/2 feet of 22-gauge cable. The 1000-Hz resistance is for a current of 0.5 mA. These are the coil numbers, not the case numbers that most telephone company personnel would use.

Ralph continues that the toroid nearly everyone obtains these days is the type 632, which is about 50 percent smaller than the older 622. The reduction results from the use of Formex wire; there was no change in the core material used.

Using the 88-MH Toroid in Filters

When used properly, the 88-mH toroid makes an excellent basic filter element. To lower the Q to where the bandwidth of the simple single-tuned toroid would make a good filter, resistance can be put either in series or parallel with the inductor.

The parallel impedance of such a circuit goes up with frequency, so the voltage developed across the filter will be much higher for the higher frequencies. Thus, combining mark and space filters on the same drive point in such a manner that the output voltage will be the same for both frequencies, while retaining the same bandwidth, requires some rather fancy juggling. Here empirical testing outweighs the value of the textbook formulas. As means are

added for equalizing the output voltages, the bandwidth is changed — and round and round we go. This may in some small way help clear up questions that otherwise might arise from a quick comparison of the various filter diagrams. The problems do not occur with the more complex filters because other means of combining them are used.

The following sections briefly describe the basic high-performance filters that may be used. As shown, the filters are directly compatible with the TT/L-2 demodulator described in a subsequent section, but the basic design features may be incorporated into nearly any demodulator which uses an audio input.

THE "MAINLINE 8170" FILTER (FIG. 2)

This is a narrow-shift discriminator filter (170 shift) and has a bandwidth of approximately 85 Hz. It is nearly the same as that published by Hoff in November 1965 *QST*, with minor changes that allow more balance range. Center crossover on Hoff's unit was 2209 Hz with mark at 2125 and space at 2295.

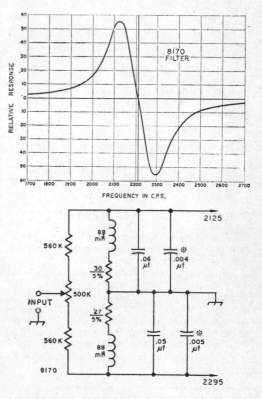

Fig. 2 — The Mainline 8170 filter for 170 shift. Each filter is about 85 Hz wide using 88-mH toroids. Capacitor values marked (*) are approximate, and should be selected to tune the toroids to the indicated frequencies.

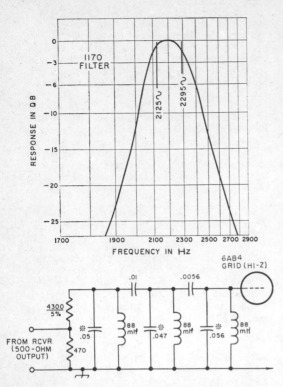

Fig. 3 — The Mainline 1170 bandpass input filter for 170-Hz shift. The band-width is about 275 Hz and the output is high impedance. Capacitances marked (*) are approximate values. Each section is tuned to the same frequency, 2200 Hz, for standard tones of 2125 and 2295.

THE "MAINLINE 1170" FILTER (FIG. 3)

This is a narrow-shift band-pass input filter of 275 Hz bandwidth, intended for tones of 2125 and 2295 Hz.

THE MAINLINE "3" SERIES FILTERS

The filters in these groups are 3-pole Butterworth designs with good skirt selectivity. They use three 88-mH toroids each.

Most commercial filters have similar input and output impedances — usually 600 ohms. The design of 600-ohm filters requires inductors of far different value than the 88-mH toroid, and to use these toroids it is necessary to allow the imped-ances to be much higher for a narrow bandwidth. This is no problem; in fact, it assists in using these particular filters in the demodulator. It also ac-

counts for the fact that the broad filters have a lower input impedance than the more narrow filters.

Every bandpass filter is potentially an imped-ance transformer. No matter how the filter is developed, its input and output impedances can be made different from one another. Therefore, in the following designs the output impedance is very high while the input impedance is only medium high. The filter then acts as a step-up transformer, and instead of having substantial voltage loss, as would most filters, it will actually show a voltage rise from input to output.

The "Mainline 3170" Filter (Fig. 4)

This filter, like the band-pass input of Fig. 3, is of a basic 3-pole Butterworth design. It is only 80 Hz wide at the −3-dB points. Two similar filters are used in the discriminator. (Other designs such as the Thomson linear-phase filters offer some theo-retical advantages for pulse reception, such as RTTY signals, but to get comparable passband characteristics at least two extra sections (for a total of five toroids in each filter) would be needed. Likely, the small advantage of the linear-phase types would be more than offset by the added difficulty of making them at home, plus the extra cost and size. If commercial filters are obtained, the four- or five-pole linear-phase types might well be considered at the higher cost. The

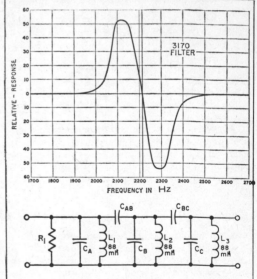

Fig. 4 — Circuit for the Mainline 3170 filter. Values are given in the table below. The capacitors should be Mylar 10-percent tolerance or better; C_{AB} and C_{BC} should be 5-percent tolerances if possible. Values for C_A, C_B and C_C are approximate; see text for tuning procedures. Where an unusual capacitance value is shown smaller values may be connected in parallel; e.g., 0.05 + 0.008 = 0.058. Capacitances are in μF except where otherwise specified. R1 — 5% tolerance.

Frequency	Bandwidth	R1	C_{AB}	C_{BC}	C_A	C_B	C_C
2125	80≈	20k	.0025	.0018	.061	.06	.062
2295	80≈	22k	.0021	.0013	.053	.051	.053

response of the 3170 filters for 170 shift is also shown in Fig. 4. The table below is representative of the performance of this type of filter. The figures given are for the 2125-cycle filter; the others are comparable:

Response in dB	Bandwidth, Hz
−3	80
−6	100
−10	122
−15	157
−20	183
−25	226
−30	261

Probably the first 15 dB of any filter establishes the primary effectiveness of the system, in which case the filter is still only 157 Hz wide at the −15 dB point. The 3-30-dB shape factor is about 3 to 1, which is quite good for such a simple filter.

Balancing the 3170 Filter

Fig. 5 shows how to install the 3170 filter in a typical demodulator circuit. Adjust the control on each filter until the filter output voltages are equal but opposite from mark to space.

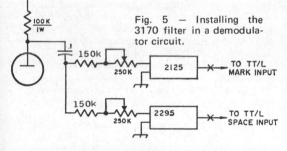

Fig. 5 — Installing the 3170 filter in a demodulator circuit.

Tuning the Filters

A digital frequency counter makes the tuning of the filters a simple task, but other schemes can be used. First let us list quickly the various items that will be needed:

1) A source of audio sine waves – an audio oscillator, a tape recorder, or the receiver itself may be used.

2) A means for determining the frequency to be used for reference. There are several possibilities:

    a) Tuning forks,

    b) Accurate audio oscillator,

    c) Musical instrument such as a piano,

    d) Tape recorder with prerecorded audio tape,

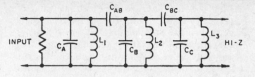

Fig. 6 — Basic layout of the three-pole Butterworth filter used for the Mainline "1" and "3" series.

    e) Capacitor decade box, or

    f) Digital audio counter.

3) A means for measuring maximum output of the filter while it is being tuned, such as:

    a) Oscilloscope,

    b) Regular VTVM with ac scale,

    c) Ac VTVM.

The biggest problem, of course, is determining just what 2125, 2295 (for 170 shift) and 2975 (for 850 shift) "really" are. (This question is discussed in detail in the Semi-Counter section, later in this chapter. As described there, the "standard" is the 88-mH toroid, which has been determined to be actually 88 mH within very close tolerances. In the setup shown for tuning a toroid to a particular frequency, an ac VTVM may be substituted for the scope.)

Tuning the toroids will actually take only a few minutes each, once the equipment has been set up. When all toroids needed are tuned, they can be wired into the filter circuit along with the associated resistors and other components.

For the simple filters such as the 8170, tune the toroids without the series resistors, and then after the toroid-capacitor combinations are finalized, install the series resistors and other components. If the toroids are tuned with the series loading resistors, the filters will be much more difficult to tune accurately because their bandwidths will be much greater.

How To Tune the Multi-Toroid Filters

Tuning the three-toroid filters, such as the Mainline 1170 or 3170 is really quite simple. It involves a few more steps, but is no more difficult than tuning a simple filter.

The basic filter diagram is shown in Fig. 6. In reality, this consists of three parallel-tuned sections, as given in Fig. 7. The capacitors on top, C_{AB} and C_{BC}, are the "cross-coupling" capacitors which establish the primary filter characteristics. The parallel capacitors, C_A, and C_B, and C_C, are used to tune each filter section to a specific frequency.

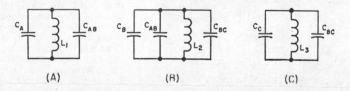

(A)   (B)   (C)

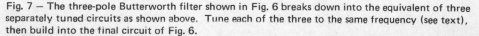

Fig. 7 — The three-pole Butterworth filter shown in Fig. 6 breaks down into the equivalent of three separately tuned circuits as shown above. Tune each of the three to the same frequency (see text), then build into the final circuit of Fig. 6.

First, set the audio source to the desired tone frequency by the tuning-fork, tape-recorder or decade-box method. Then tune each section in Fig. 7 independently to that same audio tone. In Fig. 7A do not change or remove C_{AB} but instead add to the value of C_A until the meter peaks, showing that the desired frequency has been reached. (Turns may also be added to or removed from the coil, if more appropriate.) When this section has been tuned, remove capacitor C_{AB} and connect it in the second section as in Fig. 7B. Tune this section to the identical audio frequency by varying C_B or the turns on the inductor. Set aside, removing capacitor C_{BC}, which is then used to tune the third section as shown in Fig. 7C. When this section has been tuned to the same audio frequency put the filter together as in Fig. 6, making sure no (more) turns are removed from any of the toroids in the process. This completes the filter tuning.

Other methods of tuning the filters can be used — indeed, many different schemes are possible. Elaborate and expensive equipment is not required, although in some instances it might make the job a bit easier. It would appear that an audio tape recorder in conjunction with a capacitor decade box and vacuum-tube voltmeter would be an ideal method available to most individuals. Just the decade box with a VTVM and a reasonably stable audio oscillator probably would work just as well.

THE MAINLINE TT/L-2 FSK DEMODULATOR

The demodulator described in this section is an advanced-design unit which was originally described by Petersen, W8SDZ, in *QST* for May and June, 1969. It offers high-performance fm (limiter) and a-m (limiterless) reception of RTTY signals. The earlier TT/L demodulator, as published by Hoff in *QST* for August, 1965, was the result of almost two years' work. Because of the desire to make each part of the basic design as nearly perfect as possible, the circuitry went through continuous improvements after that information was published. Nearly four years later, when it was felt by Hoff and Petersen that all circuits had been fully optimized, the TT/L-2 appeared in print.

The TT/L-2 demodulator includes band-pass filters for both 850- and 170-Hz shift. It also includes a three-speed switch for the low-pass filter stage following the discriminator detectors. This feature selects the optimum cutoff frequency for each transmission speed, 60, 75, or 100 wpm. With the increasing availability of equipment which will operate at the higher speeds, this feature is especially timely.

An effective auto-receive stage in the TT/L-2 prevents the receiving teleprinter from printing garble when there is no RTTY signal present, and completely ignores cw and other non-RTTY signals which may be within the received passband. The auto-receive circuit also controls a motor-control stage which turns off the teleprinter motor approximately 30 seconds after the signal leaves. (This delay is sufficient to keep the motor running during station identification and subsequent "turn-over" to another station.) The combination of the auto-receive and motor-control stages provides an efficient and reliable system for obtaining unattended reception of RTTY signals.

The TT/L-2 includes protection against a steady space tone, which would otherwise cause the teleprinter to "run open." This circuit also prevents the auto-receive circuit from responding to steady space signals.

The TT/L-2 incorporates a simplified mode-switching system, using a single six-position rotary switch. This feature eliminates much of the confusion which could result from using many separate switches. The switch controls four different functions, interlocking them so there is no possibility of a wrong combination which might cause improper operation.

Heavy-duty main and loop power supplies are used for cool operation and good regulation.

Fig. 1 — The TT/L-2 demodulator built for rack mounting. This unit, constructed by John Roache, W1SOG, includes a phase shift oscillograph indicator in addition to the eye-tube indicator described in the text. The main and loop power supply components are mounted on the right rear of the chassis. Plugged into sockets at the left rear are the two Butterworth input band-pass filters and the two discriminator filters, each built into a Minibox fitted with an octal plug. One of four vacant sockets may be seen at the rear of the unit. These sockets are used in conjuction with the spare positions of the discriminator filter section switch.

Fig. 2 — A look at the TT/L-2 from the rear. Suggested chassis size is 13 X 17 X 3 inches, such as a Bud AC-420. The K5BQA printed circuit board was used in the construction of this unit. The two tubes appearing on the upper left corner of the chassis are the voltage regulator tubes of the power supply. The eye-tube indicator is mounted at the opening in the front panel. Input band-pass and discriminator filters are built into Vector, cans and inserted in the filter sockets.

This is especially important when the unit is used for continuous auto-start operation. The loop supply provides a balanced-voltage output for driving a saturated diode for fsk or afsk operation. The circuit also permits automatic retransmission of received signals — such as for relaying from another band or playing back from a tape-recorded signal.

The EM84/6FG6 tuning eye is used because it is a more accurate indicator than either an oscilloscope or a meter. It shows at a glance when the signal has drifted, and is especially effective when "straddle-tuning" is necessary due to inaccurate shift by the sending station.

You will notice that no power-on indicator has been included in this design. It was purposely omitted because the tuning eye provides this indication. The TT/L-2 is pictured in Figs. 1 and 2, with an optional scope tuning indicator included.

The Circuit

The circuitry of the TT/L-2 Demodulator is shown in Fig. 3. Fig. 4 shows the schematic of the power supplies and the fsk driver.

Two input-bandpass filters are provided, one for 850-Hz and the other for 170-Hz shift. Selection of the desired filter is made with S1. V2 and V3, the limiter stages, are used for fm reception. These stages may be bypassed for limiterless reception with S2.

A four-position switch, S3, is shown in the discriminator filter section for selection of filters with different responses. Only two filters are included in this design, as it was felt that the builder might wish to add other filters at a later date, after becoming better acquainted with the operation of the TT/L-2. The narrow-band 3-pole Butterworth filters described in the preceding section on high-performance RTTY filters could be installed in the extra switch positions.

The speed switch, S5, is used to select the components for 60-, 75-, or 100-wpm signals. This switch is shown in the 60-wpm position, and may be omitted if you have no interest in 75- or 100-wpm operation. In this case, only the parts associated with the left position of the switch are required.

Special Notes

All diodes except those in the power supplies and the Zener in the auto-receive stage are type 1N2070A. It is important, especially in the ATC/ DTC stage, that the diodes have at least 200 megohms back resistance.

All controls are linear taper. Those marked 2 watts are Ohmite type AB or equivalent.

Capacitor values shown with asterisks in the input band-pass filters are approximate. Using the tune-up instructions presented in the "High-Performance RTTY Filters" section, tune individual sections of the 170-Hz filter to 2200 Hz. The 850-Hz filter requires no tuning if 5% tolerance capacitors are used. Otherwise, tune filter sections A and C to 2400 Hz, and section B to 2300 Hz. Figs. 6 and 7 of the preceding section of this chapter show these filter sections.

Capacitor values in the discriminator filters are approximate. Choose values for resonance with the appropriate toroid at the desired frequency.

Construction Notes

The layout used for construction of the TT/L-2 should be similar to that used in a high-quality audio pre-amplifier. This type of layout is desirable because of the very high-gain circuitry used. Be sure to shield all audio and high-impedance dc leads which might otherwise pick up extraneous signals or noise because of physical length or placement.

The wiring associated with the grids of V1, V5A, V6A and V11B should either be very short or else be shielded.

It is most important that T1 and T2 be mounted in such a way that they will not pick up inductively from each other, from T3 and T4, or from the power supply transformers and chokes. The best method is to mount each of the four transformers on different axes. Do not mount one above and one below the chassis in an effort to avoid inductive coupling, because the usual aluminum chassis used will not provide inductive shielding. Also be sure the 350-H choke in the low-pass filter section is not mounted near any of the power supply transformers or chokes.

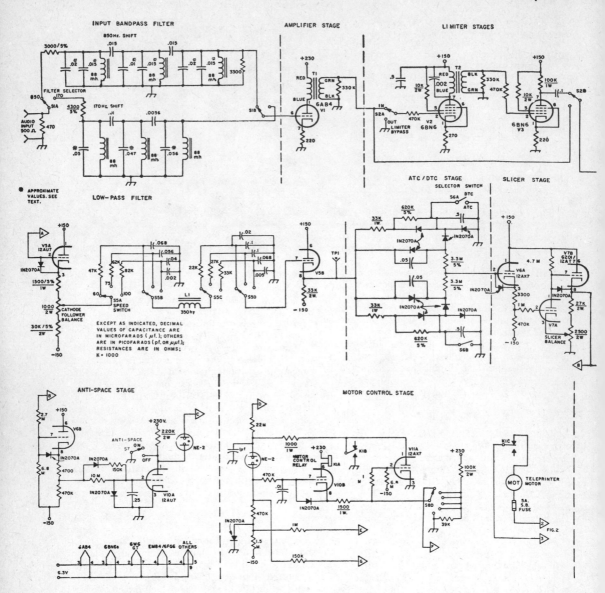

The 5-volt ac winding of the main power transformer, T6, is not used, and the leads should be insulated and secured to prevent their shorting out. This winding is a spare, for possible future use. Particular attention should be paid to the indicated connection of the secondary of transformer T2 for proper phasing to avoid feedback.

Shield all leads associated with the limiter bypass switch, S2. The 0.47-megohm series grid resistors for V2 and V3 should be located right at the grid pin for each tube socket. All switches except S7 should be mounted on the *front* panel. S7, the anti-space ON-OFF switch, is used for test purposes only, and may therefore be mounted on the rear panel since it is not used in normal operation.

The test point located at the cathode follower output of the low-pass filter should be mounted in a convenient spot on or near the rear panel.

The auto-receive sensitivity control and the indicator sensitivity control should be mounted on the *front* panel. All other potentiometers should be mounted on the rear panel.

The RECEIVE and STANDBY neon indicators may be mounted on the front panel, if desired, to show when the unit is ready to receive a signal. Be sure the sockets do not contain any resistors. If the builder does not wish to include these indicators for front panel use, the RECEIVE STANDBY neon must be retained, however, as it is used as a coupling device. Many neons (about 20%) are not good performers due to manufacturing tolerances,

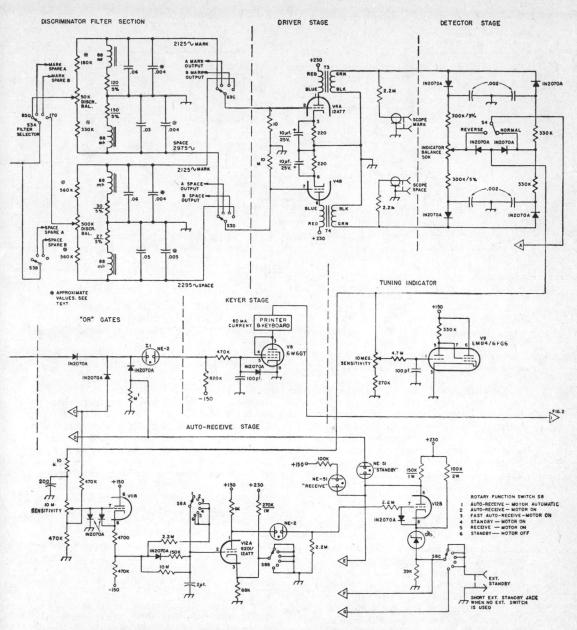

Fig. 3 — Circuit of the Mainline TT/L-2 FSK Demodulator unit. All resistors are 1/2-watt, 10% tolerance, unless otherwise indicated. All capacitors are mylar, 10% tolerance, except those indicated in pF which are mica, and those with polarity indicated which are electrolytic. See *QST* "Ham-Ads" for obtaining 88-mH toroids.

CR1 — Zener, 10 volts, 1 watt (International 1AC10T10).

I1 — For text reference.

K1 — 110-volt dc relay (Potter and Brumfield KAP-11DG or KRP-11DG).

L1 — 350 henrys, 5 mA (Stancor C-2345).

S1, S2 — Dpdt rotary, non-shorting (Centralab 1464).

S3 — Miniature phenolic rotary, 2 sections, 4 poles, 5 positions (1 position unused), non-shorting (Centralab PA1013).

S4 — Spdt toggle.

S5 — Same as S3 except 2 positions unused.

S6 — Dpdt toggle.

S7 — Spst toggle.

S8 — Miniature ceramic rotary, 2 sections, 4 poles, 6 positions, shorting (Centralab PA2010).

T1, T2, T3, T4 — Interstage audio, 1:3 primary: secondary turns ratio; 10 mA (Stancor A-53).

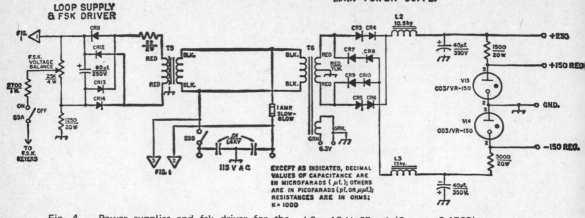

Fig. 4 — Power supplies and fsk driver for the TT/L-2 Demodulator.
CR3-CR14 incl. — Silicon, 800 PIV, 500 mA (Sarkes-Tarzian F-8).
L2 — 10.5 H, 110 mA (Stancor C-1001).

L3 — 13 H, 65 mA (Stancor C-1708).
S9 — Dpst toggle, 15 A, 125 volts.
T5 — 115 V, 35 VA (Triad N-51X).
T6 — 550 V ct, 110 mA; 6.3 V, 5 A; 5 V, 2 A (Triad R-12A).

so an extra few should be purchased. If any trouble is experienced with either the auto-receive or the motor-control stages, the builder should try another neon.

ADJUSTMENT INSTRUCTIONS

Allow the unit to warm up for at least fifteen minutes before any adjustments are made. The tubes will age during the first few days of operation, so it is wise to repeat the entire adjustment procedure approximately a week after inital setup has been performed. These adjustments should always be done in the order shown below, or improper operation will result.

Cathode-Follower Balance

The first adjustment to be made is the cathode follower balance control in the low-pass filter stage. Connect a senstive VOM or a VTVM to the test point, TP1. Remove the audio input from the TT/L-2 by unplugging the input cable. Set the limiter bypass switch to the OUT position. Adjust the cathode follower balance control for zero volts dc at the test point. If it is not possible to reach zero, and a new tube has already been tried, change the value of the 1500-ohm resistor in the cathode circuit of V5A as necessary so the adjustment can be made properly.

Slicer Balance

The slicer balance adjustment is also made with no audio input and with the limiter bypassed. The anti-space switch, S7, should be set to the OFF position and the rotary function switch, S8, should be set to position No. 5 (RECEIVE — MOTOR ON) for this adjustment. Turn the slicer balance control until the teleprinter "runs open." Then turn the control in the opposite direction until the printer returns to the marking condition. Note

these two points, and set the control midway between. No further adjustment is necessary.

Return the anti-space switch to the ON position.

Discriminator Filter Section

The discriminator filters should be tuned to resonance for the desired tone frequencies by varying the capacitors marked with asterisks. When adjusting the filters for resonance, the resistors in series with the ground connection of the toroids should be shorted out temporarily. Be sure to remove these shorts after the tuning is completed, or severe distortion of the received teleprinter signals will result. For additional tuning hints, refer to the section on high-performance RTTY filters.

The resistors marked with asterisks on either side of the balance controls should be chosen for each filter so that the dc voltages developed from mark and space tones, when balanced, do not exceed ±60 volts at Test Point 1. If adjustment is required, change both resistors by an equal amount, so as to maintain a balance within the range of the control.

Adjustment of each discriminator balance control is made with the limiter bypass switch set to the IN position, and the normal-reverse switch, S4, set in the NORMAL position. Alternately apply a mark and space tone to the input of the TT/L-2. Adjust the discriminator balance control so that the mark and space dc voltages are equal, but of opposite polarity, at the test point.

Indicator Balance

After the discriminators have been balanced, set the normal-reverse switch in the REVERSE position. Now adjust the indicator balance control for equal mark and space dc voltages at the test point. Observe the tuning eye. Carefully adjust the indicator balance control to eliminate any eye

Fig. 5 — The inside of the TT/L-2. Components at the left are those of the power supplies. The concentration of parts inside the partially shielded compartment is associated with the phase-shift indicator circuitry. Most small components are mounted on the opposite side of the printed circuit board.

movement when alternating between mark and space tones. No further adjustment is necessary.

FSK Voltage Balance

Set the rotary function switch, S8, to position 4 (STANDBY — MOTOR ON). Connect a test voltmeter from the FSK DRIVER output to ground. Disconnect the external fsk keyer lead during this adjustment. Alternately open and close the printer loop by pushing the "break" key or opening the keyboard contacts at the teleprinter. Adjust the fsk voltage balance control for equal but opposite mark and space dc voltages. The mark voltage should be approximately −45 volts and the space voltage should be approximately +45 volts. No further adjustment is necessary.

CORRECT VOLTAGE CHECKS

With a 1.5-volt peak-to-peak 2125-Hz tone at the grid of V1 and the limiter switched in, there should be approximately 40 volts peak-to-peak at the plate of V1, 10 volts peak-to-peak at the grid of V2, 45 volts peak-to-peak at the grid of V3, 40 volts peak-to-peak at the center of the discriminator balance control, and 40 volts peak-to-peak at the plate of V4A. There should be about 120 volts at the secondary of T3.

Dc voltages are present from this point on. The grid of V6A should be approximately −50 volts with the ATC/DTC switch at DTC, and about −28 volts at ATC. All of the following voltages should appear with the switch at DTC. The cathode of V6A should be about −50 volts, the grid of V7A −45 volts, and the grid of V8 between 0 and −0.2 volt. With a space tone at the input and with the anti-space switch turned off, the grid of V8 should be about −50 volts. The junction of neon I1 and the two resistors in the keyer stage should be at +10 to +20 volts with a mark-tone input.

OPERATION

The proper audio input level for the TT/L-2 is that which produces the same amount of tuning-

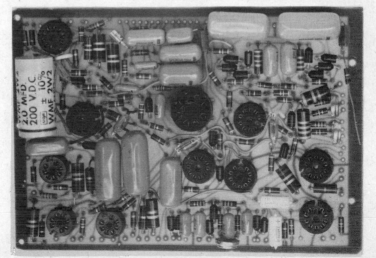

Fig. 6 — A close-up of the K5BQA printed board with all components mounted. Measuring approximately 6 X 9 inches, the board contains tubes and components of the amplifier, limiter, driver, detector, low-pass filter, ATC/DTC, OR gate, keyer, anti-space, motor-control, and auto-receive stages. (Jim Salter, K5BQA, 11040 Creekmere, Dallas, TX 75218.)

eye closure in either the fm (limiter) or a-m (limiterless) mode of operation. You will find that this is slightly above normal room volume, and it will be necessary to install a pad in the speaker circuit to bring its volume down to a suitable listening level. The pad also offers the advantage of decoupling the variable impedance of the speaker from the receiver output circuit.

It is best to use your receiver's 100-kHz crystal calibrator or an actual signal to make the auto-receive sensitivity adjustment. Set the rotary funct-ion switch to position 2 (AUTO-RECEIVE — MOTOR ON). With no signal (just noise) input to the TT/L-2, adjust the auto-receive sensitivity control to a point just below that where the teleprinter prints garble. The printer should now remain quiet. Now adjust the sensitivity control so that when a signal is applied there is a 3- to 4-second delay before the RECEIVE neon indi-cator lights. If your adjustment is correct, the teleprinter should print five or six letters after the signal leaves, and then remain quiet.

The auto-receive circuit was designed to be used only when receiving in the fm (limiter) mode. When the a-m (limiterless) mode is used, the rotary function switch, S8, should always be placed in the No. 5 position (RECEIVE — MOTOR ON). The motor-control stage works only when the auto-receive circuit is in operation.

The tuning-indicator sensitivity control is pro-vided so that the user may control the amount of eye closure during operation. The best setting is one where the eye just closes with the signal tuned properly. If the signal drifts, the eye immediately starts to open, signaling the operator to retune.

S6 is used to select the Automatic Threshold Corrector or the Decision Threshold Computer. The DTC is used at all times except for reception of mark-only or space-only signals.

During transmission, the EXT. STANDBY switch must be opened, so that the signal will not feed back into the loop. When retransmitting or transmitting from tape-recorded signals, the switch must remain closed.

THE MAINLINE ST-4 RTTY DEMODULATOR

What are the minimum RTTY demodulator requirements for reception of both vhf and hf? When receiving RTTY signals on vhf, many of the problems associated with the hf bands just do not occur. Such things as selective fading, adjacent-channel QRM, static due to thunderstorms, and so forth, are rarely encountered. In addition, fm is often used together with repeaters, where fluctua-tions in signal strength are not a problem. Squelch is normally available to lock the receiver into standby if there is no signal present. Cw inter-ference is rarely encountered, and so few stations are present that crystal operation is frequently used, keeping adjacent-channel interference to a minimum.

As a consequence, the most elementary TU or demodulator is often quite enough, and many of the unique problems of the hf bands are of no concern to the vhf enthusiast. The schematic of the typical vhf RTTY TU amply demonstrates the simplicity possible. On the other hand, almost none of the units designed for vhf are really much more than barely adequate when used in the hf bands.

At hf we get into problems which are rarely experienced on higher frequencies. Probably the worst problem of all is cw interference, and next is adjacent-channel interference (other stations close by). Static, high noise levels, selective fading, improper shift, and drift all contribute to the "nightmare" of hf RTTY. To minimize cw inter-ference (probably the toughest of all the prob-lems), you can turn the receiver avc off and go to limiterless copy with sharp filters. This takes a rather advanced demodulator design, such as the Mainline TT/L-2* with the sophisticated threshold computer and narrow Butterworth filters.* This is

*See preceding sections.

also the answer for selective fading and adjacent-channel interference. Not much can be done to eliminate static and high-noise-level problems.

What are the minimum requirements for both vhf and hf? This is a somewhat difficult question to answer because it depends so much upon your own experience. First of all, you need a good limiter. (Let's omit "limiterless" demodulators from the minimum-requirements discussion.) Few demodulators have offered a really decent limiter in the past, other than the TT/L or TT/L-2, which limit to around −60 dB. (Zero dB is defined as 0.774 volt across a 600-ohm load, a condition producing 1 mW of power in the load. However, the dB reference here is made to the voltage level rather than the power level, because the impedance throughout the circuit is not necessarily 600 ohms. The −60 dB refers to the minimum input signal level at which the sine wave starts becoming limited.)

You will also need well balanced filters to develop similar voltages for both mark and space tones, and to obtain good noise cancellation when there is no signal. You should have a high-voltage loop supply of at least 120 volts and preferably more, 150 to 250 volts. Although the RTTY machine itself can work on voltages as low as 24 volts and even less, immense amounts of distortion are added. It has been shown that printers operated in a 12-volt loop can easily exceed 60 percent spacing bias. This amount is essentially intolerable. Raising the loop potential to 36 volts can still result in as much as 30 to 33 percent spacing bias. If the incoming signal is also distorted, this can create an immense number of printing errors at times when others may copy perfectly. With a 150-volt loop, the bias can be reduced to 2 percent or less, an insignificant amount.

Automatic Printer Control

All of these points so far have been related to copying the signal in a decent manner. Now we can discuss the "optional extras." The most important of these, particularly on vhf, is some sort of automatic arrangement that will energize the printer whenever a signal (RTTY only, of course!) comes on the frequency. On vhf where squelch is employed and where cw is rarely used on an RTTY frequency, the most elementary means can be employed. A simple system consists of a capacitor across a relay, so that it takes 4 or 5 seconds of steady mark to turn the unit on, and either no signal at all (squelch, again) or a steady space for 6 or 8 seconds to turn it off. This system suffers from problems, though. It requires a special "turn-on" signal, and the turn-off method is not always satisfactory, particularly if a voice signal comes on the frequency immediately after the tone signal has stopped.

On 3 to 30 MHz, automatic printer control is just as desirable. But here, cw signals are the main problem. You now need a system that will turn on without any special procedure, a system that does not respond to cw, and preferably a delay system that will keep the motor running for at least a half-minute or so while the other station is identifying by cw. (This keeps the motor from turning on and off after each RTTY transmission.)

The term "autostart" has been used in the past to mean fixed-frequency monitoring, such as on net frequencies. But automatic printer control and autostart need not be considered in equal terms at

Fig. 1 — ST-4 demodulator for receiving 170-Hz-shift RTTY signals. Being completely solid state, the device can be housed in a relatively small enclosure. Only four switches are required on the front panel. The meter is optional, and provides a tuning indication for use in the hf amateur bands. An aluminum chassis is used for a cabinet. A decorative self-adhesive paper provides the grained-wood appearance.

all. If you have an RTTY printer, you will have a use for automatic printer control.

Fully automatic printer control (autoprint) is useful for *any* frequency, because the operator need not be present. The machine will respond to an RTTY signal, and return itself to standby if the signal ceases. Soon afterward, the printer motor will also turn off. If you walk out to the kitchen

Fig. 2 — The bottom cover removed for a look inside the demodulator. On the lower right corner of the etched circuit board are three toroidal inductors associated with the band-pass input filter; nearer, the center of the board are the two toroids associated with the discriminator. The 12-volt and 160-volt power supply transformers are located off the board, in the lower portion of this photo.

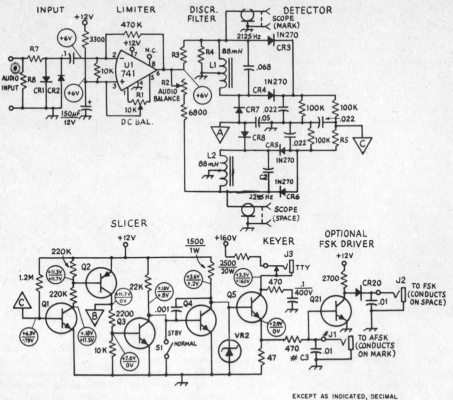

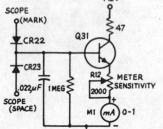

EXCEPT AS INDICATED, DECIMAL
VALUES OF CAPACITANCE ARE
IN MICROFARADS (μF); OTHERS
ARE IN PICOFARADS (pF OR $\mu\mu$F);
RESISTANCES ARE IN OHMS;
k =1000, M=1 000 000

Parts for optional tuning-indicator circuit:
CR22, CR23 — Silicon diode, 50 PRV or greater (1N4816 or equiv.).
M1 — 0-1 MA dc meter (Shurite 8336 or equiv.)
Q31 — Audio transistor, npn silicon (Motorola MPS 3394 or equiv.)
R12 — 2000-ohm linear-taper control, sub-miniature, for horizontal circuit-board mounting (Mallory MTC 23L4 or equiv.).

for a moment during a QSO and the other station turns it back to you unexpectedly, without some automatic feature you may get back to find the machine running "wild," printing only random garble and turning up the paper like a child in the bathroom. Autoprint would have locked the unit in standby when the signal stopped.

If you want to monitor an interesting QSO and still leave the room to eat dinner, mow the lawn, watch televison, or even go to the office, you can do so with autoprint, knowing full well the machine will go back to mark (standby) when the stations have stopped transmitting. Some operators even leave their equipment running when they are out of town for several days at a time.

You can find this feature to be extremely useful for MARS participation, also. Tune in the

frequency using autoprint, and come back an hour or two later to see what went on. Only on RTTY can such a simple but fully automatic arrangement be set up.

DEVELOPMENT OF THE ST-4

The ST-4, Figs. 1 through 5, was developed for those interested only in 170-Hz shift, and is particularly useful for autostart purposes. It is perhaps the first demodulator intended solely for narrow shift reception ever offered the RTTY enthusiast.

The particularly outstanding features of the ST-4 are the autoprint section, the high-voltage loop, and the extraordinary limiting available with

AUTOPRINT AND MOTOR DELAY

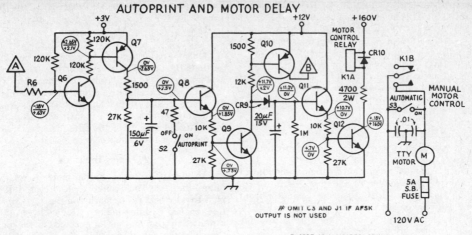

OMIT C3 AND J1 IF AFSK
OUTPUT IS NOT USED

POWER SUPPLY

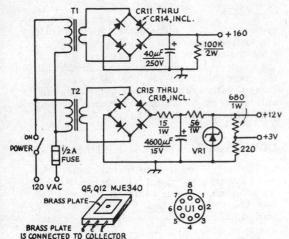

EXCEPT AS INDICATED, DECIMAL
VALUES OF CAPACITANCE ARE
IN MICROFARADS (μF) ; OTHERS
ARE IN PICOFARADS (pF OR μμF);
RESISTANCES ARE IN OHMS;
k =1000 , M=1 000 000

Q1, Q6, Q8, Q9, Q11, Q21 — Audio transistor, npn silicon (Motorola MPS3394 or equiv.).

Q2, Q7, Q10 — Audio transistor, pnp silicon (Motorola MPS 3702 or equiv.).

Q3, Q4 — General-purpose transistor, npn silicon (Motorola MPS 2926 or equiv.).

Q5, Q12 — Audio transistor, npn silicon, 300-V collector-emitter rating (Motorola MJE340 or equiv.).

R1 — 10,000-ohm linear taper control, sub-miniature, for horizontal circuit-board mounting (Mallory MTC-14L4 or equiv.).

R2 — 5000-ohm linear taper control, sub-miniature, for horizontal circuit-board mounting (Mallory MTC53L4 or equiv.).

R3 — 6800 ohms.

R4 — 4700 ohms.

R5 — 91,000 ohms.

R6 — 0.11 megohm.

R7 — Use 1000-ohm value if audio input is connected directly to receiver output; if input band-pass filter of Fig. 5 is used, value is 4700 ohms.

R8 — 560 ohms; omit if input band-pass filter of Fig. 5 is used.

S1-S4, incl. — Spst toggle.

T1 — Power; primary 120 V; secondary 125 V (Chicago-Stancor PA-8421 or Triad N51-X or equiv.).

T2 — Power; primary 120 V; secondary 12 V, 350 mA (Chicago-Stancor P8391 or equiv.).

U1 — Integrated-circuit operational amplifier, μA741, TO-5 package.

VR1 — Zener diode, 12-V, 1-W (Sarkes-Tarzian VR-12 or equiv.).

VR2 — Zener diode, 4.3-V, 400-mW (1N4731 or equiv.).

C1 — Not used.

C2 — 0.56 μF, paper or Mylar, 75- or 100-volt rating.

C3 — .01 μF Mylar or disk, 600 volt. Omit if af keying output is not used.

CR1, CR2, CR7, CR8, CR9, CR15-CR18 incl., CR20 — Silicon diode, 50 PRV or greater (1N4816 or equiv.)

CR3-CR6, incl. — Germanium diode, type 1N270.

CR10-CR14, incl. — Silicon rectifier, 400 PRV or greater (1N4004 or equiv.).

CR19, CR21 — Not used.

J1, J2 — Phone jacks. Omit J1 if af keying output is not used.

J3 — Phone jack, single circuit, shorting.

K1 — 110-V dc relay, dpdt contacts with 10-A minimum rating (Potter and Brumfield type KA11DG or equiv.).

L1, L2 — 88 mH toroid.

Fig. 3 — The ST-4 RTTY demodulator (by Hoff — from *QST*, April 1970). Unless otherwise indicated, resistors are 1/4-watt 10 percent tolerance. Capacitors with polarity indicated are electrolytic. Dc operating voltages are indicated in the limiter, slicer, keyer, and autoprint and motor delay circuits. All voltages are measured with respect to chassis ground with a VTVM. In the slicer and keyer stages, voltage values above the line should appear with a mark tone present at the demodulator input, while values below the line appear with a space tone present. In the autoprint and motor delay circuit, voltage values above the line occur with a mark or space tone present while those values below the line are present with only receiver noise applied at the demodulator input.

the new integrated-circuit front end. The overall features are as follows: The demodulator

1) Adapts to a variety of audio input schemes.

2) Has a low-cost linear integrated operational amplifier (op amp).

3) Has at least −60dB of limiting.

4) Has a well-balanced filter design with excellent noise cancellation.

5) Has a simple but effective low-pass filter (*RC* type).

6) Has a very high gain in the "slicer" section allowing reception of shifts under 5 Hz.

7) Uses an inexpensive 300-volt loop-keyer transistor.

8) Has a most unique automatic printer control (autoprint) that ignores cw and voice.

9) Has motor delay to keep the motor from needlessly turning on and off.

10) Is dc coupled from input to printer for minimum distortion.

12) May be used easily for repeating (retransmitting).

13) Uses only parts available from any general distributor.

14) Is low cost. Total cost of all parts is about $75.

OPTIONAL FEATURES

An Optional Normal-Reverse Switch

In normal RTTY operation, the audio tone of 2125 Hz for mark is shifted higher in pitch for space – to 2975 Hz for 850-Hz shift, or to 2295 Hz for 170-Hz shift. In the hf bands, this will occur only when the signal is tuned as if it were a "lower sideband" transmission. On rare occasion, a station will be transmitting backwards from normal, or "upside down." This happens so infrequently that no normal-reverse switch was added to the basic diagram. After all, one can go to upper sideband to copy the fellow, or ask him to invert his shift. If you feel it necessary to have an upside-down switch, use that shown in Fig. 4. This involves only an additional dpdt switch mounted on the front panel. However, such a switch is almost super-

fluous and hence was not placed on the basic schematic.

Band-Pass Input Filter

A band-pass input filter is always beneficial, particularly on the 3- to 30-MHz bands. One such as that shown in Fig. 5 may be added. This filter may be driven directly from either a 500-ohm receiver output or with a transformer. You can also wind about thirty turns of small wire around the input toroid and drive the filter from a 3.2-ohm source. Other filters may also be used.

A Tuning Indicator

On vhf with afsk, a tuning meter is relatively unimportant, as fixed audio tones are used. If you plan to use the ST-4 primarily on the 3- to 30-MHz frequencies, a tuning indicator is nice to have. You can use an oscilloscope connected to the points shown in the detector circuit, and the display will be something like that pictured in an earlier section of this chapter under "Selective Fading."

A VTVM can be hooked to point A of Fig. 3 and used as a tuning indicator, or you may add the optional tuning-indicator circuit shown in Fig. 3. When the mark and space signals are equally tuned the meter will not flicker, but will stand still while the sending operator types. You can also copy less than 170-Hz shift by tuning in this manner, although now the unflickering meter will read somewhat less than for full shift.

CONSTRUCTION AND ADJUSTMENTS

You may, if you wish, completely eliminate the entire autoprint and motor delay section. Without the autoprint or motor control features, the total cost would run only about $50. You will find it hard to build something remotely decent for much less money.

You can utilize the junk box to a great extent on this unit. Diodes CR3 through CR6 are germanium, type 1N270, and here we suggest you do not substitute other types. The 88-mH toroids will cost about 60¢ each and may be purchased from various advertisers in the Ham-Ads section of *QST*. The relay, K1, and an external plug for the printer motor should be wired directly to 120 V ac. The 1/2-A fuse in the power supply section of Fig. 3 is only for the actual demodulator itself; the printer should already have a fused motor circuit.

If you orient the switches correctly, you can place them all "up" for fully automatic operation. This is convenient, since you can merely glance at the unit to be sure it is set for auto-print, and then leave the room.

S1 (NORMAL-STANDBY) should be open when up (NORMAL).

S2 (AUTOPRINT ON-OFF) should be open when up (ON).

S3 (MANUAL MOTOR CONTROL) should be open when up (AUTOMATIC).

S4 (POWER) should be closed when up (ON).

When you connect the high-voltage power supply, the voltage on standby (mark) may not be

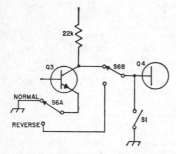

Fig. 4 — Normal-reverse switch. S1, Q3, Q4, and the 22-kΩ resistor appear in Fig. 3, and are shown here only to indicate the points in the circuit which are switched by S6.
S6 — Dpdt toggle.

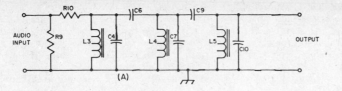

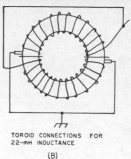

TOROID CONNECTIONS FOR
22-mH INDUCTANCE

(B)

Fig. 5 — Band-pass filter for ST-4. Filter output should be connected directly to audio input shown in Fig. 3. R7 of Fig. 3 should be 4700-ohm value and R8 should be omitted. All capacitors are mylar, 75- or 100-volt rating.

C4, C10 — 0.22 μF.

C5, C8, C11 — Not used.

C6, C9 — 0.022 μF.

C7 — 0.18 μF.

L3, L4, L5 — 22 mH toroid; made from usual "88 mH" toroid except windings are parallel-connected as shown above, rather than series-connected.

R9 — 560 ohms.

R10 — 1600 ohms.

Adjust ST-4 filter sections listed below for resonance at 2195 Hz; it will be necessary to remove turns from the toroids. One turn off each winding simultaneously will raise the resonant frequency about 6 Hz.

L3 with C4 + C6.

L4 with C6 + C7 + C9.

L5 with C9 + C10.

160 volts, depending upon the power transformer used. Measure the current through the printer magnets, and if it is not between 50 and 70 mA, change the 2500-ohm current limiting resistor in the collector lead of Q5 to a value giving the proper current. (No meter is needed permanently at this position.) At the same time, check the current to the winding of K1. You may need to change the 4700-ohm resistor to another value if you do not read within about 1 or 2 mA of the 11 mA current the relay needs for optimum operation.

Then measure the current through the Zener diode in the low-voltage supply (VR1). If necessary, change the value of the 56-ohm 1-watt resistor until the Zener diode conducts between 10 and 25 mA current.

Adjust the discriminator filters for resonance at the frequencies shown in Fig. 3. Because of manufacturing tolerances, most 0.068-μF capacitors will be a little too large in actual value for resonance at 2125 Hz, so remove turns from the 88-mH toroid to raise the frequency of the mark filter. Take an equal number of turns off each of the two half-windings before permanently joining the two sections of the toroid together. Similarly, most 0.056-μF capacitors will be too large in value for resonance at 2295 Hz for the space frequency in the ST-4. Again, remove an equal number of turns off each winding of the toroid. Adjustment of the limiter circuit is performed in the following manner. With a VTVM, measure the +12-V supply potential. Ground the audio input to the demodulator, and connect the VTVM to pin 3 of the 741 IC. Adjust R1 throughout its total range, and note that the voltage changes from approximately 1.6 V

at either extreme to about 6 V at the center setting of R1. Perform a coarse adjustment of R1 by setting it for a peak meter reading, approximately +6 V. Move the VTVM lead to pin 6 of the IC. Slowly adjust R1 in either direction, and note that adjustment of just a *small fraction* of a turn causes the voltage to swing from approximately 1 V to 11 V. Carefully perform a fine adjustment of R1 by setting it for a voltmeter reading of half the supply voltage, approximately +6 V. With the VTVM, again measure the voltage at pin 3. If the potential is approximately 6 V, R1 is properly set. If the voltage is in the range of 2 V or less, R1 is misadjusted, and the procedure of this paragraph should be repeated.

There is one other adjustment to be made. Attach a VTVM to point A in the detector circuit. Tune for maximum reading on a mark tone, and note the reading, around −2.5 volts. Then tune for maximum reading on a space tone and note the reading, again around −2.5 volts. If these two voltages are not equal, adjust R2, the audio balance control at the output of the limiter circuit, until the voltages are equal.

The 2000-ohm control in the optional meter circuit lets you set the meter to some desired reading when mark is tuned in to maximum. It is convenient if adjusted to read about 80% full scale at that time.

It normally takes about 0.6 volt to cause a silicon transistor to conduct. The 1.2-megohm resistor at the base of Q1 causes Q1 to conduct. A very tiny amount of negative voltage will cause the stage to be cut off, and a very tiny positive amount will cause it to saturate. By hand-selecting an appropriate-value resistor, you can cause the printer to go to mark for all input signals lower in frequency than 2210 Hz, and to go to space for all frequencies higher. However, the 1.2-megohm value should be an excellent choice, depending upon how carefully and accurately you were able to tune the discriminator filters to the mark and space frequencies. If you lack some fairly accurate means of determining the necessary frequencies, disable the autoprint stage by closing switch S2 (autoprint OFF), and select a resistor value that causes the printer to print garble on receiver noise.

The network at the base of Q6 in the autoprint stage does the same thing. Here, you select a value for R6 to determine the sensitivity of the autoprint stage. With a 110-kΩ value, the bandwidth is about ±50 Hz before the printer goes into standby. This value should give adequate tolerance for signals that drift or have improper shift, or both. By increasing the value, toward 120 kΩ, you can decrease the bandwidth, and by going the other direction, toward 82 kΩ, you can increase the bandwidth, but then you run into the problem of more frequent accidental turn-ons.

Use as a Repeater

If an audio signal is fed into the demodulator, it will soon activate the autoprint section, as well as the relay. Thus, a signal on one band can be used to activate a transmitter on another frequency. This is called "retransmitting" or "repeating," and is used frequently on vhf at remote sites. The relay can control the push-to-talk circuit on the transmitter, or if it is used infrequently, can control the 120-V ac power to the transmitter instead.

RTTY INDICATOR SYSTEMS

Various types of indicators, used as aids in the accurate tuning of incoming RTTY signals, are described in this section. Prepared by Hoff, the information originally appeared in *QST* for October, 1965.

In regular cw reception, the beat-frequency oscillator can be adjusted for any tone that is pleasing to the ear. RTTY, however, involves filters in the demodulators that are designed for specific audio tones for optimum reception. Since RTTY demodulators work best when the mark and space frequencies correctly match these filters, some means is needed for tuning the receiver to the optimum tones. Most indicators rely on human eyesight to make a visual comparison between mark and space signals, but aural comparison of the mark tone with a standard reference can be quite simple, inexpensive and yet accurate.

TUNING BY EAR

Some copy will be printed if the receiver is merely tuned until the printer *does* work. After some experience in listening to the audio tones which are required, an adept operator can tune the receiver fairly well by "guessing." However, this seldom gives better than second-rate results with a demodulator that does not incorporate a threshold

corrector such as is used in the TT/L-2 demodulator.

With the threshold corrector, automatic balance is maintained for mark and space voltages at the slicer input. This feature allows great latitude in tuning accuracy (or for drift tolerance). Without this feature few demodulators can tolerate any mistuning without introducing bias into the post-detector signal. Of course the printer can handle a surprisingly high amount of bias, if in proper adjustment, so the typical operator is seldom aware that he may be getting less than optimum results if there is no tuning indicator to show otherwise. It is ironic that the units requiring the most precise tuning – those without some type of automatic threshold correction – are often those with the least suitable tuning indicators.

INDICATING LAMPS

Some demodulators (usually quite simple types) use neon lamps as triggering devices. These normally have one lamp for mark and another for space. If these lamps are panel mounted, they provide a means for tuning the incoming signal to *some* extent.

Sometimes neon lamps are used in the mark and space channels merely to indicate which channel the signal is coming from at the moment. Some commercial units offer these lamps in addition to a more precise indicator; their use assists in rapid tuning and in quickly identifying "upside-down" copy.

"EYE" TUBES

Quite often the outputs of the mark and space channels are sampled and then combined in some visual type of indicator. While the cathode-ray oscilloscope is most often used by the advanced enthusiast, the 6AF6G electron-ray tube is a much cheaper and more simple arrangement. This tube indicates visually, by means of two shadows on the fluorescent target, the effects of changes in the controlling voltages. A typical circuit for a 6AF6G tube is shown in Fig. 1.

This type of indicator is viewed from the end and looks something like Fig. 2A. The shadows alternately open and shut on the upper and lower bright areas as the signal goes from mark to space, and the receiver is tuned to the signal so this alternating pattern results. With some experience,

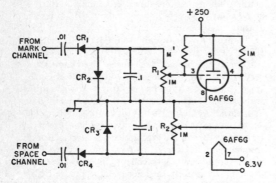

Fig. 1 – "Magic-eye" tuning indicator circuit. The display is similar to Fig. 2A when the receiver is properly tuned. Capacitances are in μF; capacitors may be paper or Mylar as convenient. Resistances are in ohms; fixed resistors are 1/2-watt.
CR1-CR4, incl. – Silicon, 100 volts PIV or more (Sarkes-Tarzian F4 suitable).
R1, R2 – Audio-taper control.

most operators are able to get good results with this type of indicator. If the shift does not closely match the filter tones, the indicator becomes increasingly difficult to use with accuracy since the relative size of the openings diminishes as the shift narrows. The 6AF6G is seldom used any longer except in the most simple demodulators, as other indicators are now available that give superior results.

Newer types of dual-shadow eye tubes have been developed, such as the Telefunken EMM-801. This is a bar-type fluorescent indicating tube with two targets, amounting to a dual 6FG6 in one envelope, and viewed the length of the tube, rather than through the end. The EMM-801 has parallel bar patterns, and may be connected to the demodulator so that one pattern is used for mark and the other for space. This provides a nice comparison for best tuning.

The EM84/6FG6 Eye Tube

The 6FG6 is currently used in many fm tuners in hi-fi installations and exhibits a pattern of the type shown in Fig. 2B. In the past, eye tubes have not been very popular with the serious enthusiast, and for good reason. When receiving a steady carrier, the pattern was steady and it was possible to tune the receiver quickly and accurately. However, when the fsk RTTY signal was received and mark would alternate with space, the eye tube would flicker so rapidly, because of the short retention time of the phosphors used in the manufacture of the tube, that accurate tuning was difficult at best. The 6AF6G pattern (Fig. 2A) is also somewhat hard to see satisfactorily in a well-lighted room.

The indicator system used in the Mainline TT/L2 Demodulator (see earlier section) is unique since it uses a single display pattern for both mark and space signals. In all other indicator systems commonly used, it is necessary to compare two different displays and then make some correction to bring these into agreement with each other for optimum reception.

In the TT/L-2, a dual-detector scheme is used so that both mark and space present voltages of the same polarity to the indicator. Since mark alternates with space, the indicator will not flicker when the mark voltage is the same as the space voltage which replaces it as the fsk signal is received. Thus rapid and highly accurate tuning is possible. Tuning becomes increasingly easy as the correct frequencies are approached, as the flicker will completely stop at the optimum point.

This sytem is particularly outstanding when receiving shifts other than normal. Most other indicator systems fail to give displays that can be easily interpreted when the shift is substantially less than normal, because of the interaction of the filters at the point at which the displays are sampled. In the TT/L-2, the dual-detector system automatically back-biases the opposite channel to eliminate this problem. The single-bar 6FG6 electron-ray tube becomes a very precise means of tuning quite narrow shifts, giving a usable display down to less than 10 Hz shift while using the

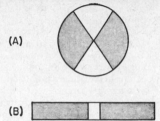

Fig. 2 — "Eye" tube displays. (A) is typical of the 6AF6G tube; (B) is the bar pattern of the 6FG6.

discriminator intended for 850-Hz shift. Actually it will be quite unusual for the operator to encounter transmissions of less than about 100 Hz, since the very narrow shifts fall in the realm of experimentation and have very little practical use at the present time.

OSCILLOSCOPE PATTERNS

The cathode-ray oscilloscope offers an excellent means of correctly tuning the RTTY signal, and many different types of patterns have been in use. The most common is the standard "+" display, where the mark channel is presented horizontally and the space channel is presented vertically (some

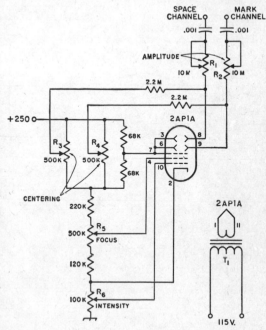

Fig. 3 — Oscilloscope indicator circuit. Resistances are in ohms (K – 1000); fixed resistors are 1/2-watt. Capacitances are in µF.
R1, R2 — Audio-taper control.
R3, R4, R5, R6 — Linear-taper control.
T1 — Filament transformer, 6.3 V, 0.6 A (Stancor P-6465).

systems use the opposite configuration; either is equally acceptable).

A typical oscilloscope hookup is shown in Fig. 3. R1 and R2 are independently adjusted for equal deflection in the mark and space channels when the input voltages are correct for the demodulator. In the case of the TT/L-2 demodulator, the pickup points for such a scope arrangement would be on the secondaries of the step-up transformers in the plate circuits of V4, the two jacks identified as SCOPE MARK and SCOPE SPACE.

If simple filters are used, the oscilloscope pattern might look something like Fig. 4A. This merely indicates that the channel separation in the filters is quite moderate. With multisection filters exhibiting sharp skirt selectivity, the pattern becomes more like Fig. 4B.

If a narrow-shift signal is tuned between these sharper filters, the pattern may look more like Fig. 4C, but if the same signal is tuned on the broader filters, it may have a quite distorted appearance as in Fig. 4D, which is of little value for tuning purposes.

However, we should mention that the more simple filters actually would work much better, in most cases, on these narrower-than-normal shifts than the patterns would suggest, and even though the oscilloscope pattern appears to be worthless, it does not mean that the demodulator cannot copy those signals. It just means a different indicator should be used for these shifts. The primary value of the "+" pattern is for copying normal shifts and using high-quality multisection filters. Some operators have added sharp filters just to the scope input to get a pattern resembling Fig. 4B, while retaining broad filters in the actual demodulator. This again gives a somewhat erroneous presentation although "improving" the scope display. Displays other than the "+" type would be more useful over a greater range of fsk shifts.

The "phase-shift" display (which resembles an "X" pattern) is occasionally used. Regular 850-Hz shift might look like Fig. 4E. Narrow shift when properly tuned might then look like Fig. 4F and normal shifts incorrectly tuned might look like Fig. 4G. The phase-shift display is much better than the "+" display for tuning less-than-normal shifts. However, it requires additional circuitry over the oscilloscope hook-up in Fig. 3, which already is fairly complex and expensive.

Another type of oscilloscope display which offers excellent potential is often used on military equipment, and might be called the "flipping-line" display, Fig. 4H. The 60-Hz power-line frequency is commonly used for the horizontal sweep. The vertical input is direct coupled and connected to the output of the detector stage of the demodulator. With no RTTY signal present, a single line appears at the reticle center line of the display (horizontal broken line at the center of the display,

Fig. 4 — Scope displays of various types for RTTY signals. See text for explanation.

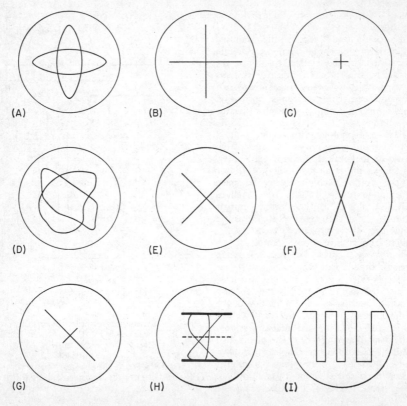

(A)   (B)   (C)

(D)   (E)   (F)

(G)   (H)   (I)

Fig. 4H). When a mark tone is present at the demodulator input, the single line is deflected upward, and when a space tone is present the line is deflected downward. With alternate mark and space tones applied, the line alternately "flips" up and down, and because of the persistence of the display, appears as shown in Fig. 4H. Proper tuning will keep this line equally above and below the center of the scope display as an fsk signal is received. (As the sweep signal is not necessarily synchronized to the switching between marks and spaces, faint trace lines may appear on the display between the mark and space lines. These lines are simply ignored during operation.) One of the big advantages of such an arrangement is that the gain of the scope may be increased as the operator tunes very narrow shifts, enabling copy of shifts of less than 6 or 8 Hz. However, the cost of the dc scope would prohibit many from buying or building such a circuit, particularly when the results are compared with the inexpensive display on the TT/L-2, which is equally good to at least 10-20 Hz shift.

If a linear sweep on the dc scope is slowed to around 6 Hz, the pulse formation of the various characters can be studied as in Fig. 4I. If the same character is repeated a few times, bias and other problems can be quickly isolated.

Other scope patterns are possible also, but again the associated circuitry is complex and expensive besides taking a disproportionate amount of chassis space. One such display, shown in Fig. 5, is a panoramic display of the audio spectrum from the receiver. As the mark signal is tuned a vertical pip moves along the base line, becoming the highest in amplitude at the point of optimum tuning. The same occurs for the space signal. The height then shows optimum tuning and the distance between indicates the shift. The tube used is rectangular in shape. The primary application for such a display is in commercial transmissions using "Twinplex" where there are actually four signals being transmitted at one time. Conventional displays would be useless in this case. An audio device of this type but not exhibiting amplitude sensitivity to frequency was described for home construction in *QST* for November, 1972, by Olson and VanGeen, "The FVGT Box." The "box" is used in conjunction with an oscilloscope, and employs the Fast Van-Geen Transform in an audio "spectrum analyzer."

METER DISPLAYS

Some operators have used meters for tuning the fsk signal rather than more costly and complex scope patterns. Such meters have normally been a center-zero type that would swing one direction for mark and the opposite for space, when hooked to the detector output. Supposedly, when receiving fsk signals, the meter would hover around mid-scale. At best this was doubtful, as most RTTY signals favor mark to some extent, even at machine speed. However, if the operator would send "RYRYRYRYRYRYRY" at machine speed the meter would be reasonably accurate. Such an arrangement is of little value for the customary

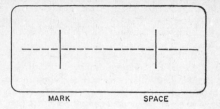

MARK   SPACE

Fig. 5 — The "audio-spectrum-analyzer" scope display.

amateur conversation, which is invariably at moderately slow hand-speed typing.

Another type of meter arrangement offers a very useful tuning aid, however. Such an arrangement is used as the optional tuning indicator in the Mainline ST-4 Demodulator (see earlier section of this chapter), and is based on the principle described above for the 6FG6 eye tube. The trick is to apply mark and space voltages of the *same polarity* to the meter. When the receiver is correctly tuned with fm or limiter reception, the meter will not flicker as the received signal shifts from mark to space. Such an arrangement is unsuitable for a-m or limiterless copy, however, because selective fading and other phenomena can cause severe flickering of the meter, even though the receiver is tuned properly.

LIMITERLESS RECEPTION

In limiterless reception the operator is going to have some difficulty no matter what visual system he uses, since the indicator amplitude will change because of the varying signal strength, in addition to changing because of the frequency of the signal. This makes it impossible for the operator to be certain whether the signal has drifted or faded. Since the mark and space signals often fade at independent rates (selective fading), the tuning is made more difficult by this as well. Thus the visual indicator systems require an operator to be quite alert.

Many operators solve the problem indirectly by turning the limiter on momentarily until correct tuning is assured and then turning it off once more to take advantage of the limiterless features of the demodulator.

To compound the problem further, most serious advocates of limiterless copy have obtained quite narrow channel filters, and here again even a little drift will quickly make a noticeable change in the indicator presentation. Also, with filters of this type, mistuning can quickly produce unacceptable levels of distortion.

Thus for limiterless reception some method in addition to visual indicators should be used, although this is somewhat a new concept in amateur reception.

Tuning by Tone Comparison

We have now made the full circle back to "tuning by ear" once more. However, the system to be described is a far cry from "guessing" by ear.

It can be an extremely accurate means of assuring oneself that the signal is correctly tuned whether for limiterless reception or for normal use of the limiter.

All that is needed is some means of generating an audio tone that matches the mark filter frequency. An audio oscillator such as is found in many amateur stations for test purposes can be put to work (one way to get your money's worth out of the thing at last!) or tuning forks can be obtained. Some musical instruments, such as mouth organs, will work very nicely.

The system is simplicity itself, and merely ,compares the incoming signal against a standard reference tone that has been adjusted to that of the mark filter. The operator just sets the tuning so the mark signal agrees with the standard tone. This system works very well for wide shifts, but is not as easy to use on narrow shift, as it is hard to pick out the exact mark pitch from the space tone for comparison purposes.

At some time prior to receiving an incoming signal, the receiver is tuned to a crystal-calibrator spot on the dial (or the transmitter is turned on to give a steady carrier) and then adjusted to give maximum output from the mark detector while looking at a meter or the tuning indicator. The audio oscillator is then adjusted to equal that tone in pitch. While receiving an fsk RTTY signal, the receiver is merely tuned until the mark tone matches the pitch of the audio reference tone. This can be done with extreme rapidity and with exceptional accuracy when compared with normal visual indicators such as the "+" scope pattern.

One of the advantages of such a system is that the operator need not continuously look at the indicator to see if any readjustment is necessary — he can hear when the signal differs in pitch from the standard tone. This is quite nice, particularly for contest work where limiterless copy with very narrow filters gives an important edge over other participants. Since the operator is listening and not looking, the system works equally well with or without the limiter.

It may be that the incoming signal shift is not a standard shift, exactly, and in this case perhaps the standard audio tone is not the best. A simple adjustment can be quickly made: the limiter is turned on and the signal tuned normally by visual reference to the indicator. Then the audio oscillator is adjusted to match this mark tone and the limiter can be turned back off.

The primary disadvantage in using this type of tuning aid is that it is necessary to hear the incoming signal as well as the standard tone source at the same time. Many operators do not care to listen to the receiver at any time while on RTTY, but this is the opposite extreme. Others prefer to listen not only to their own signal but the incoming signal as well. Both techniques have some merit, but it would seem that monitoring the signal by ear has much merit.

The audio comparison method has an important fringe benefit — it is very simple to match the local transmitter to the incoming signal quickly and accurately. Thus for breaking into a contact the frequency can be set "right on the money" in an instant, and if it is not correct that fact becomes immediately evident. Again this requires that the operator be able to hear the signal while transmitting. It would seem that a bypass switch across the speaker could be easily installed for this purpose, so it would operate during transmissions. There is no need to kill the receiver during transmission as the demodulator standby switch makes that unnecessary. Having the receiver operate during transmission will also enable the operator to observe the tuning of the local station to compare its frequency with the incoming signal for accuracy. From listening to amateur RTTY contacts it would seem that very few operators pay any attention to their own frequency while transmitting, for how else could they be so far off the station they are talking with?

CHECKING RTTY SHIFTS

Accurate setting of frequency shift for transmitting radioteletype is probably the most difficult task encountered by amateur operators. A related problem is accurate tuning of the filters used in the demodulator, for optimum reception of incoming signals.

Audio oscillators are often used, but accuracy is normally rather poor because the high range (typically 2,000 to 20,000 Hz) must be used; it would be easy to miss the correct frequency by 100 IIz or more, and this is intolerable. Tuning forks may be purchased for standard RTTY tones and this system works very well indeed for those who have obtained them. Again, striking certain notes on the piano will give 850 or 170 shift quite accurately, and K8UFU for years used a harmonica for setting his shift! Also, audio tapes that have the standard RTTY tones may be obtained; this method is not only about the cheapest of all, assuming that the operator owns or has access to an audio tape recorder, but approaches the accuracy of a digital counter. However, each of these methods is good only for certain limited aspects.

A simple and relatively inexpensive technique, but one which is highly accurate for audio frequency measurements, has been named the Mainline TT/O Semi-Counter by Hoff. The Semi-Counter consists of two extremely sharp filters of 20-25 Hz bandwidth, one of which is tuned to a fixed frequency of 2125 Hz and the other adjustable by means of a precision capacitor substitution decade box. The two filters are connected to an oscilloscope that displays a "+" pattern when the signal is properly tuned. The TT/O Semi-Counter is not particularly designed to replace the normal visual display on the demodulator, but to complement and augment such a display when used "on the air." It is also readily adaptable to other applications, such as:

1) Aiding in the tuning of filter sections to specific audio frequencies;

2) Measuring the shift of any RTTY signal being received.

3) Setting the transmitter quickly and accurately to an incoming signal without using loudspeakers or headphones.

4) Keeping a "cold" transmitter on frequency.

5) Estimating transmitter drift over, say, an hour's time with reasonable accuracy.

6) Quickly and accurately setting the fsk shift of the local transmitter to shifts other than 850 or 170, and then returning to the previous setting accurately.

The 88-mH Toroid

The common 88-mH toroid, Fig. 1, has a very high Q, around 118 at 2125 Hz, and the Q rises linearly to about 157 at 2975 Hz. When isolated properly to take advantage of this high Q, a simple tuned-circuit filter using the toroid will have a bandwidth of 17-20 Hz (see Fig. 2). It is unlikely that such isolation can be conveniently achieved, but it is easily possible to keep the bandwidth down to 20 to 25 Hz. The Qs of the filters in Mainline TT/O Semi-Counter are about 85 at 2125 Hz and 120 at 2975 Hz. For a number of reasons, such filters are much too narrow for general reception of 60-wpm RTTY signals, but they certainly make optimum displays possible for tuning purposes, for setting the transmitter on frequency and maintaining that frequency, for adjusting the fsk shift, and other worthwhile applications.

Little we have said so far will be very new to many readers. The new "twist" to the Mainline TT/O Semi-Counter is the use of a decade capacitance box.

Several experimenters have found, after working with many 88-mH toroids from a variety of suppliers, that for the most part they are wound to extremely close tolerances. In checking the resonant frequency with the same capacitor across a dozen different toroids, a variation of only 10-15

Scrape insulation and solder for series connection of windings.

Fig. 1 — The 88-mH toroid. The two windings must be connected in series to give an inductance of 88 mH.

Hz will be noted. However, using various capacitors across the same toroid is something else again!

Take the mark tone of 2125 Hz, for instance. A 0.068-μF capacitor is often used across an 88-mH toroid to tune to this frequency. If the capacitor has a 10% rating (about the best you will find in the local store or mail-order catalog) it can vary from 0.0612 to 0.0748 μF and be within limits. In frequency this would correspond to 1962 to 2169 Hz. Quite a variation! – *over 200 Hz* for a 0.068-μF capacitor that is within limits. With a 1% capacitor the variation would be around 20 Hz.

The answer, of course, is to use 1% capacitors, at least for one standard reference filter from which others can then be duplicated. Here is where the decade capacitance box comes in.

The Decade Capacitance Box

The decade capacitance box uses all 1% capacitors, and is adjustable in 100-pF steps from zero to 0.111 μF. These boxes are available in kit form (such as the Heathkit IN-27). The box will be useful not only in the Mainline TT/O Semi-Counter for day-to-day use, but also for tuning filters that may be constructed for the demodulator and in other applications around the RTTY station. Tuning filters is a job that most dread to such an extent that very few even bother, but with a piece of test equipment such as the capacitor decade box tuning filters quickly and accurately is quite easy.

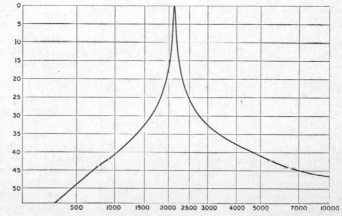

Fig. 2 — Response of single-tuned 88-mH toroid filter for 2125 Hz. This circuit has a very high unloaded Q of 118. The bandwidth is only 18 Hz. Vertical axis in dB, horizontal axis in hertz.

Tuning Toroids

An 88-mH toroid that appears to be "brand-new" and has had no turns of wire removed from it should be chosen for use in conjuction with the decade capacitance box as a standard reference. Other toroids and capacitors to be used in filters are then tuned against the reference combination. Their actual values will be rather immaterial — either a few turns of wire will be removed from the toroid to match the capacitor, or a few smaller capacitors may be connected in parallel to achieve the proper frequency. This process does not take long, nor does it require expensive components of close tolerance.

If the capacitance box is connected across the standard reference toroid, any specific frequency from 2125 to 3150 may be "tuned" immediately by referring to Table I. This enables the operator not only to select specific audio tones for various purposes, such as tuning filters, but also to measure the frequency of an unknown tone. It forms the basis of reading shifts with the Semi-Counter.

TABLE I
Calibration Chart for 88-MH Toroid and Decade Box
Shift is measured in hertz with respect to 2125 Hz.

μF	Shift	Freq.	/100pF	μF	Shift	Freq.	/100pF	μF	Shift	Freq.	/100pF
0.0290	1026	3151	5	0.0410	525	2650	3	0.0530	205	2330	2
0.0295	999	3124	5	0.0415	509	2634	3	0.0535	195	2320	2
0.0300	973	3098	5	0.0420	493	2618	3	0.0540	184	2309	2
0.0305	947	3072	5	0.0425	477	2602	3	0.0546	170	2295	2
0.0310	922	3047	5	0.0430	462	2587	3	0.0550	163	2288	2
0.0315	898	3023	5	0.0435	447	2572	3	0.0555	152	2277	2
0.0320	874	2999	5	0.0440	433	2558	3	0.0560	142	2267	2
0.0325	850	2975	5	0.0445	418	2543	3	0.0565	132	2257	2
0.0330	828	2953	4	0.0450	404	2529	3	0.0570	122	2247	2
0.0335	806	2931	4	0.0455	390	2515	3	0.0575	112	2237	2
0.0340	785	2910	4	0.0460	376	2501	3	0.0580	103	2228	2
0.0345	763	2888	4	0.0465	363	2488	3	0.0585	93	2218	2
0.0350	743	2868	4	0.0470	350	2475	3	0.0590	84	2209	2
0.0355	723	2848	4	0.0475	337	2462	3	0.0595	74	2199	2
0.0360	703	2828	4	0.0480	324	2449	2	0.0600	65	2190	2
0.0365	683	2808	4	0.0485	311	2436	2	0.0605	56	2181	2
0.0370	664	2789	4	0.0490	299	2424	2	0.0610	47	2172	2
0.0375	646	2771	4	0.0495	286	2411	2	0.0615	38	2163	2
0.0380	627	2752	4	0.0500	274	2399	2	0.0620	30	2155	2
0.0385	609	2734	4	0.0505	262	2387	2	0.0625	21	2146	2
0.0390	592	2717	4	0.0510	251	2376	2	0.0630	13	2138	2
0.0395	574	2699	3	0.0515	239	2364	2	0.0635	4	2129	2
0.0400	558	2683	3	0.0520	228	2353	2	0.0637	0	2125	
0.0405	541	2666	3	0.0525	217	2342	2				

These represent 500-pF steps on the decade capacitance box. The small figures between steps are the hertz for each 100 pF. For example, suppose the decade box reads 0.0321. This is close to 0.0320, so subtract 5 Hz from 874 for resultant final shift of 869. The decade capacitance box has 1-percent capacitors, and the practical results are usually within 2 to 3 Hz of these figures with an unmodified 88-mH toroid.

Setting Up The TT/O

Referring to Fig. 3, the 2.2-MΩ resistor provides suitable isolation to keep the Q of the toroid quite high, and thus very sharply resonant. (The input resistance of the scope will typically be 3-6 MΩ and also has little effect on the Q.) By changing the capacitance between points A and B, the frequency to which the filter will respond will be changed accordingly. This is the circuit used in setting up the Mainline TT/O.

Use the standard reference toroid and the capacitor box for L and C, respectively. Referring to Table I, set the box to 0.0637 μF. The filter will now be tuned to within a very few hertz of 2125 — again, of course, assuming that the 88-mH toroid you selected was "new." Adjust the audio source so that the scope shows maximum indication. (The audio source can be an audio oscillator, a receiver tuned to a 100-kHz calibrator point to give steady tone, a tape recorder, or other oscillator of some type. In any event, allow the audio source ample opportunity to warm up so that it will be stable — in the case of the audio oscillator, a few hours; in the case of the receiver, overnight. The setting of the audio source is then left unchanged and it in turn becomes a "standard" against which the 2125-Hz fixed-frequency filter can be tuned. The following steps outline the procedure used in tuning the 2125-Hz filter.

1) Remove the standard 88-mH toroid and replace it with any other 88-mH toroid.

2) Connect a 0.06-μF capacitor across the toroid, leaving the decade box in the circuit.

3) Set the decade box for maximum scope indication.

4) Read from the decade box the additional capacitance that must be added to 0.06 μF to tune the toroid to 2125 Hz.

5) Add the required amount and again adjust the capacitance decade box, to see if any small additional capacitance is needed. If not, and the indication is not as great on the scope as with the decade box alone, the added capacitance was too large. In this case, remove a few turns of wire from the toroid. Each turn removed will raise the frequency about 3 Hz around 2125 Hz.

6) After you think the 2125 filter is adjusted about right, remove the decade box and readjust the audio source to show maximum deflection on the scope.

7) Remove the 2125 filter, and replace with the standard reference 88-mH toroid and decade box. Again adjust the decade box for maximum scope deflection without touching the audio source.

8) Read the value on the decade box and compare against the values in Table I to see if any small corrections could advantageously be made to the 2125 filter. From Table I, each 100 pF added will lower the tone about 2 Hz, and each turn removed from the toroid will raise the tone about 3 Hz. (At 2975 Hz, each 100 pF added will lower the tone about 5 Hz and each turn of wire removed will raise the tone about 4.5 Hz.)

Many variations will become apparent as the operator gains a bit of experience. At any rate, the

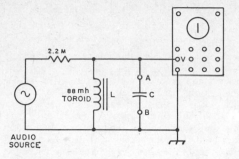

Fig. 3 — Tuning the toroid to a specific frequency. The audio source can be a variable-frequency audio oscillator, a receiver tuned to a 100-kHz calibrator point, or a tape recorder with a standard tone. Use only Mylar or polystyrene capacitors.

use of the method explained and retention of a standard reference toroid will make tuning filters simple and easy — and best of all, very likely will surpass any accuracy previously achieved.

Checking Shifts

Most demodulators amplify the audio tones used for mark and space prior to rectification in the detector stage. These ac potentials usually reach 50-100 volts or more. The Mainline TT/O Semi-Counter is connected to the demodulator at these points through very high resistances to keep the filters extremely narrow for optimum tuning. This also makes possible the basic purpose of the Semi-Counter, that is, to measure shifts by utilizing the very sharp filters appropriately.

Fig. 4 shows how the Mainline TT/O can be quickly connected for checking RTTY shifts. It should be easy to adapt the Semi-Counter to whatever demodulator is in use.

In checking fsk shifts, first tune the receiver for maximum mark indication on the scope. Then vary the capacitor decade box for maximum space presentation. Note the setting on the box and refer to Table I.

Checking Transmitter Drift

Most receivers (after 5-6 hours warmup) are quite stable. Many of the newer receivers will hold a frequency within a few hertz in an hour's time. (Temperature variations in a room will change this picture considerably, of course.) Transmitters, on the other hand, seldom will match a receiver for stability regardless of how long they have been running. While it is not unusual to run a receiver 24 hours a day (many enthusiasts never turn their receivers off, and this is indeed highly recommended), few would care to turn on a transmitter more than a few minutes prior to its use.

Under these circumstances, all but crystal-controlled transmitters will drift considerably more than most individuals would think, during the first hour or two. If the owner is curious as to just how stable his transmitter really is, the Mainline TT/O Semi-Counter will show him very quickly. Let the receiver warm up overnight at least so it can be relied on as much as possible as an accurate standard. Then turn the transmitter on. Tune it for a beat tone of say 2700 Hz with the decade box on the Semi-Counter set at 0.0395 μF. Then, at time intervals selected as convenient, vary the decade box for maximum scope presentation. By comparing against Table I the transmitter drift can be rather accurately estimated. By keeping track over a period of a few hours, it will become obvious just how long it really takes for the transmitter to settle down.

Keeping the transmitter on frequency is one of the fringe benefits of the Semi-Counter. The filters are so sharp that drifts of 15 or 20 Hz will cause nearly a 25-percent change in the size of the scope pattern. As a result, any drift will be quickly noticed. Thus the operator can come on frequency with a "cold" transmitter, and although frequent adjustments may be needed they can be made quickly and accurately in order to stay on a specific frequency.

Accuracy

The Semi-Counter won't compete directly against a digital audio counter for accuracy. However, with a little care in tuning the 2125 filter accurately, and with some practice in the use of the Semi-Counter, an operator with normal skill can readily enough determine shifts to within 5-10 Hz. You will soon discover that very few amateurs apparently have the foggiest notion of what 850 or 170 shift really is, and you will be amazed at the actual shifts in common use.

The Semi-Counter could well become one of the most useful items in the RTTY station.

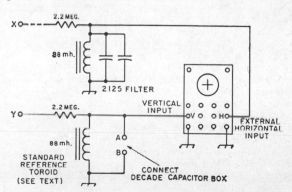

Fig. 4 — Basic circuit for the Mainline TT/O Semi-Counter.

STATION CONTROL, ASSEMBLY OF EQUIPMENT, OPERATING PROCEDURES

As additional equipment is added to the station, questions arise as to the most convenient way to connect things. Indeed, merely hooking up a station to operate at all often becomes a problem. Such things as antenna changeover relays, choice of several different antennas, cw monitors, "bugs," electronic keys, monitorscopes, Pan-adapters, SWR indicators, speaker muting for transmitting on voice, uhf equipment – the list can become quite long, and the problem of where to put what and how to connect it can become quite acute. Many setups are so complex that an outsider would have little idea of how to operate the station even if he owned similar equipment.

The addition of Teletype equipment only makes things more difficult. However, with a little common logic, it need be no more troublesome than adding one of the items listed above.

The "normal" RTTY station consists of a printer, a demodulator, a receiver and a trans-

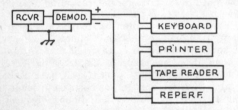

Fig. 1 – How to add extra items of RTTY equipment to the station.

mitter. The input of the demodulator is connected to the output of the receiver, usually across the 500-ohm tap so that headphones may be plugged in without interrupting the RTTY signal. The output of the demodulator is connected to the teleprinter. Modern demodulator circuits allow the printer selector magnets and keyboard to remain hooked in series for the greatest convenience and flexibility, while the transmitter is keyed directly from the same loop supply.

As equipment is added, the switching systems become increasingly complex. A typical station would involve a printer, a reperforator to cut tape either from the incoming signal or from the local station, and a tape reader to play the tape at machine speed automatically. Fig. 1 shows how these might be arranged so that reasonable flexibility can be attained.

Essentially all RTTY equipment is hooked in series. Since the keyboard and tape-reader contacts are merely switches they cause no current drain, and thus numerous units can be added. The selector magnets in the printer and reperforator each total 50 ohms when wired in parallel for 60-mA operation, and numerous units can be hooked in series without causing concern. It is quite unlikely that the average station would ever accumulate enough printers to cause unsatisfactory

operation with all of them connected to the output of the demodulator at the same time. Each unit does develop about 75 volts of inductive kick, in a 60-mA loop, when the circuit is broken, as in a space pulse. Thus with several units in the circuit at one time, substantial voltage can be developed momentarily. The 6W6 and other vacuum tubes often used as keying tubes can easily handle this voltage, but care must be exercised when using transistor circuits.

In all but the most complex RTTY stations, one local loop in addition to the demodulator's own loop system is ample. This gives a flexibility that is quite sufficient for nearly any purpose. Fig. 2 shows how the various units can be changed between the demodulator loop and that of the local loop for cutting tape or for running local checks.

Fig. 3 shows how this can be accomplished with instant switching, a system that has been used with success for some time. By adding extra 4 pdt switches similar to the one shown, the operator can have complete control over the various units in the system. Make-before-break ("shorting-type") switches should be used. If the current through the machine is in the same direction for both loops there will be no interruption in the circuit when the switch is thrown. Otherwise the circuit will be momentarily open, as an ordinary switch has no such make-before-break, and an error invariably results if the switch is thrown while receiving an incoming signal. The voltage rises momentarily as the switch goes through the midposition, but this need not cause concern.

Figs. 2 and 3 can also be combined, for utmost flexibility. The only limiting factor on switching circuits is the operator's imagination. These two simple circuits should satisfy all but the most unusual requirements.

Transmitter Switching

Here again, the method used will vary considerably with the demands of the operator. The simplest system would be one similar to that shown in Fig. 4. The two switches could be placed on or near the printer so that one would need to reach only a short distance to have complete control over the printer for receiving and transmitting. With such an arrangement all that is needed to go from receive to transmit is to close S2 and type. Surprisingly enough, few stations so far have such one-switch simplicity, yet without it station operation becomes most cumbersome. If the transmitter has no push-to-talk line, it has some means of being placed on the air by pushing or twisting a switch – and that switch can be paralleled by the second section of S2 for flexibility similar to that shown in Fig. 4.

For greater convenience, other functions can be switched at the same time the transmitter is placed on the air. For instance, the tape reader can be switched so that it will automatically start when

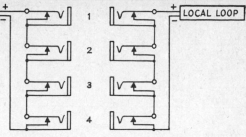

Fig. 2 — Wiring for a simple control panel. If each item of equipment is provided with a cord and plug, it can be connected into either loop easily and quickly. Cords and plugs could be provided, for example, for the keyboard, printer, tape reader, and reperforator.

NOTE: ALL JACKS MUST BE INSULATED FROM THE CHASSIS

the station begins transmitting, as in Fig. 5. Additional switches have been included so that manual control as well as automatic control of the tape reader can be achieved. A manual control switch for the demodulator standby line has been added in Fig. 5 in the event that "retransmit" is desired from an incoming signal. Normally, the demodulator standby line is closed automatically for transmit (Fig. 4) so that the transmitted signal may still be monitored through the receiver without having the demodulator attempt to trip the transmitter while the operator is typing (in voice circles this would be called "feedback").

Other Switching Circuits

The diagrams shown in Figs. 1 to 5 should satisfy all but the most unusual requirements. They should also give the operator some ideas on how to proceed in designing other switching circuits he might need or prefer. Certainly there are a multitude of ways of achieving equipment flexibility, and figuring out switching circuits is a fascinating aspect of assembling an amateur radio station.

To name a few things that might be done, Hoff has devised a system to do the following: A model 28ASR is programmed through the "transmit" switch not only to play the tape reader automatically, but also to change the printer and keyboard over to 100 speed for cutting tape if desired. Also, if the blank key is struck while in the transmit

configuration, a cw identification machine starts up, interrupts the tape, sends the required cw, and then turns the tape back on — all automatically. When in the receive configuration, an incoming blank key has no effect on the system. At the end of a transmission, striking SPACE FIGURES H will turn the transmitter off. An incoming signal sending the same SPACE FIGURES H will turn the transmitter on again for complete automation. Thus a tape can be left on the tape reader and an incoming signal will turn on the transmitter; the proper cw identification is automatically inserted and the transmitter turned off at the end of the tape.

Such switching circuits are an immense personal pleasure to figure out and wire up, and certainly add to the fun of RTTY. Other circuits have been in use by various people, and no doubt from time to time some of these will receive additional publicity.

Transmit-Receive Changeover

Since RTTY consists of 100 percent key down, "instant carrier" occurs when the push-to-talk circuit is activated. The push-to-talk system usually operates an internal relay that does several things: (1) removes cutoff bias on one or two stages in the transmitter, (2) applies voltage to the antenna changeover relay, (3) mutes the speaker for trans-

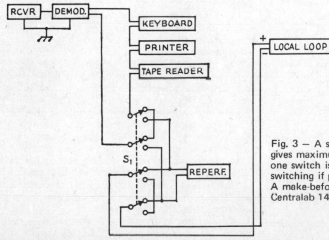

Fig. 3 — A system using switches rather than jacks gives maximum convenience. (For simplicity, only one switch is shown.) No interruptions occur when switching if polarities of both circuits are the same. A make-before-break (shorting) switch such as the Centralab 1459 should be used.

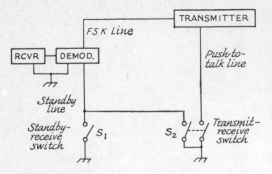

Fig. 4 — Typical station control system offering rapid send-receive switching. S1 is a single-pole single-throw toggle and S2 a double-pole single-throw toggle. Both switches should be mounted close to the printer for greatest convenience in operating.

mitting, and (4) usually provides an extra set or two of contacts for other purposes. Full output of the transmitter exists as soon as the relay closes. Unfortunately, the antenna changeover relay is energized *after* the PTT relay closes, and it would be impossible for a mechanical relay to close before the rf voltage hits its contacts. In fact, it is merely beginning to close at the time that full rf voltage is present. With a full kilowatt this can be a serious problem, and the RTTY enthusiast can go through antenna changeover relays very quickly if high power is consistently used.

There is a very simple remedy for this: Fix the contacts on the antenna changeover relay to control the cutoff-bias on the transmitter. Since the PTT relay normally grounds the cutoff bias, just lift this wire off its ground connection and install a jack as shown in Fig. 6. If no plug is inserted into the jack everthing operates normally as in the "before" illustration. By inserting a plug connected to the auxiliary contacts of the antenna

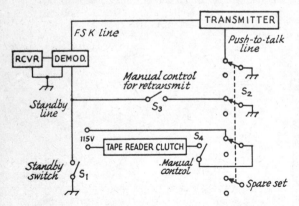

Fig. 5 — An advanced station-control system offering "retransmit" as well as automatic control of the tape reader for transmitting. S3 is seldom used, and S4 is an integral part of the tape reader. S1, S3, S4 — Spst toggle.
S2 — 4-pole double-throw rotary (Centralab 1938 or equivalent).

changeover relay, the cutoff bias cannot be removed until *after* the antenna changeover relay is already on the line, thus providing the necessary timing sequence. Now the antenna changeover relay should not be subjected to the high rf voltage that builds up when the transmitter is momentarily without load, and arcing at the relay contacts cannot occur. Also, additional protection is afforded the receiver by eliminating this arcing. A fringe benefit is that generation of undesired frequencies by the contact arc is eliminated. Television sets in the neighborhood should stop jumping when you key the transmitter.

Distortion and Bias

Distortion occurs when the pulses are not of the standard 22-millisecond duration at normal 60 wpm. Several kinds of distortion occur in practice:

1) *Bias.* If the timing of the signal is such that all the mark pulses are longer or shorter than 22 ms (which automatically makes the space pulses shorter or longer), this is a uniform or systematic type of distortion called "bias." This type of distortion can be corrected at the receiving station by changing the trigger point on the slicer — or more easily, in most cases, by merely moving the range selector on the printer magnets enough to compensate.

However, if the demodulator controls are properly set and the printer's range selector is in the middle of its best printing range, some ±45 percent bias distortion can be tolerated by the printer. This means that the transmitted signal must really be horrible when it will not print. The chances are that you will never hear a signal *that* bad. With a good threshold corrector in the demodulator, little or no need would exist for a distortion or bias control. Some demodulator designs use mechanical relays having "bias windings," and by varying the voltage on such windings distorted signals can be compensated for. However, such circuits introduce serious disadvantages which far outweigh the minor correction possible.

If the mark pulses are longer than normal, it is called "marking bias;" if the space pulses are too long, it is "spacing bias."

2) *Fortuitous distortion* is nonuniform (random) distortion caused by noise bursts, QRM, mechanical trouble, and similar unpredictable phenomena.

3) *Characteristic distortion* involves timing errors introduced by improper filter design in the demodulator, where the rise time of the filter adversely affects the pulse timing. This is quite typical in certain simple demodulator designs using one 88-mh toroid in each channel filter. However, the printer will accept rather large amounts of distortion, so very few amateurs recognize the fact that their units may have much greater inherent distortion than they believe. Published circuits would indicate that few designers of amateur RTTY demodulators have concerned themselves at all with characteristic distortion.

4) *Systematic waveform distortion* is introduced in the sending setup; an illustration is

contact bounce on the keyboard or tape reader. Many fsk systems using a shift pot and partially saturated diode have this systematic waveform distortion — often so badly that just by listening to the signal it will be immediately noticed. As Merrill Swan, W6AEE, has often said, "It sounds like a wet mop or a man walking through heavy, sticky mud."

There are probably other types of distortion, but these are the ones of most interest to the amateur. In general, with a well-designed fsk system on the transmitter and a properly designed demodulator on the output of the receiver, distortion will be minimal. If it does exist, in all probability the keyboard contacts on the printer or tape reader should be cleaned.

Narrow Shift

The use of narrow (170-Hz) shift offers many advantages over 850, and is used almost exclusively at hf these days. Of course, the transmitter stability and receiver tuning become five times more critical when compared with 850 shift, but with the current high-quality ssb equipment used by many RTTY stations, there is no reason why

spectrum you were wasting before between the mark and space frequencies.

It is probably true that less selective fading occurs on 170 shift, and this upsets some of the more enthusiastic proponents of limiterless "two-tone" demodulators (such as the Mainline TT/L-2 with the limiter switch off), as they like to go looking for signals showing selective fading — instead of folding up shop as previously! If a limiterless unit is *not* used, the reduction in selective fading becomes an advantage.

Maintenance

The Teletype Corporation publishes manuals on each of the machines it has manufactured. The U.S. Government publishes many manuals for the correct maintenance and adjustment of the various machines it has bought. Procurement of these manuals should not be too difficult, and many times they are advertised for sale in *QST* and other publications. Also, it may be possible to induce a local repairman working for the Teletype section of the Bell System to come over on one of his free evenings and "routine" your machine once a year — all it will need with normal ham service. It is also

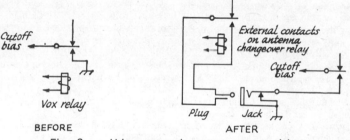

BEFORE   AFTER

Fig. 6 — Using external contacts on coaxial antenna switch to prevent arcing at the antenna contacts. Transmitter cutoff bias line cannot be grounded until antenna-relay contacts have closed.

good operation on 170 shift cannot be realized. For one thing, the signal takes only a fraction of the bandwidth that 850 consumes, and thus conserves space in our already-crowded bands. (On more than one occasion when the hf band was *very* crowded, cw operators have made successful contacts while operating on a frequency *in between* the mark and space radio frequencies of an RTTY station using 850-Hz shift.) However, the real advantage of narrow shift lies in the reduced bandwidth possible in the receiver; optimum selectivity for 170 shift is only 275-300 Hz. As a result, nearly all extraneous signals can be rejected.

An additional benefit not to be overlooked is the absence of Morse stations in or near the same frequency. This is based on physiological aspects of the human ear — basically, it is hard to pick out a Morse signal near a narrow-shift fsk signal in the audio beat-note region that is normally used for cw reception. Thus, if you have been badly bothered by Morse interference on 850 shift it is probable you will no longer be bothered by it when using 170. At the same time, the Morse operator benefits because you allow him to have some of the

possible that after one time with such an experienced person, you will henceforth be able to do ordinary oiling and maintenance yourself. One of the fascinating things about RTTY is working with the machinery, although in a few isolated cases this will not be practical.

As a quick summary, oil all felts which appear to be provided for the purpose; use a flashlight and search out all places where mechanical motion seems evident and give them a drop of oil. More damage can be done on the typical machine by lack of oil then by over-oiling. Some amateurs, at periodic intervals, give their printers a liberal "spraying" with a pump-can oiler, then allow them to drain overnight over a stack of waste newspapers. When finished, be sure to clean off the keyboard contacts, as a thin film of oil is often sprayed on them by the various rotating mechanisms which flip it off.

Ribbons

Ordinary typewriter ribbons can be used, but it seems they only last a short time. Actually, the ribbon does not wear out, but even one roll of paper represents a great deal of printing. As a guess, one double roll of Teletype paper might be roughly the equivalent of a ream of typing paper. So it is not unusual for a ribbon to print quite lightly at the end of a large roll of paper.

The average amateur will make a ribbon last until he can barely read the paper. Actually, the ribbon may still be in excellent condition but simply have used up most of the ink it originally had. Several inexpensive "re-inkers" are on the market for those who would rather do a little work on the ribbon than spend the $1.50 to $2.50 that a new ribbon will cost.

Where To Find Amateur RTTY

Typical RTTY frequencies on the various bands are:

80 meters: 3605 to 3640 kHz
40 meters: 7090 ± 5 kHz
               7140 ± 2-3 kHz (usually local daytime only
20 meters: 14,085 to 14,100 kHz
15 meters: 21,090 ± 5 kHz
10 meters: 28,090 ± 5 KHz
 6 meters: 52.6 MHz
 2 meters: 145.7 MHz

With the exception of vhf, where the activity depends entirely on the local area, most of the operation at night is on 80 meters, while in the afternoon and early evening it is on 20 meters. Occasionally, especially during contests, signals will be heard on 10 and 15 meters. On Sunday mornings a group will be heard around 7140 kHz, where most of the 40-meter activity at one time existed. Since the Europeans are limited to 7100 and below, the suggested frequency for the 40-meter band is now 7090, but signals are heard on the old 7140 frequency nearly as often.

Technique on the Air

When first coming on the air, remember that some operators may be receiving you on automatic copy, and their printers may be producing mostly garble when you send your Morse identification. Thus (although very few operators do this) it would be most kind when beginning a transmission to push the LETTERS key five to ten times to let the other operator's printer get back into operation properly, and *then turn up two new lines of paper*. This will isolate the Morse garble so it will not interfere with quick scanning of the paper. The same thing should be done at the end of the message, just prior to sending the final Morse identification, to leave a little empty space between what you last sent and the Morse. Many operators just quit in the middle of the line and send Morse, forgetting that at the other end garble will result. Also, the carriage may be caused to return to the beginning of the line where it might wipe out the copy already typed, by overprinting.

At the end of each line, the operator should get in the habit of sending

CARRIAGE RETURN
CARRIAGE RETURN
LINE FEED
LETTERS keys

It is amazing how many unfortunate variations of this correct procedure have been invented by various operators. As many machines have now been adapted to various types of nonoverline protection, systems other than this may and often do turn up unwanted extra lines.

Breaking into a Round-Table

On voice and Morse, it is customary to send a quick "Break" and then stand by. On some ssb frequencies this technique merely infuriates those already on the frequency. On RTTY, many operators take the cw key and send "BK" in Morse, but it is seldom they are acknowledged when this occurs, as most teleprinters do a poor job of receiving Morse. A method that normally works quite well is for the station intending to break to ascertain previously that he is on the correct frequency so that when he starts transmitting he will be heard instantly.

When "Henry" has finished his transmission and has just turned it over to "Dusty," Henry must finish his transmission with a Morse identification. The best possible time to throw your carrier on is while Henry is still sending his Morse, as Dusty is already reaching for the switch. If you wait until Henry finishes and has killed his carrier, you probably are already too late to break in.

So while Henry is on Morse, start to transmit and send ten to fifteen LETTERS keys to let Dusty's printer get synchronized once more, as he probably turned it to standby while Henry was on Morse. Then indicate your intention of breaking, follow with your call letters, send your Morse, and then kill the carrier. Dusty will in this case undoubtedly hear you and let you in on the round-table.

Other methods may work, but this is one of the most reliable.

Unshift-on-Space

Some machines, particularly those used by the military and many Europeans, do not have unshift-on-space. (This was discussed to some extent earlier in this chapter.) This means that once you have gone to FIGURES case, the machine will remain in FIGURES case until a LETTERS character is received. This can be a most aggravating nuisance on RTTY, and is certainly most undesirable for ham operating. We only mention it at this time because hams all over the world should realize that most amateurs use machines that *do* have unshift-on-space, so the printer goes back to LETTERS case immediately after hitting the space bar between words. Many Europeans who wish to send: "73 73 73 73" do not send a new FIGURES character after each space bar, and thus are printed by most of us as: "73 UE UE UE." People on both sides of the Atlantic should always remember that a LETTERS key should be sent to return to LETTERS case (that is, don't use the space bar for lower case), and that any time the space bar *is* struck a new FIGURES character will be needed for any subsequent numbers or punctuation.

Abbreviations

On Morse it is quite advantageous to use as many abbreviations as possible, hence the "Q" code and number code (such as "73" and "88"). Unfortunately, many operators seem to think that such abbreviations are suited to RTTY operation as well. RTTY should be conducted just as you would write a personal letter either on a typewriter or in longhand.

Station Identification

As with any other mode of amateur operation, the station transmitting RTTY must identify itself at the beginning and end of each transmission or exchange of transmissions, and at least once every ten minutes. The required identification *must* be made either by voice or by cw. When operation is at hf, identification must therefore be by cw, because voice and RTTY operations are allocated to different sub-bands. Identification via the RTTY keyboard once was, but no longer is, a legal requirement under FCC regulations. Even so, most operators customarily type the call letters of the station they are working, followed by their own call, at the beginning and end of RTTY transmissions. This is done as a courtesy to those who may be monitoring the frequency but are not actively participating in the round-table, and also because it provides a means of identifying the source of the typed material when it is read at some later time.

It is important to remember that identification must be made *at the beginning and end* of each transmission. Stations may frequently be heard failing to meet this requirement, by omitting cw (or voice) identification at the beginning of their transmissions when more than 10 minutes has elapsed. Even though identification is usually made via the RTTY keyboard, the omission of the cw (or voice) identification is in violation of existing regulations.

If afsk is in use, the identification requirement may be met in different ways. The operator may announce his call letters by voice into the micro-phone, he may use code keying to frequency shift the tones, or he may use code keying to turn either tone on and off.

When fsk is in use at hf, many amateurs key the carrier on and off, usually at the mark frequency. A few key at the space frequency. Others use frequency-shift keying in Morse code, at either the full shift or at reduced shift. A few even use reduced shift and key the carrier in the opposite frequency direction from normal RTTY shifting. If cw identification is made by automatic means, the code speed, by regulations, must be no faster than 20 wpm, and if by fsk, should use a shift greater than 100 Hz.

Nearly all receiving operators dislike the Morse code fsk at the full shift, because it resembles RTTY but creates wild activity at the teleprinter. For the same reason, many operators with demod-ulators containing fade-compensating circuitry dis-like the keyed-carrier Morse, but an effective mark-hold circuit will prevent the wild printer activity from occurring with this type of keying. Reduced-shift code keying is favored by a large number of amateurs because it does not actuate the circuitry of most demodulators in the way that either full fsk or cw does. However, reduced shifts are often difficult to read, and there is no amateur standard as to which frequency represents key-up and key-down. Some operators prefer cw identi-fication, primarily because it is easiest to read. Also, with full break-in capability on cw, even though the cw identification at the beginning of a transmission may already have been started, it is possible to hear breaking stations who may be slow in coming on the air.

A method of identifying in Morse which was originated by K1MIA is becoming quite popular. He calls this method "compatible cw identi-fication." The letters-shift and blank keys of the keyboard, when manipulated in the proper se-quence and at the correct interval, make quite readable fsk dots and dashes. Although this keying does actuate the printer, it is an orderly action, and no printing occurs on the paper.

KOX — KEYBOARD-OPERATED TRANSMISSION ON RTTY

Most persons who operate RTTY, at one time or another, have had thoughts about fast-break no-switch RTTY operation. After all, look how easy and effortless it is to use voice-controlled break-in operation (VOX) with ssb transmissions. With such a system, you can simply start typing at the keyboard and the carrier comes on for your transmission. Stop typing and, after an adjustable delay, the carrier goes off and your station returns to the receive mode. Everything is electronically controlled, with no switches to throw. Using fast-break techniques, the half-duplex operation available to subscribers of the commercial landline services can be approached!

Local-Loop Connections

A VOX-type circuit is wired into the local loop. This circuit, by sampling the loop voltage, detects the interruption of the local-loop current when any keyboard key is depressed, or when the TD is started. In turn, a relay is energized. This relay controls the switching of the station between receive and transmit. An adjustable time constant holds the relay closed for a brief period of time after the TD or typing has stopped.

The circuit presented here is intended for use in a system where the keyboard and TD are con-nected in series with a loop power supply and some form of dc load. Fig. 1 shows a typical local-loop arrangement where the TD, keyboard, printer selector magnets, and possibly the keyer section of an RTTY demodulator, are all connected in series. Points A, B, and C, shown in Fig. 1, are for connection of the KOX detector circuit shown in Fig. 2.

In Fig. 1, point C for most installations will be chassis ground or common, and points A and B will

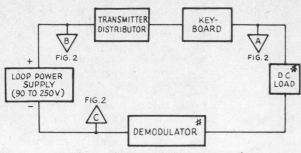

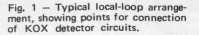

Fig. 1 — Typical local-loop arrangement, showing points for connection of KOX detector circuits.

✱ – *Printer, polar relay winding, current-adjust control, or other load.*

– *Keyer stage or polar relay contacts of demodulator, if not in separate loop.*

correspond to the keyboard-printer junction and the power supply output, respectively. In the Mainline fsk keying system of the TT/L-2 where a polar-output keying signal is developed, point A corresponds to the junction of the printer winding and the keyboard contacts, while points B and C correspond respectively to the positive and negative sides of the 80-μF filter capacitor. In any system where the demodulator keyer is used in the keyboard loop, it is important for proper KOX operation that the printer selector magnets be connected *between* the keyer stage and the keyboard contacts, as shown in Fig. 1.

Referring to Fig. 1, it may be seen that as long as the TD and keyboard contacts remain closed, the power-supply voltage is presented at Point A, the input of the KOX detector circuit. When either a perforated tape or typing is started, the contacts open, and the voltage at point A momentarily drops to zero.

Detector Circuit

Fig. 2 shows the KOX detector circuit. The power requirement is 12 volts dc at 5 mA. Point A is the sampled voltage input. Satisfactory operation will result with any dc level above 12 volts applied at this point. Point C represents the ground or common connection.

R1 and R2 divide down the loop voltage. Q1 acts as a switch, controlled by the voltage at Point A, and turns Q2 on or off. The holding time is determined by C1 and R4. With the circuit values shown, the "dropout" delays may be adjusted from about 1/2 to 4 seconds. Different supply voltages have some effect on the operational ranges. Depending on your typing speed and your particular circuit requirements, you may wish to use different holding times. Larger values for C1 may be used for longer holding times.

Adjustments

The only "adjustment" required is to select the final value for R1. The value should be found experimentally, and will depend upon the amount of loop supply voltage and how well it is filtered. Connect a milliameter to read the current through the coil of K1 (clip the meter leads across S1, leaving the switch open). With only the KOX 12-volt power supply energized, the current should be more than sufficient to close the relay — a few milliamperes. Now temporarily connect a jumper lead across R3, shorting it out, and again note the relay current. This current should be less than that required to hold the relay closed, something like 0.5 mA. If more than this amount of current is read, the value of R5 should be changed to 1

Fig. 2 — KOX detector circuit. Capacitances are in microfarads (μF); resistances are in ohms, k = 1000, M = megohms. All fixed resistors are 1/2 watt.
C1 — Electrolytic.
CR1 — Any small-signal silicon diode.
K1 — Sensitive relay, 1000-ohm, spst contacts (Sigma 48RO-1000G/SIL or equiv.).

Q1 — Silicon pnp audio or rf transistor (Motorola MPS6516 or HEP 57 or equiv.).
Q2 — Silicon npn audio or rf transistor (Motorola MPS3394 or HEP 50 or equiv.).
R1 — See text.
R2, R3, R5 — For text reference.
R4 — 50,000-ohm linear-taper control, low wattage.
S1 — Spst toggle.

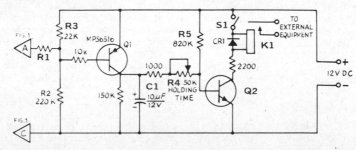

megohm. Now with the jumper removed, energize the loop power supply, and select the highest common value for R1 which provides approximately the same current as with R3 shorted out. For well-filtered loop supplies of 50 to 250 volts, values between 1.5 and 10 megohms will be required; lower values will be needed for lighter filtering. The final value isn't at all critical, but shouldn't be less than a half megohm per hundred volts of loop supply voltage.

Once the value for R1 has been determined, tap the LETTERS key of the keyboard one time. The relay should close for a short period of time, and then open. The time the relay remains closed should be adjustable with R4.

Operation

When you type, there is some slight delay on pull-in of the relay, so the first character you type may come out garbled on the receiving end. The use of two LETTERS functions at the beginning of each transmission is suggested, the first to turn the carrier on, and the second to assure that the receiving printer is in a position to type letters instead of figures.

For fast-break operation, there is no real need to use carriage returns, line feeds, or cw identification between short transmissions. (Of course you must identify your station every ten minutes.) When you finish your comment or question, even if right in the middle of a line, just type BK, or simply stop typing, and let the other fellow continue from there to the end of the line.

Soon after this circuit is incorporated, you'll discover that there are times when it is undesirable to have fully automatic operation. One of these times is when you are "reading the mail" on a round-table, with all of your station equipment "fired up" and tuned to zero beat. Should you then decide to make a carriage return with a few line feeds locally, your carrier plopping right in the midst of the round-table probably won't be appreciated. Opening S1 will disable the "automatic" circuitry, and perhaps save you an embarrassing moment.

A SIMPLE CW IDENTIFIER

Cw identification of hf amateur RTTY transmissions, as required by FCC, becomes a simple matter when an automatic cw identifier is used. Such a scheme can be implemented mechanically with a teleprinter transmitter-distributor, or TD, and perforated RTTY tape, and the result is the generation of perfectly proportioned Morse code. A simple modification to the TD is required, but the modification can be completely removed in a few minutes time. It has no effect on normal use of the TD for RTTY operation. See Fig. 3.

The scheme requires the addition of a polar relay, the contacts of which do the actual cw keying. (The relay can be one relegated to the junk box after changing to electronic keying, or might be acquired through surplus channels for a few dollars — see *QST* Ham-Ads.) One winding of the relay is used to close its keying contacts upon command from the TD, starting a dot or a dash element. The second winding of the relay, upon a separate command from the TD, opens the contacts and ends the Morse code element. The duration of the dots or dashes is controlled by altering the times between turn-on and turn-off commands, through appropriate RTTY letter combinations on the tape.

In operation for cw keying by this method, one teleprinter character (163 milliseconds in duration for a 60-wpm TD) is used for a Morse dot and its succeeding space. Thus, a string of dots will occur at the rate of 6.13 per second. A dash and its succeeding space is equal in duration to two teleprinter characters, so a string of dashes will occur at the rate of slightly more than three per second. One can determine the code speed by multiplying 2.4 times the number of free-running dots per second, and for a 60 wpm TD this equates to a maximum cw keying rate of 14.7 wpm. For a TD geared at 75 speed, the maximum code speed in 18.4 wpm, and 24.0 wpm for a 100-speed TD. Of course by allowing more time between turn-on and turn-off commands or using long spaces between cw letters, slower cw speeds can be sent.

Fig. 3 — The transmitter-distributor and polar relay interconnected for keying Morse code from teleprinter tape. Octal socket and plug fittings on the interconnecting cable facilitate easy separation. Should it be desired to remove the relay from the circuit, a plug with appropriately jumpered pins restores the connections required for RTTY operation of the TD.

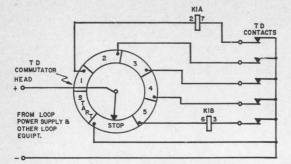

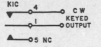

Fig. 4 — Typical polar keying relay installation with a Teletype Corp. model 14 transmitter-distributor. Satisfactory operation of the relay will result with loop currents ranging from 60 mA down to 2 or 3 mA, depending on how well the relay is adjusted. See text regarding connection polarity of relay windings. K1 — Polar relay, Western Electric 255A or 314A or equivalent (see *QST* Ham-Ads).

Installation

Fig. 4 shows a typical wiring diagram for installing the relay. The contact-closing winding of the relay is placed in series with the TD commutator segment for the first selector pulse. As a perforated tape is played through the TD, any character containing a mark in the first selector pulse position will energize this winding, which will close the keying contacts. Because of the nature of the polar relay, the contacts will stay closed even after the current through this winding is removed. They will remain closed either until a current of the opposite polarity is passed through this winding, or until a current of the proper polarity is passed through the second winding. In effect, the relay latches itself closed.

The contact-opening winding of the relay is placed in series with either the fourth or the fifth selector-pulse commutator segment, at the operator's preference. The fifth position gives almost a perfect 1:1 dot-to-space ratio for 60-, 75- or 100-wpm TDs (dot ON time equals 54 percent), but for Western Union and other TDs set for 65 wpm the fourth position might give a more pleasing weighting.

Be sure to observe the correct polarity for connecting the relay windings. If either winding is reversed, no keying will result. If both windings or the polarity of the power supply voltage is reversed, contacts 1 and 4 of the relay will close during the "key up" period, but to correct this situation it might be easier merely to use contacts

Fig. 5 — Teleprinter tape perforated for the cw message QST DE W1AW. A blank separates the cw letters; three blanks separate the words.

1 and 5 of the relay for the cw keying, rather than to rewire the two windings or to change the power supply connections.

Operation

To prepare a tape for transmission of cw, simply punch the teleprinter letter "B" for each dot and punch "UM" for each dash. Although other characters will also yield the desired results, the Bs and UMs have short and long sounds, making it convenient to say "B UM B" to yourself when you might ordinarily say "dit dah dit" for the cw letter R, for example. Use either a blank or a space-bar function for spacing between cw letters and use three blanks between cw words. These spacings will result in a perfect 1:3:7 ratio for element, letter, and word spacing. Use five spaces for the separation of paragraphs or the equivalent.

A tape punched for the cw identification QST DE W1AW would read like this, occupying about five inches of perforated tape: UMUMUMBUM BBB UM UMBB B BUMUM BUMUMUMUM BUM BUMUM. In the above example, spaces are shown where blanks may be used while perforating the tape. Fig. 5 shows a tape punched for this cw message.

Probably the simplest method of sending slower than the maximum code speed is to use the same pattern as above for keying individual cw letters, and to use a greater number of blanks for spacing between letters and words. Using this idea, 8 blanks between cw letters and 24 blanks between cw words results in an overall code speed with a 60-speed TD of 5 wpm (although the individual letters are still sent at the maximum rate). To send properly proportioned code at a lower speed, with a 60-speed TD, punching "UM" followed by a blank for a Morse dot, "U Blank Blank Blank M" followed by a blank for a dash, and using 3 additional blanks for cw letter spacing or 9 additional blanks for word spacing will result in a code speed of 4.9 wpm with a 51.3-percent dot-to-space ratio. Although we did not try the idea, faster speeds might be obtained with a 60-wpm TD by an arrangement of two polar relays connected to various commutator segments of the TD and with the relay keying contacts placed in parallel.

One thing is important if your fsk input is permanently wired into the transmitter — the frequency-shift keying must be disabled while playing the cw tape! Otherwise you will end up with simultaneous A1 and F1 emission, likely an invitation to hear from an FCC monitoring station.

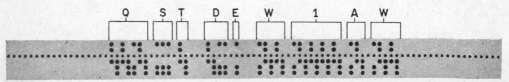

HANDLING TRAFFIC BY RADIOTELETYPE

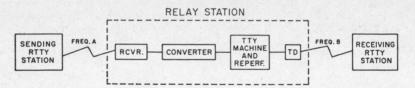

Fig. 1 — One of the advantages of RTTY is its ability to relay automatically. This diagram shows how a properly equipped RTTY station can be used to relay by using the received signal to operate the teletypewriter and reperforator to punch a tape containing the incoming message which is then fed into the transmitter-distributor for transmission to the destination station.

RTTY is becoming more involved in handling record traffic, a use to which this mode is admirably suited. While basic message forms and procedures apply to RTTY just as they do to voice and cw, there are many special procedures used in RTTY. Most of them arise from the fact that this mode automatically converts the intelligence from signal to paper. No intermediate mental conversion is needed, as in other modes.

This doesn't mean, of course, that handling traffic by RTTY does not require one to use his head. On the contrary, the use of a proper and standard procedure is just as important here as it is with other modes — and as in other modes, a standard form is required. The differences arise mainly in having the knowledge and skill to operate a teletypewriter (quite a bit different from an ordinary typewriter, as we shall see) so that messages transmitted will, when printed automatically at the other end, be identical with messages received by any other mode, and be readily transferrable from one mode to another.

RTTY Message Handling

RTTY is best employed when there is a considerable volume of traffic between two points, preferably between two stations. Given the stack of traffic at one point and the capability of transmitting it at a steady 60, 75, or 100 wpm speed to the other point, then there are two principal problems: first, collecting it at the transmitting point and second, distributing it from the receiving point. Usually, some degree of versatility will be required on the part of operators at both ends in utilizing modes other than RTTY both in collecting and distributing.

Assuming the availability of traffic at both ends, a number of arrangements can be made for handling it. One method is automatic relaying, in which an incoming signal actuates a tape perforator. The tape feeds into the TD which actuates a transmitter on a different frequency and relays the traffic to another point within seconds after being received. See Fig. 1. Such a setup could be used, for example, on a transcontinental circuit with the relay half way between, when direct reception between transmitting and receiving points is not good enough; or, if necessary, a number of such relays could be utilized with the loss in time being only the few seconds it takes between reperforation and retransmission multiplied by the number of relays.

Although "break-in" is not normally feasible on RTTY, a variation of it can be made available, given the equipment, by establishment of "dual contact" between stations, one by RTTY and another by phone or cw. The phone or cw channel can then be used to ask for fills or tape reruns in case garbling is so bad that this becomes desirable. Thus, while the tape is going through and the receiving printer is chattering away, the two operators can discuss the quality of reception and have the tape stopped in case of interference or fading disruptions. Then part of it can be rerun. This is even better than cw break-in, but it does require separate transmitter, receiver and antenna facilities.

"Duplex" can also be used, if you have the equipment and enough separation, either in frequency or physical distance or both, between your receiver and transmitter. This consists of sending and receiving at the same time and will require two machines at each location. Naturally, enough separation will have to be present to prevent your transmitted signal from blocking the one you are trying to receive. Where a circuit is so full that there is necessity for both sending and receiving at all times, a "duplex" circuit can handle twice as much traffic as a "simplex" one.

There are many other variations used in commercial and military practice that are possible also on amateur circuits, but generally speaking amateurs do not at present possess the equipment or the facilities, or even the need, to put them to use.

RTTY Traffic Nets

At present there are not a great many RTTY traffic nets, but there will likely be more of them in the future as use of the mode increases, as it seems destined to with more machines becoming available to amateurs. Consequently, all we have to go on for net procedure on RTTY are, first, the procedure used in amateur nets using cw and phone, second, the procedure used in commercial and military RTTY circuits, and third, the procedure used by those few amateur RTTY circuits which do exist. Out of this, we have come up with an RTTY procedure, leaning most heavily on the third of the three factors mentioned.

The NCS opens the net with a call-up and test tape which he runs for about three minutes; such tape might print the following: CQ CQ CQ RATTS NET DE W6CAL W6CAL W6CAL QND QND QNZ QNZ . . . This is followed by about thirty seconds of uninterrupted carrier on the "mark" frequency for zero beat purposes. This is very important on RTTY because the tuning tolerance is considerably less than other modes received by ear.

Then comes the call-up. This may vary considerably from net to net, but one should bear in mind that its purpose it to gather the clan and to instruct them on reporting procedures as briefly as possible. If the net is close-knit and there are not likely to be visitors who don't know the procedure, the call-up can be kept very short, such as: CQ CQ RATTS NET DE W6CAL QNI QNI KKK. If it is an "open" net, as most are, brief instructions such as the following may be included: CQ CQ CQ RATTS NET DE W6CAL W6CAL RTTY STATIONS ARE INVITED TO QNI FOR TRAFFIC AND BULLETINS ON THIS NET OPERATING AT 0400 GMT MONDAY THURSDAY AND FRIDAY. MESSAGES SHOULD BE LISTED BY DESTINATION AND PRECEDENCE AND PRETAPED FOR IMMEDIATE TRANSMISSION IF POSSIBLE. TRAFFIC WILL BE DISTRIBUTED ON THIS NET OR RELAYED VIA THE ARRL NATIONAL TRAFFIC SYSTEM. CQ RATTS NET DE W6CAL QNI QNI KKK.

Stations then check in and list their traffic, much the same as in a cw net. For example: W6CAL W6CAL DE K6DYX K6DYX QNI MONTEREY QTC. . . . When all stations appear to be checked in, NCS directs stations with traffic when and on what frequency to transmit it. Usually the net frequency is used, but when there is to be an exchange of several messages, or a batch, they are directed to QNY. (Incidentally, use of Q signals and other cw abbreviations is encouraged on RTTY nets.) NCS identifies by sending his call by cw (not required to send the other stations's call) at least once every ten minutes; otherwise identification exchanges include both his call and that of the station he is calling or in contact with.

With RTTY, as with phone, use of a "squelch" on the receiver is practical, and thus a pre-set frequency may be used for continuous monitoring. On vhf, RTTY setups use audio frequency shift keying (afsk) in which a steady carrier is modulated by an audio tone which shifts its audio frequency just as fsk shifts its radio frequency. Thus a receiver on "squelch" can be activated by the carrier, which can also, with an "auto-start" system, actuate the teletype machine so that any station may transmit messages to other stations even though no operator is present at the latter. Suffice it to say that such a setup is readily feasible with RTTY, especially at vhf, and is actually in use by many stations, presenting an advantage definitely not available by any other mode. On some portions of the vhf amateur spectrum, the use of "intercom" communication with "autostart" is common. This type of setup is not really a net and has no NCS until or unless traffic becomes heavy, at which time a station may assume the role of NCS until things quiet down, after which monitoring with squelched receivers can continue.

RTTY Message Format

There are several differences between message formats and transmission procedures using the three principal modes of emission – cw, voice and RTTY. On phone and cw, what is actually transmitted doesn't always appear on the copy – for example, the many procedural signs (prosigns) used on cw and the pro-words used on phone. On RTTY, use of signs and symbols that do not appear on the printed page are restricted to what is available on the keyboard. Every combination of teleprinter pulses is used for some motion of the teletypewriter carriage, although some of them are not printing motions – for example, space, line feed, carriage return, and the shifts for letters and figures. Nearly every other pulse combination results in a printed letter or figure on the page. The problem is to adapt the format generally used by RTTY to use by other modes, and this in turn means the elimination of prosigns that would not be transmitted on cw or phone. So any consideration of RTTY message format should meet the following requirements:

(1) Contain all the elements of the standard ARRL format.

(2) Be readily transferrable to phone or cw with a minimum of required changes.

(3) Provide uniformity and a practical degree of ease in composition.

(4) Allow the receiving and relaying operators to double check the information which is most critical to accurate delivery.

(5) Resist the effects of poor conditions, atmospherics and QRM.

(6) Employ techniques which are the least susceptible to variations in machines and random errors.

(7) Provide adequate spacing on tape between messages sent manually or from tape to allow the separation of messages recorded on reperforated tape.

(8) Use the minimum practical number of lines on the page so the receiving operator will not have to chase messages down the back of his machine to detect errors – especially when a large volume of traffic is being handled.

(9) Provide adequate, but not excessive, separation between messages on the page for east of reading.

The following sample best meets all the requirements involved:

RYRYRYRYRYRYRYRYRY . . . .

(Just a short length of test tape so receiving operator can tune you in for optimum copy, required only before the first message.

NR 28 R W6CAL CK 25 NORTH HOLLYWOOD
CF 0157Z NOV 1
TO JOHN J BROWN 1234 TEMPLE ST EL
CAMPO CF TEL 987-6543
BT
DID YOU ASK HOW TO INCREASE TELE-
 PRINTER SKILL QUERY THE
BEST WAY IS REGULAR TOUCH TYPING
 PRACTICE ON LOCAL LOOP
AND ON AIR X REGARDS
BT
SGD AVERY JONES
CFM BROWN 1234 TEMPLE ST 987-6543
AVERY JONES ARAR

Note that the preamble is identical to that which would be copied by cw. On cw, the CK is sometimes omitted, but it can be sent, so no harm in its appearing on the TTY printer.

In the address, we balked at the inclusion of the word TO because we thought there was no RTTY reason why this should be included when we discourage it on cw and do not write it down on phone. However, on RTTY this short word is a tipoff in case the line-feed or carriage-return function is lost, enabling the receiving operator to identify the beginning of the address or perhaps even to line-feed or carriage-return manually before the address actually starts, if he is on his toes. Teletypers transferring an RTTY message to a cw circuit will just have to remember not to send the TO when transmitting the message.

The necessity for spacing between the parts of the address poses a problem. Considering everything, if you agree that such separation is necessary, the easiest, quickest, most economical way to indicate it on RTTY is to send an extra letter space.

Two CR, one LF and one LTRS is the standard method of changing lines; the last provides time for a sluggish machine, or one that "bounces" at the left hand margin, to come to rest before the printing pulses start.

The message should be preceded by not less than ten LTRS, so it is easy to read between messages on reperforated tape and still leave an adequate leader for insertion in a TD. This advances the tape but makes no printed symbol on the page.

Don't send space to unshift the receiving machine after sending numbers, because the receiving machine may not be set up that way; send LTRS to unshift.

It is customary on phone and cw to spell out all punctuation, except to use STOP or X for a period and QUERY for a question mark. Teletypers often use different abbreviations, such as PD for a period, CMA or CMM for a comma, CLN for colon, PRN for parentheses, etc., per military usage. We think PD is an especially bad abbreviation because about 50% of cw operators, not being used to it, copy it as AND. STOP has its disadvantages, too. We think the best compromise is X. As for other punctuation, in the text or elsewhere, avoid it wherever possible. Nine times out of ten, no punctuation is necessary except a period (X) now and then. Originators please cooperate! This is important! Whatever the originator uses for punctuation is carried through in the same form to delivery. Standardization on this has to be effected by the originator.

Note that the text contains ten words to a line, with an extra space between the fifth and sixth words. This makes it easy to "check the check" to be sure it is correct, and even though it might waste a line here and there, in general we feel it is worthwhile. When ten words exceeds one line we carry over to the next line, indenting five spaces. Luckily, this doesn't happen often.

The signature line begins with SGD, for the same reason that we begin the address line with TO. It is not sent (neither is SIG) when transferred to a cw circuit.

After the signature line on RTTY comes another line not usually included by other modes. Certain types of copy are more subject to error caused by sudden noise or fading than others. In common words and text it is often possible to fill this in or correct it if printed wrong, but unusual names or numbers can easily be garbled on RTTY, so teletypers use a CFM line after the signature line to repeat such things as unusual names, street numbers or addresses, telephone numbers, etc., in any part of the message, in the order in which they were sent. Just make sure the CFM line doesn't change something that was right the first time!

Since much traffic on RTTY is reperforated as it is received (this makes relaying very simple and convenient), the making of changes because of improper format or procedure is decidedly inconvenient. Therefore, frequently an operator will add an "operator's note" manually after the CFM line to point out changes that should be made in the message prior to deliver – for example, a correction of the check, separation of parts of the address, anything else in the message that needs changing before delivery. "Operator's notes" are a pain in the neck on phone and cw. They are more convenient on RTTY where they can be printed with the message without operator exasperation. Where an operator's note becomes lengthy or cumbersome, let's throw out the reperforation and perforate a new tape; but don't forget, relaying operators *never* make changes in message content, only in form if it is incorrect.

After the AR, send two carriage returns and four line feeds to leave space between messages. Then send at least ten LTRS, so there will be space at the end of the reperforated tape. If another message follows send ten more LTRS before starting it, so the tape for this one can have an adequate leader. More than four line spaces separation between messages is a waste of paper.

When handling a high volume of traffic, sending five messages at a time is about right. The receiving operator can lift the paper for about that length to scan what has been received; more than that and he has to crawl over the back of his machine.

FUN WITH TAPE

Many RTTYers enjoy exchanging special features that are peculiar to tape-sent transmissions. One of the most compelling reasons for owning a reperforator is the possibility of copying these tapes, and for owning a tape reader, of playing them.

For example, by proper manipulation, Ralph Larsson, Chief of the Equipment Exhibits Department of the Teletype Corporation, has made numerous portraits of various important executives, including Presidents Eisenhower, Kennedy and Johnson. As tapes of this type become available to various amateurs, a popular activity is demonstrating this enjoyable aspect of RTTY to visiting firemen by asking the other operator to send any pictures he may have on tape.

At Christmas time various interesting pictures are exchanged by the more ambitious individuals. Nearly as interesting and just as enjoyable is playing "Jingle Bells" by tapes. Here the timing between the bell characters is all-important. Clever individuals have been able not only to get a tape that taps out "Jingle Bells" in authentic rhythm, but at the same time writes the words "MERRY

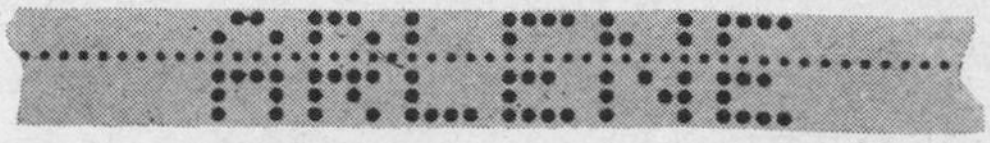

Fig. 1 — Punching the actual characters of the alphabet can be done by using a code such as the one given in Table I.

CHRISTMAS AND A HAPPY NEW YEAR TO ALL."

Others enjoy typing special QSL cards on tape for later transmission. Some of these represent hours of hard work and are most enjoyable to receive.

"Brag Tapes"

Most operators owning tape equipment like to type up precut tapes telling of the station's equipment. These are very interesting, and some of the fellows exhibit a real sense of humor. A lot can be discovered about the person's preferences in equipment in this manner, and quite often some of the tapes include information on the operator's occupation, family and other interests.

Fun with Tape Lettering

Table I is a chart for typing various letters of the alphabet onto perforated tape. This makes the tape print garble if run through a tape reader, but if held up to the light it looks quite readable. See Fig. 1. You could cut such a tape and send it, assuring the other operator that although it will garble badly on the printer, it will be quite unique when scanned visually after being copied on a reperforator or retyped on his perforator. Best results are obtained if the reperforator in use punches the holes cleanly (chad tape). With chadless perforations, a small "lid" is left over each hole, making the alphabetic characters nearly impossible to read.

RTTY Art*

Creating RTTY art, such as that shown in Figs. 2 and 3, is a great deal easier than you might think. There is much basic art work available from which RTTY pictures may be made. Comic strips, magazines, newspapers, gatefolds, photographs and copies of works of art may all serve as bases for pictures. While these may not be the right size, an inexpensive child's pantograph or some types of Xerox machines may be used to enlarge or reduce them. A portrait of Washington was made from the etching on the dollar bill. Also, if you have a little sketching talent, that will help (or enlist the help of your wife and friends). Be sure to keep your left and right margin distances in mind when sizing your art and in selecting portions of large basic material. Remember that the width limits of most teleprinters will permit a picture of only a little over seven inches wide.

Table I	
A	VSSV
B	LTRS YYR
C	CZZR
D	LTRS ZZC
E	LTRS YYZ
F	LTRS SSE
G	CZBR CARRIAGE-RETURN
H	LTRS SPACE SPACE LTRS
I	ZZ LTRS ZZ
J	CARRIAGE-RETURN TTK
K	LTRS SPACE RZ
L	LTRS TTT
M	LTRS LINE-FEED SPACE LINE FEED LTRS
N	LTRS LINE-FEED SPACE CARRIAGE-RETURN LTRS
O	CZZC
P	VSSI
Q	CZBCT
R	LTRS SFP (OR VSFP)
S	LYYD
T	EE LTRS EE
U	KTTK
V	ANTNA
W	LTRS CARRIAGE-RETURN SPACE CARRIAGE-RETURN LTRS
X	ZR SPACE RZ
Y	E LINE-FEED M LINE-FEED E
Z	ZBYWZ

1	L LTRS T	6	CYYN
2	BYYL	7	ZDSA
3	ZYYC	8	FIGS YY FIGS
4	U SPACE SPACE LTRS	9	LINE-FEED YYC
5	JWWF	Ø	ECZYBCT

---

* By Don Royer, WA6PIR. Reprinted by permission from *RTTY Journal*, September, 1974.

After selecting your subject and sizing the art work, run about four feet of paper from your printer. Use the center portion and carefully tape or glue the drawing or photo to the paper. Trim the edges to the same width as your paper. Now remove the paper stock from your printer and insert the four-foot sheet whereby the sketch is presented to you as it rolls over the platen. Carefully align the edges of the paper on the platen. Use your line feed to bring the top of the sketch into view. You are now ready to type the first run of your proposed picture directly upon the sketch, punching a tape as you go.

A small selection of characters is all that is needed to produce either outlined or shaded pictures. Study the letters and other characters to learn their individual densities. For example, the M and W are the darkest, followed by the H or X and then by the I. Thereafter, you can use the upshifted characters such as the : or ; followed by the ” or − or , and the like, depending upon where you want the print to fall. In this way, you may add the shading that you desire or leave certain areas blank like this:

MMHMHHIHII:I::.:.’. .’.::I:IIHIHHMHMM
going from dark to light and back to dark again. Due to their shape, you may also desire to use the V, A, F or L at the beginning and ends of dark areas to obtain smooth edge lines and perhaps accompanied by an apostrophe or period. With a little practice, you will be able to tell just where any character will strike the paper. Do leave blank or white areas whenever possible and don't try to fill the entire line with characters since this is a black and white (we hope you have white paper) picture and you must rely upon the contrast to produce the desired detail. Continue the typing process over the entire sketch.

Now remove the sketch from your printer and reinsert your paper stock. Play out the tape you have made. You will probably be pleasantly surprised. Use a red pen to indicate on the print where additions, corrections and any changes are to be made. Rerun the tape (having folded the marked-up print and following it line-by-line using the paper holder and line guide on the printer) to make corrections, punching a new tape at the same time. In most instances, a good picture may be made with a series of five or six correction tapes.

When typing on the sketch, it helps to have a strong light directed onto the sketch in your machine. This is particularly true if the contrast of the sketch is poor, as may be in color photos. Also, since you will be unable to see the part of the sketch below the ribbon, a pencil may be used to outline the areas where the shading will change from one density to another. You may thus be able to produce a more complete picture the first time through. Some of the RTTY artists have found that it helps to make Xerox prints of the original sketches or photos and to use those for their art work, as this eliminates some shading and provides a black and white format from which to work.

Keep the detail of the original art work as large as you can and don't be afraid to experiment with different letters and techniques. Do clean up your

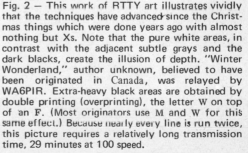

Fig. 2 — This work of RTTY art illustrates vividly that the techniques have advanced since the Christmas things which were done years ago with almost nothing but Xs. Note that the pure white areas, in contrast with the adjacent subtle grays and the dark blacks, create the illusion of depth. "Winter Wonderland," author unknown, believed to have been originated in Canada, was relayed by WA6PIR. Extra-heavy black areas are obtained by double printing (overprinting), the letter W on top of an F. (Most originators use M and W for this same effect.) Because nearly every line is run twice, this picture requires a relatively long transmission time, 29 minutes at 100 speed.

HARRY J. DANNALS, W2TUK

PRESIDENT, AMERICAN RADIO RELAY LEAGUE

Fig. 3 — RTTY portrait of Harry J. Dannals, W2TUK, President, American Radio Relay League. This portrait was originated by John Sheetz, K2AGI, of Murray Hill, N.J., and was presented to President Dannals at the ARRL National Convention in July, 1974.

tapes. This may be done during the first run-through after the typing to remove any extra characters that crept in by mistake. To give you some idea of the time required to complete the pics, about 20 hours is needed for one that runs 30 minutes or so. Most of this will be in making the corrections and in rerunning the tape. Even after they are apparently finished, hang your creation across the room to see how it looks from a distance and then make a final tape with the finishing touches, increasing or decreasing contrast in certain areas and cleaning up edge lines. Time and patience!!

As many modern machines have nonoverline features, it is generally well to avoid overline printing. Good, nonoverlined pics may be made by using the various character densities to create desired contrast. Stay within a 72-character line. Start and end the tape with a series of LTRS or blanks, a single carriage return and about ten line feeds. Keep in mind those machines which downshift on space as well as those which do not. If you are upshifted, and then space and wish another upshifted character, put in another FIGS character. Of course, the same applies when you want a letter following a space after an upshifted character and another LTRS must be added. At the start of each line, use one carriage return, the line feed and one LTRS unless the first character of that line is upshifted and requires a FIGS.

Again, make your tapes as short as possible by taking out any unneeded characters, extra LTRS, FIGS followed by LTRS and things like extra spaces or LTRS at the end of a line. Above all, be sure to put your credit line at the end, with the hope that others will follow your lead and keep it there.

There is one further situation you may wish to consider. An increasing number of machines do not use the standard communications keyboard. On these machines, the apostrophe and the bell are switched from the more normal arrangement of the apostrophe over the "J" and the bell over the "S." To enable the pictures to be printed on either machine, it is only necessary to use both of these characters. That is, every time you use an apostrophe follow it immediately with a bell. This, of course, will produce a lot of bell ringing during reception but will enable full and accurate print on either type of keyboard arrangement. Most of the commercially available picture tapes are formatted in the suggested manner.

If you make or obtain pictures that are in several panels, it is very important that your paper is very tight on your platen. Otherwise, the panels will not line up. In putting these panels together, trim the border from the left edge of the second panel and carefully align it with the appropriate edge of the first panel. You may have to compensate if the print is off a bit. The panels may be secured together with plastic tape or, better yet, with a small amount of white glue. For wall display purposes, if your paper is thin, the overlapped areas may be hidden by backing the finished print with blank paper.

So if RTTY pictures excite your imagination, how about trying your hand at making at least one? You may find some hidden talent.

Space Communication

Exciting communications possibilities are afforded through the use of amateur satellites. They function much in the same way as terrestrial repeaters, to relay signals over greater distances than normally feasible. With satellites, the area is usually international in scope. Thus, DX communication on frequencies unable to support ionospheric propagation is possible.

Three amateur communications satellites have been orbited to date. Oscar 3, used in early 1965, was a 144-MHz in-band repeater; Oscar 4, launched in late 1965, repeated 144-MHz signals in the 420-MHz band; Oscar 6, launched in October, 1972, is a long-lifetime translator, repeating 144-MHz signals in the 28-MHz band. Oscars 1, 2, and 5 were beacon satellites for scientific and training purposes.

Current amateur plans for satellite systems involve the use of the 28-, 144-, and 420-MHz bands. Crossband repeaters are favored. Thus, expected combinations might be: 144 uplink, 28 downlink; 420 uplink, 144 downlink; or 144 uplink, 420 downlink. There is a trend toward designing amateur satellites with higher system gains (i.e., higher sensitivity and greater output). The objective is to permit the use of these satellites by average-sized amateur ground stations. Future satellite lifetimes of one year or more can be expected. Effort will be made for successive satellites to utilize similar frequency combinations to alleviate the need for equipment changes in ground stations.

A principal factor in determining how far one can communicate via a particular satellite is the orbit. Higher altitude orbits put the satellite within line-of-sight of greater areas of the earth. Fig. 1 can be used to determine your map range for a satellite according to its altitude. For example, a satellite at 910 miles would give a map range of 2450 miles. For illustration, draw on a map a circle centered on your location with a radius equal to the map range. Each time the satellite is directly over any point within this circle, you will be able to use it for communication. Contact can be made with any other station having the satellite within its range at the same time. This is shown in Fig. 2. Thus, the maximum map distance for communication would be about two times your map range.

The time duration for which a satellite will be within your range depends on two factors: the satellite's altitude and the distance between the subsatellite point (the point on the earth directly below the satellite) and your station. Higher altitude orbits increase the size of your range or acquisition circle, thus providing longer exposure to the satellite. Also, the longest duration for any given altitude will occur on orbits which pass directly over the station location. For example, a satellite in a 1000-mile orbit would be line-of-sight to a ground station for about 25 minutes on an overhead pass. At a map range of 1000 miles the duration would be 20 minutes, and at 2000 miles, the availability would be about 10 minutes.

Conventional transceiver-type operation may offer some problems with satellites because of the Doppler phenomenon. Separate frequency control of the ground station's transmitter and receiver is desirable. (In some cases an "incremental tuning" feature on a transceiver will suffice.) Doppler is a frequency-shifting effect resulting from the motion

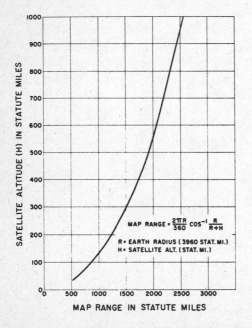

$$\text{MAP RANGE} = \frac{2\pi R}{360} \cos^{-1} \frac{R}{R+H}$$

R = EARTH RADIUS (3960 STAT. MI.)
H = SATELLITE ALT. (STAT. MI.)

MAP RANGE IN STATUTE MILES

Fig. 1 — Satellite altitude above earth versus ground station map range (statute miles).

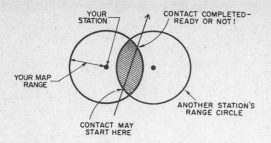

Fig. 2 — Satellite passes through the range of two stations, enabling contact.

of the satellite. It is a function of the transmitting frequency and the velocity of the satellite relative to the observing station. (Velocity is further a function of satellite's altitude.) Fig. 3 compares Doppler shifts for frequencies up to 500 MHz for satellites in 200- and 1000-statute-mile orbits. The reason why Doppler shift requires a special consideration with transceiver operation is because two stations in contact would go through a series of frequency compensations, thus "walking" themselves across (and perhaps out of) the band! The frequency of a satellite moving toward a ground station appears higher than the actual satellite transmitter frequency. It drops as the satellite nears the ground station. At the exact point of closest approach, the observed frequency will be the same as the true frequency. Past this point, the satellite's signal will continue to drop lower in frequency as the satellite moves away.

There are two types of repeaters likely to be employed in future amateur satellites. A channelized repeater for fm would operate much like the ground-based fm repeaters used by amateurs; one station could use a channel at a time. Several contacts could be accommodated by a multi-channel satellite. The other approach is called a frequency translator. It receives a segment of one band, say 100 kHz at 144 MHz, and retransmits the segment on another band, say 28 MHz. With a frequency translator, as many contacts as can be accommodated by the translator's bandwidth can take place simultaneously, and all modes can be used. Doppler shift from the fm repeater would be the same as expected for a transmitter on its downlink frequency. With a translator, however, the amount of Doppler shift is influenced by both the up- and downlinks. By employing a frequency inversion technique in the satellite's design, these amounts of Doppler will subtract; the resulting shift is then found from Fig. 3 by using the frequency difference between up- and downlinks.

An aid to satellite communication is to monitor your own downlink signal coming from the satellite, while you are transmitting. This permits you to avoid interference from other stations, to compensate, where appropriate, for Doppler shift, and to adjust your transmitter power and antenna direction for maximum efficiency in sharing the satellite's output.

EQUIPMENT REQUIRED FOR SATELLITE COMMUNICATION VIA AMSAT-OSCAR C

Your first hurdle is in getting a signal on 2 meters. The satellite receives signals between 145.9 and 146.0 MHz and retransmits them in the segment 29.45 to 29.55 MHz. Any mode appearing within the 2-meter input passband will be repeated, but cw and ssb offer the most efficient use of Oscar. You should aim for about 100 watts of effective radiated power (erp). This can be achieved with 10 watts into a 10-dB antenna, 100 watts into a nondirectional antenna, or some such combination.

Transmitting Converters

An expedient way of getting your signal on 2 meters is through use of a transmitting converter. Of course, a receiving converter is not needed for AOC operation, but should be included if you anticipate direct two-meter operation, also. Most 2-meter "transverters" can be used with any 14- or 28-MHz exciter. To minimize exciter interference in your own receiver with Oscar's 10-meter downlink signals, 14 MHz rather than 28 MHz is recommended as the transverter input band. The transverter crystal frequency should be 43.9333 MHz. This will provide for conversion of 14 MHz to 145.8 MHz. The satellite's input band would then be tuned on your exciter's VFO dial from 14.1 to 14.2 MHz.

A transmitting converter designed for use with a 6-meter rig is described in the League's *VHF Manual* (page 121 in editions 1 and 2; page 125 in the 3rd edition). It uses a 6360 as a final amplifier, with a rated output of about 12 watts PEP. Power can be increased by use of a linear amplifier; or, about 9 dB of antenna gain (excluding line loss) will bring the 12 watts up to par.

Cheap and Easy

As is true in other areas of amateur radio, cw can provide the simplest and most straightforward

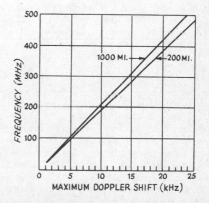

Fig. 3 — Satellite transmitter frequency versus Doppler shift for satellite in 200- or 1000-statute-mile orbits. For a translator, use the difference between uplink and downlink frequencies as the "frequency."

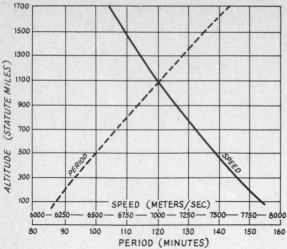

Fig. 4 — Satellite altitude versus its period (time for one revolution) and speed.

The antennas you use for AOC can contribute much to the effectiveness of your station. A particularly important item is the 10-meter receiving antenna. While simple antennas will work, superior performance can be acheived by employing a gain antenna. With a directive array, the strength of signals from AOC will be improved by the amount of antenna gain. Also, the directivity of the antenna will serve to provide immunity to noise sources not within the antenna's main lobe, thus further improving the signal-to-noise ratio.

A typical amateur installation with a 10-meter rotary beam or tribander at about 50 feet above ground should perform well for AOC work. An antenna mounted higher, thus having a lower angle of radiation, will be superior for maximum DX communication which occurs when the satellite is near your horizon. For passes closer to your station (at higher elevation angles), the lower antenna will pay off because of its higher take-off angle.

Signal levels of stations coming through Oscar will not all be the same. Thus, the stations with really effective receiving antennas will be the most successful in pulling out signals. However, if you don't have a beam, don't despair. Many AOC signals are expected to be strong enough for usable reception on a dipole. Even such a simple antenna should be rotated so that it can favor the heading of Oscar. A crossed dipole or turnstile antenna will produce a more onmidirectional pattern so that rotation becomes unnecessary.

While gain is of importance on 10 meters, your 2-meter transmitting antenna can be a simple

means of getting on the air. A cheap and easy way to put a signal into AOC is through use of a commercial surplus fm transmitter strip, modified to key the carrier. Most "high-band" rigs readily cover the 2-meter band. Some of the older taxicab and police gear is obtainable at low cost. Since fm won't offer the most efficient use of AOC, such rigs are best modified for cw operation. In general, use of grid-block keying in two of the doubler stages will do the trick. If you should wish to key a transistor-type fm rig, keying could be applied to the emitters of the doublers. In order to use surplus fm gear — designed primarily for mobile operation — an ac power supply of conventional design will be needed.

Receiving

Almost any good amateur receiver of modern design, capable of tuning the 29.45 to 29.55 MHz range, will serve well for receiving signals from AOC. Because of the high level of man-made and galactic noise at 10 meters, an extremely good receiver front end is not required. But, if your receiver sensitivity and performance at 10 meters are suspect, consideration should be given to the addition of a preselector.

Details on an 80- through 10-meter preselector appear in the 1974 *Handbook* beginning on page 265. The unit described is built on a 4 × 5-inch etched-circuit board and provides the necessary improvement to the receiver lacking in sensitivity. Some older or inexpensive receivers may also offer stability and calibration problems at 10 meters. In many cases, the solution lies in utilization of a converter, permitting the receiver to tune a lower frequency range, such as 80 meters. A down-converter of suitable design is described in the 1974 *Handbook*, page 274. Output is from 3.5-4.0 MHz. To tune AOC's down-link, the frequency of Y1 should be 33.3 MHz.

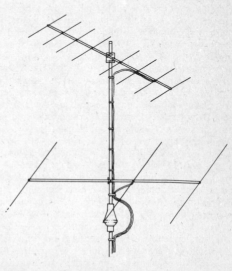

Fig. 5 — A practical antenna set-up for Oscar is a 10-meter beam (boom horizontal) plus a 2-meter Yagi mounted with an approximate elevation angle of 30 degrees.

dipole and still provide maximum (100 watts erp) performance. This is possible because you can use increased transmitter power to compensate for low gain. Indeed, 80-100 watts into a dipole will give you a "full power" signal at the satellite. Any signal stronger than this will either overload the repeater or cause agc action to reduce Oscar's sensitivity. So, the 100 watt erp maximum should never be exceeded. If your rig's output is less than 100 watts, you can compensate by increasing antenna gain. For example, 50 watts to your antenna (after subtracting transmission line loss) is a ratio of 2:1 (100 watts erp required, to 50 watts output), and an antenna gain of 3 dB is needed for the desired erp.

If a gain antenna is used for transmitting, it becomes necessary to consider aiming it at the satellite. A moderate gain (less than 10 dB) two-meter antenna can be mounted at a fixed elevation angle of about 30 degrees (see Fig. 5). The take-off angle will then be high enough and beamwidth sufficiently broad to catch most AOC passes. For the greatest DX performance, however, the antenna should be mounted normally with the boom horizontal for the low-angle shots.

An azimuth-elevation mount can be used with the two-meter antenna for effective results. It will allow for pointing of the antenna directly at Oscar.

The polarization of the satellite's signals will be changing due to tumble and Faraday rotation. Thus, use of circular polarization on the ground will tend to maximize fading. Antennas such as a crossed yagi or helix have been used with good results by many amateurs. You'll need an extra 3 dB of gain, however, if you should use a circularly polarized antenna. Little difference will be experienced between use of conventional vertical or horizontal polarization, a distinction which loses meaning when the antenna is pointed skyward. But, aimed at the horizon, a vertical 10-meter beam will tend to receive a higher noise level than a horizontal antenna. Horizontal polarization thus has an advantage in this case.

Late Information

QST carries information about recent developments in Oscar. Since ground station requirements are dependent on the bands, modes, etc used by the satellite, the amateur wishing to become equipped for space communication should consult ARRL headquarters to determine current amateur satellite plans.

CIRCULARLY POLARIZED CROSSED YAGI ANTENNAS

With the advent of space and satellite communications, amateurs should consider the effects of polarization and angle of elevation, along with the azimuth of either a transmitted or received signal. Normally, provisions for polarization are unnecessary on the hf bands, since the original polarization direction is lost after the signal passes through the ionosphere. A vertical antenna will receive a signal emanating from a horizontal one, and the converse is true when transmitting and receiving antennas are interchanged. Neither is it worth the effort to make provisions for tilting the antenna, since the elevation angle is so unpredictable. However, with satellite communications, the polarization changes and a signal that would disappear into the noise on a normal antenna might be S9 on one that is insensitive to polarization direction. Angle of elevation is also important from the standpoint of tracking and avoiding indiscriminate ground reflections which might cause nulls in signal strength.

Circular Polarization

The ideal antenna for random polarization would be one with a circularly polarized radiation pattern. Two commonly used methods for obtaining circular polarization are the crossed yagi and the helical antenna. The crossed yagi is mechanically simpler to construct, but harder to adjust than its helical counterpart.

Mathematically, linear and circular polarization are special cases of elliptical polarization. Consider two electric-field vectors at right angles to each other. The frequencies are the same, but the magnitudes and phase angles can vary. If either one or the other of the magnitudes is zero, linear polarization results. If the magnitudes are the same and the phase angle between the two vectors (in time) is 90 degrees, then the polarization is circular. Any combination between these two limits gives elliptical polarization.

Crossed Linear Antennas

A dipole radiates a linearly polarized signal, its direction depending upon the orientation of the antenna. Figs. 6A and 6B are the electric field patterns of horizontal and vertical dipoles. If the two outputs are combined with the correct phasing (90 degrees), a circularly polarized wave results, and the electric field pattern is shown in Fig. 6C. Notice that since the electric fields must be identical in magnitude, the power from the trans-

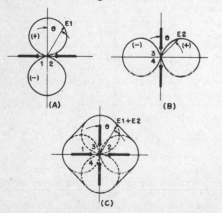

Fig. 6 — Radiation patterns looking head-on at dipoles.

mitter must equally divide between the two antennas; hence the gain of each one is decreased by 3 dB, when taken alone in the plane of its orientation.

As previously mentioned, a 90-degree phase shift must exist between the two antennas. The simplest way to obtain the shift is to use two feed lines with one section a quarter wavelength longer than the other one. These two separate feed lines are then paralleled to a common transmission line which goes to either the transmitter or receiver. Therein lies one of the headaches of this system, since the impedance presented to the common transmission line by the parallel combination of the other two sections is one half that of either one of them taken alone (normally not true when there is interaction between loads, as in phased arrays). Another factor to consider is the attenuation of the cables used in the harness, along with the connectors. Good low-loss coaxial line should be used, and connectors such as type N are preferable to the UHF variety.

A CIRCULARLY POLARIZED AZIMUTH-ELEVATION ANTENNA SYSTEM

The basic considerations in the design of this system were low cost and ease of assembly. In the matter of choice between a crossed-yagi system and a helical antenna, the main factor was that yagi antennas can be bought off the dealers shelf, but most helical antennas can not.

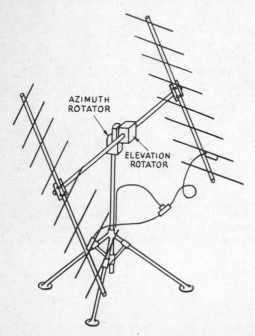

Fig. 7 — The antenna system can be assembled using off-the-shelf components such as Hy-Gain Yagis, Cornell-Dubilier or Blonder-Tongue rotators, and a commercially made tripod.

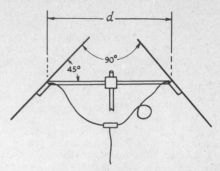

Fig. 8 — An end-on view of the antennas show that they are mounted at 90 degrees to each other, and at 45 degrees to the cross boom.

Fig. 7 shows the overall assembly of the array. The antennas used are Hy-Gain Model 341 eight-element Yagis. Fig. 8 is a head-on view of the array, showing the antennas mounted at 90 degrees with respect to each other and 45 degrees with respect to the cross arm.

Coupling between the two Yagis is minimal at 90 degrees and is somewhat greater at 45 degrees, following the greatly simplified formula:

$$E = E_o \cos \theta$$

Where E = induced voltage
E_o = inducing voltage
θ = axial angle between the two yagis

By setting the angle at 45 degrees with respect to the cross arm, coupling is minimized but not eliminated.

Length d in Fig. 8 should be the minimum necessary for the elements to clear the tripod base when the array is pointed straight up and rotated. A five-foot section of TV mast may serve the purpose.

The Phasing Section

One antenna must be fed with coaxial cable that is one-quarter wavelength longer than the feed line to the other. The preferred method is to use a grid-dip meter to check the sections of coax for correct length. The characteristic impedance of these sections should be such that, when paralleled, they match the main feed line. One possibility is to use RG-63/U (125 ohms) for these lines. There is some mismatch when connecting to a 50-ohm main feed line, but not enough to warrant additional matching networks. Care should be taken when other types of coax are considered, especially if you are unfamiliar with them.

The Mounting Tripod

A mounting tripod could be made by using aluminum railing, called "NuRail," which comes with all manner of swivels, crosses, and T fittings. However, the cheapest method is to purchase a TV tower such as Lafayette No. 18-56233W, which is a collapsible tripod. It is made by the South River Metal Products Company, South River, NJ 08820.

Their model number is HDT-5. This tower sells for such a low price that there is little point in constructing your own. Spread the legs of the tripod more than usual to assure greater support, but be sure that the elements of the antenna will clear the base in the straight-up position.

Elevation-Azimuth Rotators

The azimuth rotator is a Cornell-Dubilier AR-20. The elevation rotator is a Blonder-Tongue Prism-matic PM-2. The latter is one of the few on the market which allows the boom of the yagi to rotate on its axis when supported at the center. Fig. 9 shows the detail of the method of mounting the two rotators together. Notice that the flat portion of the AR-20 makes an ideal mounting surface for the PM-2. If you want to utilize commercially fabricated components throughout, a mounting plate similar to that shown in Fig. 9B can be purchased. Blonder-Tongue makes an adapter plate for their heavy-duty CATV antennas. It is called a YSB Stacking Block. The PM-2 rotator fits horizontally on this plate even though this was not the intended application. The adapter plate may be used to fasten two PM-2 rotators together.

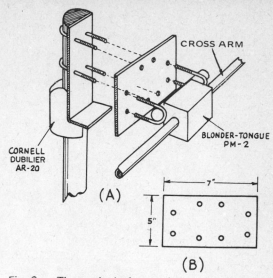

Fig. 9 — The method of mounting two rotators together. A pair of PM-2 rotators may also be used. The adapter plate (B) may be fabricated from 1/4-inch-thick aluminum stock, or a ready-made plate is available from Blonder-Tongue.

A TURNSTILE REFLECTOR ARRAY

The use of a simple antenna system for satellite work is often desirable. The following description of an effective two-meter antenna was first described in *QST* for September 1974, by K2UBC/WA3VCI. This antenna, called a turnstile-reflector (TR) array, can be built very inexpensively and put into operation without the need for test equipment. The characteristics of the TR array should make it useful to amateurs who have never operated on the 2-meter band and to experienced vhfers who already possess high-gain rotatable 2-meter arrays. The basic TR array produces a broad, balloon-like pattern with modest gain. It can be mounted close to the ground and does not require rotators. When aimed vertically, it is effective only when the satellite is within a surface distance of 1,000 miles (1,600 km) from one's station. This distance can be extended by re-aiming the array for each pass.

Background

Early experience with Oscar 6 has shown that rapid fading can be a severe problem to satellite communicators. Fortunately, the ground station has control over two important parameters affecting fading — cross polarization between ground station antennas and Oscar antenna, and nulls in the ground station antenna pattern. (Note that these two parameters affect downlink, as well as uplink, antennas). Fading because of cross polarization can be reduced by using a circularly polarized ground-station antenna. Fading because of radiation-pattern nulls can be overcome either by (1) using a rotatable, tiltable array, and continuously tracking Oscar; or (2) using an antenna with a broad, null-free pattern. A number of amateurs have demonstrated that they are capable of using high-gain, narrow-beamwidth antennas to simultaneously track and communicate through Oscar. This method has serious drawbacks, such as the expense of one or two rotators and the need for an extra set of hands. The TR array uses the easier approach — it produces a broad balloon-like pattern.

How about transmitting gain? The TR array appears to trade operating convenience and low cost for a big gain penalty. After all, circular polarization at only one end of a communications link costs 3 dB with respect to matched linear polarization. Antennas with broad patterns don't have the gain of highly directive arrays. Calculations do, in fact, show this gain penalty when the TR array is compared to an optimally oriented, high-gain, linearly polarized array. But back to reality! The TR array should be compared to an antenna that is neither oriented optimally with respect to polarization, nor aimed perfectly. So, under most real conditions the theoretical gain penalty turns out to be largely imaginary. Unless one is interested in extreme DX, antenna gain is not very important in an uplink antenna. This is because the sensitive receiver aboard Oscar and the low free-space path loss at 146 MHz require the ground station to use *less* than 100 watts erp. A greater erp may overload the receiver.

Technical Description

The turnstile antenna consists of two dipoles mounted at right angles to each other and fed 90

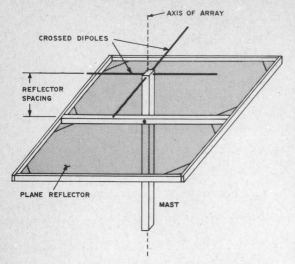

Fig. 1 — The turnstile-reflector (TR) array consists of crossed dipoles above a screen reflector.

degrees out of phase. The TR array consists of a turnstile mounted above a reflecting screen. The plane of the dipoles and the plane of the reflecting screen are parallel. See Fig. 1. The axis of the TR array is an imaginary line perpendicular to the dipoles and passing through their common midpoint. Radiation from the TR array is nearly omnidirectional about the axis — the departure is negligible and can be ignored. Along the axis of the TR array the radiation is circularly polarized. Off axis the radiation is elliptically polarized. Note that these comments on polarization and the omnidirectional character of the TR array are true for any spacing between the reflecting screen and the dipoles (reflector spacing). An omnidirectional antenna can be completely described by a single elevation pattern drawn for a plane containing the axis.

The reflector spacing has two important effects — it determines both the elevation pattern and the feed-point impedance of the antenna. Elevation patterns for certain reflector spacings can be obtained from *The ARRL Antenna Book*. The feed-point impedance of a single dipole above a perfectly reflecting screen can also be obtained from that publication. The delay line providing the 90-degree phase shift is most conveniently a section of coax cable which is *electrically* a quarter-wave in length. The characteristic impedance of the coax should be chosen to match a single dipole at the reflector spacing used. Because the two dipoles are mounted at right angles, their mutual induction is minimal. Consequently, connecting them for parallel feed yields a feed-point impedance of one half that of each dipole. Matching sections or baluns can be used as necessary.

The basic TR array uses a reflector spacing of 0.22 wavelength. At this spacing the broad, null-free elevation pattern is similar to that shown in Fig. 2A. This array can be fed using the arrange-

ment shown in Fig. 3. Note that a reflector spaced 0.22 wavelength in back of a dipole element yields a dipole impedance approximately that of one in free space. Other values of reflector spacing also produce useful patterns — we'll return to this later.

Construction

The wooden mast is 2 inches square and 8 feet long. Dipoles are formed from No. 12 copper wire taped to 1/4-inch diameter oak dowels. The reflecting screen is 20-gauge hexagonal chicken wire, one-inch mesh, stapled to a four-foot square frame made from furring strips. Hardware cloth can be used as well. Spar varnish on the wooden members will increase their lifetime. Corner bracing of the reflecting screen will provide mechanical stability. Silicone caulking compound can be used to keep water out of the coax. Dimensions for 146 MHz

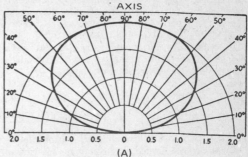

(A)

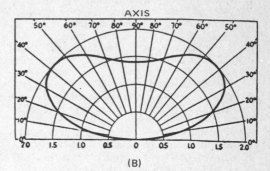

(B)

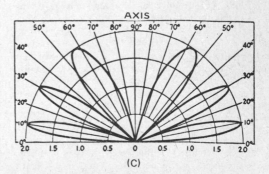

(C)

Fig. 2 — Elevation patterns for dipoles mounted over a ground plane. Pattern A is for spacing of 0.22 wavelength, B is for 0.37, and C is for 1.5-wavelength spacing.

are given in Fig. 3. See the *Radio Amateur's VHF Manual* for an alternative method of turnstile construction.

Performance

Here is a method that may be used to evaluate the performance of the uplink antenna. The basic problem is to isolate performance of the uplink system signal-strength variations on the uplink from the downlink. To do this, the amplitude of the downlink signal is compared to the amplitude of the broadband noise from Oscar. The broadband noise is easily discernible when using a low-noise receiver in a quiet location. If the ratio of the amplitudes remains constant during a fading episode, the fading is attributed to the downlink. If the signal fades while the background noise from Oscar remains constant, the fading is on the uplink.

Variations

Interesting variations of the TR array can be obtained by mounting the mast in other than a vertical direction and by using different reflector spacings. For example try placing the axis of the basic TR array at an elevation angle of about 45 degrees and aimed at the point of closest approach on a distant pass. Under these conditions, usable downlink signals can be obtained from as far away as 1,700 miles (2400 km). Such an experiment will show that one can increase the amount of time of access to the satellite by repositioning the antenna for each pass.

Another variation of the TR array which may prove useful to those with extra power available (100-300 watts) is the following: Setting the reflector to 0.37 wavelength produces the pattern shown in Fig. 3B. When aimed vertically this antenna will both decrease one's signal strength when the satellite is nearby (preventing overload)

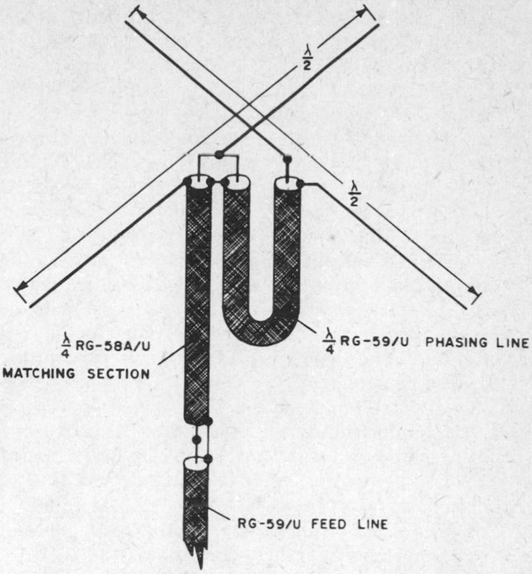

Fig. 3 — Dimensions and connections for the turnstile antenna. The phasing line is 13.3 inches of RG-59/U coax. A similar length of RG-58/U cable is used as a matching section between the turnstile and the feed line.

and increase effectiveness when the satellite is distant (increasing access time and range).

Some operators using Oscar have tried turnstile antennas without the reflecting screen. Results were often poor. Apparently this is because of the elevation patterns that result from leaving the position of the image plane to chance. Consider, for example, what happens when the distance between the turnstile and the effective reflecting plane is 1.5 wavelengths. The numerous nulls in the resulting pattern, shown in Fig. 3C, make such an antenna unsuitable for Oscar operations.

RANGE MEASUREMENTS WITH OSCAR

Trying to determine a satellite's equatorial crossing time, and particularly the longitude of equatorial corssing, by simple means is a rather difficult job. On the other hand, with range data, these orbital parameters can be calculated after observing a single pass of the satellite.

It is possible to gather range information using the satellite's transponder. By measuring the time a radio wave takes to travel to the satellite and back, the distance to the satellite can be determined, since the speed of propagation is known to be approximately 300 meters (984 ft) per microsecond.

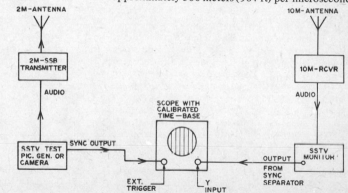

Fig. 1 — Slow-scan TV equipment configuration for ranging with Oscar 6.

The range to Oscar 6 will be between about 1500 and 4000 km (900 and 2500 miles), giving delays from 5 to 13 milliseconds for one way, or 10 to 26 milliseconds for the round trip of the signal. If the desired accuracy of the satellite's equatorial crossing time and longitude is 10 seconds and 2/3 degree respectively, then a ranging accuracy of 75 km (45 miles) is desirable since the satellite travels at a speed on the order of 7 km/second (4-5 miles). In order to achieve this accuracy, the ranging timing error should not exceed 0.5 ms. From this, it is evident that the signal-delay within the satellite transponder, which is on the order of 10 microseconds, can be neglected. On the other hand, the delay introduced by the ionosphere over the ten-meter downlink cannot be neglected.

In order to investigate the ranging concept, a very simple arrangement was tried. Standard slow-scan television equipment has a line frequency of 15 Hz, corresponding to a 66.6-ms period. The horizontal sync pulses last 5 ms. It was felt that slow-scan test transmissions could provide a useful means to carry out ranging experiments.

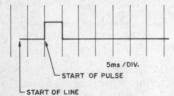

Fig. 2 — Scope pattern in short-circuit ("back-to-back") mode.

The sync pulses of a test transmission are used to trigger a scope line. The received sync pulse is then displayed on the scope (see Fig. 1). To do this, the output of the sync-separator of the monitor has to be made available. The line flyback pulse was tried, but it was found that this had too much jitter and it was impossible to tell the quality of the recovered pulse. By using the sync-separator output of the monitor, any poor return quality is immediately evident on the pulse shape (it is shortened).

The systems must be calibrated in order to account for the various delays in the station. It was found the the transmitter and receiver introduce about 2 ms delay, and the monitor another 2 ms delay.

By placing a converter in front of the ten-meter receiver, the system can be run in a short-circuit or "back-to-back" mode. The line start of the scope should be adjusted in such a way that the displayed pulse starts at a grating reticle on the oscilloscope screen. Line start and pulse start should be noted. This is shown in Fig. 2. When the system is operated through the satellite repeater, the pattern will look like that shown in Fig. 3. During a period of good reception, the start of the received pulse should be marked and the time noted. (It's best to have a second operator do the writing and time recording for you.) Now note the time delay t_d from the scope. About ten good measurements per

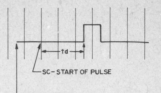

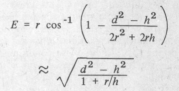

Fig. 3 — Scope pattern in ranging mode.

pass are sufficient to get the necessary information.

In order to calculate orbit formation from these measurements, it is desirable to have a calculator. At first, the t_ds are converted to distance by the formula:

$$t_d \text{ (ms)} \times 150 = d \text{ (km)}$$

where d is the slant range distance to the satellite in kilometers. To use miles, substitute "93" for "150" in the formula. In order to be able to transfer this distance into a chart, it has to be turned into a great-circle distnace (Fig. 4).

$$E = r \cos^{-1}\left(1 - \frac{d^2 - h^2}{2r^2 + 2rh}\right)$$

$$\approx \sqrt{\frac{d^2 - h^2}{1 + r/h}}$$

where E is the great circle distance between the subsatellite point and the observer, r is the earth's radius, and h is the height of the satellite above the earth.

These E-values now can be used to construct a graph. First start by drawing a vertical line to represent the subsatellite track. Next, divide this line into about 25 equal distances, representing 1-minute intervals corresponding to 425 km (265 miles) each. Choose a scale that is practical for the size of the page. Now set a compass to the first radius E_0 and draw a circle or arc from the "zero" time mark. Then, go to each subsequent one--minute interval mark, and draw an arc with a radius equal to the corresponding E value. Fig. 5 illustrates the technique, although only the ,E_0 and E_8 arcs are shown. When the corresponding arcs for all E values have been drawn, it will be possible to locate, on the graph, the position of the station.

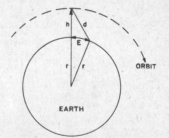

Fig. 4 — Relationship between slant-range *(d)* and great-circle distance *(E)*.

The circles do not meet in one point, because the ionosphere introduces errors as high as 500 km (300 miles) at ten meters, if the satellite is at a low angle above the horizon. Part of this error is cancelled by the approximations implied in the planar construction of this actually spherical problem, and by the approximation for the arc cosine given in the above equation. In addition, you must make an educated guess at the station's position indicated by the small circle in the figure, the nearest measurement being the most accurate. From this graph it is easy to find the distance of closest approach and the time of closest approach, which can be used to set the orbital semicircle on a meterological satellite plotting map. Working backwards, equator crossing time and longitude can be found (note that there are actually two ambiguous solutions, only one of which is correct).

For an observer in the northern hemisphere, south-to-north passes are most useful for calculating equator crossing data, while northwest-to-northeast passes can be used to check the system with known inclination, or to determine inclination.

The accuracy obtained is about one millisecond, which falls slightly short of the desired value, but nevertheless the system provides a reasonably accurate way available to amateurs to determine equator crossing information.

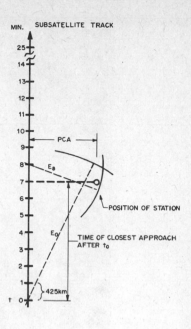

Fig. 5 — Determination of satellite position from range measurements.

SATELLITE-LOCATING AIDS

Knowing where a satellite is, and when it will be within range of the ground station, has been covered in various publications from time to time. In spite of this, finding the satellite remains a chore to some amateurs. A duo of neat station aids appeared in *QST* for May, 1974, and are also included in this section. The first is by WØCY, and the second by VE4AS. Each system has its merits; the reader can take it from here.

INSTANT OSCAR 6 LOCATOR

The instant Oscar 6 locator is the lazy-man's solution to the problem of wanting to know where the satellite is at all times — now all that is necessary is to see which light-emitting diode is blinking. No more calculations or plotting, and the accuracy is such that a high-gain antenna can be pointed with precision. In addition, the locator is an excellent demonstration unit for showing the real-time motion of a satellite when you are talking to a science club or other interested group.

Some plotting methods do not take into account the motion of the earth during the pass, and consequently Oscar 6 is five degrees west of the plotted location at the end of the pass. This represents about 350 miles at the equator or almost the east to west distance across the state of Kansas. The instant locator shows where Oscar 6 is

to the closest minute of time in the northern hemisphere, and to the closest five minutes in the southern hemisphere. The photographs pretty well explain the project, which consists of three parts: the globe, a Plexiglas ring with LEDs mounted on the periphery, and a rotary switch to control the voltage to the LEDs.

Construction

The globe is mounted on a double ball-bearing support and driven by a 1-rph clock motor through a 24-to-1 gear chain. A knob on top of the globe releases it for timing and for correction after a power failure. One of the new felt-tipped non-

Fig. 1 — The globe and accompanying switch mechanism make an attractive station accessory. The ring surrounding the glove has LED indicators on the periphery.

Fig. 2 — The Plexiglas ring has eyelets pressed into it to aid in making connections to the LEDs. The groove in the ring carries the wires from the LEDs to the base. A 2500-mile circle is shown centered on Salina, Kansas.

permanent marking pens may be used to draw a 2500-mile radius circle centered on your location. If the next Oscar should be at a different altitude, the non permanent ink can be removed with soap and water.

The second part, the Plexiglas ring, is scaled so that the top represents an orbit 900 miles above the globe, and supports the LEDs that mark Oscar's progress. In the northern hemisphere, an LED is mounted every minute of time, and in the southern hemisphere, every five minutes. At this location, about all you want to know is the approximate location in the southern hemisphere, and about how soon Oscar is going to cross the equator. One of the LEDs is always on, so it is no problem to spot where Oscar is at the moment. The ring is mounted at an angle of 102 degrees, corresponding to the approximate inclination of the Oscar 6 orbit. Diffused-light type LEDs are used which can be seen easily from twenty feet in a well-lighted room. They only draw 10 mA, and therefore No. 28 wire is adequate to connect them to a terminal board in the base. Small eyelets were pressed into the perimeter of the ring, making it easy to join the small leads on the LEDs to the wire. Removing a bad LED is no problem when

this type of mounting is used — a couple of them did get overheated in soldering and had to be replaced.

The third section is a 115-point rotary switch which is driven by a 1-rpm clock motor turning a single worm gear and driving the 115-tooth main gear. Therefore, the switch arm makes one rotation every 115 minutes and lights the appropriate LED. The motor must be turned off for 16 seconds every 50 orbits to compensate for the 114.9946-minute actual orbit time. Toggle switches are provided for the rotary-switch motor as well as the power supply for the LEDs. Included in the power supply is a transistor flip-flop to cause the LED to blink twice per second with an 80-percent on time; it is a lot easier to spot a blink than a steady glow. The orbit-number counter is geared to the rotary-switch shaft with a one-to-one bevel gear. The Plexiglas cover over the switch and power-supply assembly helps people resist the urge to see if the shaft can be turned by hand. It should be possible to do all that the rotary switch does by using shift registers, then everything could be mounted in the globe base. A beeper is connected to the 114th-minute point on the switch to warn that an equatorial crossing is about to occur. The beeper can be

Fig. 3 — A clock motor and worm-gear arrangement drives the rotary switch. The pc board to the left contains the power-supply components and a "beeper" circuit.

connected through a diode to any of the points should other passes become active. It is nice to go on about your work and know that you will not be late for a pass.

A SATELLITE TIMING MECHANISM

An effective satellite timing mechanism can be made from two old Tymeter or similar digital clocks that may have been retired from service because of noisy motors. This type of clock uses four wheels to display seconds, minutes, and hours in a 24 hour cycle. If clocks are used to keep track of three orbital parameters, the tedious calculations would not be necessary. The information needed is time in GMT, orbital progression west of Greenwich, and something synchronized with the 115-minute orbit of Oscar 6 to display time and degrees to the next equatorial crossing.

The station clock can provide the first information. The second information is obtained by changing the numerals on one of the old clocks to read degrees instead of time. At VE4AS this was done by using Dymo tape labels on the three wheels reading minutes and hours. The minute wheel on the right was marked to increase from 0 to 2.5 degrees in 0.25-degree steps. The next wheel reads from 0 to 15 degrees in 2.5 degree steps and the third wheel reads from 0 to 360 degrees in 15 degree steps. The first and last figures occur at the same point on each wheel but zero is marked on the wheel rather than the maximum figure (in the case of the left wheel, 000 is used rather than 360). After the two clocks are synchronized at a known equatorial crossing the current orbital plane can be read continuously by adding up the readings on the three digit wheels. For example, when the left wheel reads 090 degrees, the center wheel reads 12.5 degrees and the right wheel reads 1.75 degrees then the orbital path os 104.25 degrees west of Greenwich.

The remaining information required could be obtained by fabricating a mechanism driven by the 1-rpm motor of the other old clock, provided that a gear arrangement was used to drive a disk one revolution in 115 minutes. The junk box produced a 1-to-60 ratio worm gear from an old command set tuning capacitor as well as an assortment of other gears. A 115-tooth gear driven by the 60-tooth gear of the worm-gear assembly would give the required ratio. However, the junk box was sadly lacking in such a gear. After counting the teeth on each of the available gears it was found that two of them could be used to obtain the required 1.9166 hours per revolution. These two were a 72-tooth gear and a 138-tooth gear. The method used for calculating the ratio was to try a gear in the following formula and then establish if the required matching gear was available:

$$\frac{60}{(72)} = \frac{115}{X} \text{ or } 60X = 8280 \text{ and } X = 138$$

Fig. 4 — The satellite timer was constructed utilizing a junk-box chassis and panel. The upper scale indicates time and the lower one reads degrees to equatorial crossing.

Fig. 5 — The hastily constructed gearing arrangement of the timer. Since the accuracy was sufficient, the unit did not get beyond the prototype stage at VE4AS.

The final gear was calibrated with two scales, one reading downward from 115 to 0 minutes and the other reading downward from 28.75 to 0 degrees. As in the case of the orbit clock, the maximum and minimum readings occur at the same point on the scales and zero is used to mark the points. When calibrating the gear or disk, a rotation of 15.65 degrees equals five minutes and 1.25 degrees. The unit is synchronized at 0 with the other two units at a time when they indicate an equatorial crossing. The next equatorial crossing then can be calculated at any time simply by adding the time and degrees to equatorial crossing, as indicated on the timer, to the time and degree readings showing on the two clocks. Times of acquisition and loss of signal as well as antenna bearings are very easily obtained from the Edler orbit calculator.

With 5-minute calibration intervals, it is best to wait until a five-minute point shows on the timer to calculate an equatorial crossing; some may wish to calibrate the minute points. However, a larger rotating disk would be required so that sufficient space is available to mark the disk with the additional numerals required. Marking a thick disk on the edge around its circumference might prove to be a convenient method to try. "Letraset" press-on lettering produces a neat scale but those with an artistic flair can hand-letter the timer dial.

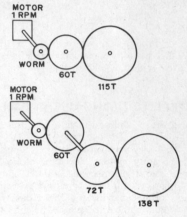

Fig. 6 — Two of the many possible gear arrangements to obtain the correct period of rotation for Oscar 6. The lower one is that used at VE4AS.

Fig. 7 — A Tymeter clock with a modified readout to indicate westward progression of the satellite orbit. The reading showing is 11.25° West.

EARTH-MOON-EARTH (EME) COMMUNICATIONS

What is perhaps the most challenging type of vhf work is currently attracting more participants, causing the ranks of those active to increase by large numbers. The greater degree of success in recent attempts at EME work results in a large part from vastly improved equipment performance. Also, it has been aided by a willingness of those in the field to share the secrets of their success with the beginner.

When reception of the first wobbly echoes of an amateur signal was reported in the pages of *QST* in 1953,* there was no more than a mere handful of amateurs who were considering EME (then called moonbounce) as a serious endeavor. Many methods were tried over the intervening years, from very slow cw transmissions and long-time integration at the receiver, to frequency-shift keying, ssb voice, RTTY, and even frequency modulation. Each small glimmer of success spurred others to join the chase and thence add a bit of knowledge.

Although equipment and techniques have improved greatly, the acheivement of EME communications is still not easy. Requirements still lean heavily on persistence, excellent equipment, and the largest antenna system that is practical to erect. Those who are able to make a contact upon almost every schedule are not content to stop there. Improvements are constantly sought, in an effort to improve the "copy" just a bit – to make the next schedule easier.

And it is getting easier. Early echoes were received by a system that included a large rhombic, aimed at a fixed "window" on the horizon. Recent successes include a contact made while using an array of stacked yagi antennas, located on top of an apartment building in Brooklyn, N.Y.

A complete discussion of the subject of EME would require far more space than is available in this volume. Coverage will be given to an important stage of EME work – locating the moon. A glossary of terminology at the end of this section

---

*This and all other references appear at the end of this section.

will aid the neophyte in understanding what the "old-timers" are talking about. Several references also appear as a guide to further reading. Additionally, a bibliography of EME articles may be obtained from ARRL headquarters by sending a business-size stamped return envelope.

A short section about operating techniques is offered as a guide to the beginner. It should be noted, however, that the details differ from one band to another in some degree. Such differences are slight, and should cause no great concern. Perhaps as the ranks grow an accepted universal operating procedure will evolve.

EME SCHEDULING

EME communication interest is growing worldwide. This increase has generated a need for more attention to scheduling, rather than relying on "looking up in the sky and pointing one's antenna accordingly." In this section, a set of scheduling guidelines will be discussed. Then several methods for locating the moon and common "windows" will be presented. This information, by W6FZJ, first appeared in *QST* for July, 1974.

Scheduling Time

The best days to schedule are *usually* when the moon is at *perigee* (closest to the earth) since the path loss is typically 2 dB less than when the moon is at *apogee* (farthest from the earth). The moon's perigee and apogee dates are listed monthly in *Sky and Telescope.*[1] If the distances are located on the EME Path Loss Nomograph, Fig. 1, the nominal EME path loss can be determined readily for the most popular frequencies. The moon follows a sine-wave orbit pattern. Hence, the day-to-day path changes at apogee and perigee are minor. The greatest changes take place at the time when the moon is traversing between apogee and perigee.

Also the S.D. (semi-diameter in minutes of arc), listed in the *Nautical Almanac,*[2] can be translated

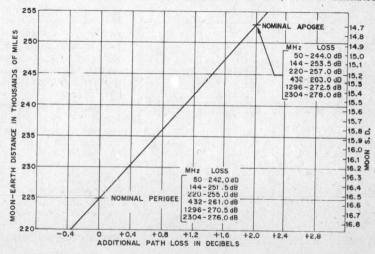

Fig. 1 — Variations in EME path loss can be determined from this graph. S.D. refers to the semi-diameter of the moon, which is indicated at the bottom of each page in the *Nautical Almanac.*

into apogee and perigee by use of the EME Path Loss Nomograph. An S.D. of 16.53 is an approximate earth-to-moon distance of 225,000 miles (typical perigee) and an S.D. of 14.7 is an approximate distance of 252,500 miles (typical apogee). However, there are several other factors that must be considered for optimum scheduling besides the path loss.

If perigee occurs near the time of a new moon, one to two days will be unusable since proximity of the moon to the sun's orbit will cause increased sun-noise pickup. Therefore, schedules should be avoided when the moon is within 10° of the sun (and farther if your antenna has a wide beam or strong side lobes). Lately (1974), perigee usually occurs near new moon in the summer and near full moon in the winter. These references to seasons apply only to the northern hemisphere. Hence, it is usually easier to schedule in the daytime in the summer and during the nighttime in the winter. The fall and spring seasons are a toss-up. The moon's perigee does shift during its 18-19 year cycle so this rule will not always apply and must be modified accordingly.

Low moon declinations and low aiming elevations generally produce poor results and should be avoided if possible. Conversely, high moon declinations and high elevation angles should yield best results. Good results are usually obtained when both stations are using similar elevation angles, since then both stations are looking through comparable electron densities. Generally, low elevation angles increase antenna-noise pickup and increase tropospheric absorption, especially above 420 MHz, where the galactic noise is very low. This situation cannot be avoided when one station is unable to elevate the antenna above the horizon or when there is a great terrestrial distance between stations. Ground gain (gain obtained when the antenna is aimed at the horizon) has been used very effectively at 144 MHz, but has been more elusive above 420 MHz. It is hoped that current tests on 144 and 432 MHz, using this mode of propagation, will yield more predictable results.

Usually, signals are stronger in the fall and winter months and weaker in the summer. Also, signals are generally better at night than during the day. This may be attributable to decreased ionization or less Faraday rotation.

Whenever the moon crosses the galactic plane (twice a month for 3 to 5 days each occurrence), the sky temperature will be higher.[3,4] Hence, some degradation (1 to 2 dB) may be observed, especially above 420 MHz where the normal background sky temperature is lower. Areas of the sky to avoid are the constellations Orion and Gemini at northern declinations and Scorpius and Sagittarius at southern declinations. Positions of the moon with respect to these constellations can be checked with *Sky and Telescope* magazine or the *Nautical Almanac*. The galactic plane is biased toward southern declinations, which will cause southerly declinations to be less desirable (with respect to noise) than are northern declinations.

Finally, the time of the day and the day of the week must be considered since most of us have to work for living and cannot always be available for schedules. Naturally, weekends and evenings are preferred, especially when perigee occurs on a weekend.

Fig. 2 — A sample portion of a page from the *Nautical Almanac*. In the example shown, the position of the moon on the 19th day, at 0600 GMT, is found to be 305° 39.9' GHA and 13° 25.5' north declination. At the bottom of the column for moon positions can be seen the S.D. (semidiameter) of the moon in minutes of arc for each of the three days on the page.

1974 MAY 19, 20, 21 (SUN., MON., TUES.) 103

G.M.T. d	h	SUN G.H.A.	SUN Dec.	MOON G.H.A.	v	MOON Dec.	d	H.P.
19	00	180 54·3	N19 38·3	218 38·6	11·5	N12 19·6	11·1	57·3
	01	195 54·2	38·6	233 09·1	11·3	12 30·7	11·1	57·3
	02	210 54·2	39·4	247 39·4	11·2	12 41·8	11·0	57·3
	03	225 54·2 ··	39·9	262 09·6	11·2	12 52·8	11·0	57·4
	04	240 54·2	40·5	276 39·8	11·1	13 03·8	10·9	57·4
	05	255 54·1	41·0	291 09·9	11·0	13 14·7	10·8	57·4
	06	270 54·1	N19 41·5	305 39·9	10·9	N13 25·5	[illegible]	57·5
	07	285 54·1	42·1	[illegible]	[illegible]	[illegible]	[illegible]	57·5
	08	300 54·1	42·6	334 39·6	10·7	13 47·1	10·7	57·5
SUNDAY	09	315 54·0 ··	43·2	349 09·3	10·6	13 57·8	10·6	57·6
	10	330 54·0	43·7	3 38·9	10·5	14 08·4	10·6	57·6
	11	345 54·0	44·2	18 08·4	10·5	14 19·0	10·5	57·6
	12	0 53·9	N19 44·8	32 37·9	10·3	N14 29·5	10·4	57·7
	13	15 53·9	45·3	47 07·2	10·3	14 39·9	10·4	57·7
	14	30 53·9	45·9	61 36·5	10·1	14 50·3	10·3	57·7
	15	45 53·8 ··	46·4	76 05·6	10·1	15 00·6	10·2	57·8
	16	60 53·8	46·9	90 34·7	10·0	15 10·8	10·2	57·8
	17	75 53·8	47·5	105 03·7	9·9	15 21·0	10·1	57·8
	18	90 53·8	N19 48·0	119 32·6	9·7	N15 31·1	10·0	57·9
	19	105 53·7	48·5	134 01·3	9·7	15 41·1	9·9	57·9
	20	120 53·7	49·1	148 30·0	9·6	15 51·0	9·9	57·9
	21	135 53·7 ··	49·6	162 58·6	9·5	16 00·9	9·8	58·0
	22	150 53·6	50·1	177 27·1	9·4	16 10·7	9·7	58·0
	23	165 53·6	50·7	191 55·5	9·3	16 20·4	9·7	58·0
20	00	180 53·6	N19 51·2	206 23·8	9·2	N16 30·1	9·5	58·1
	01	195 53·5	51·7	220 52·0	9·1	16 39·6	9·5	58·1
	02	210 53·5	52·2	235 20·1	9·0	16 49·1	9·4	58·1
	03	225 53·5 ··	52·8	249 48·1	8·9	16 58·5	9·3	58·2
	~~04~~	~~240 53·4~~	~~53·3~~	~~264 16·0~~	~~8·9~~	~~17 07·8~~	~~9·2~~	~~58·2~~
	~~05~~	~~255 53·4~~	~~53·8~~	~~278 43·9~~	~~8·7~~	~~17 17·0~~	~~9·1~~	~~58·2~~
21	00	180 52·7	N20 03·7	193 14·0	6·9	N19 53·4	7·2	58·8
	01	195 52·7	04·3	207 39·9	6·8	20 00·6	7·0	58·8
	02	210 52·6	04·8	222 05·7	6·7	20 07·6	6·9	58·9
	03	225 52·6 ··	05·3	236 31·4	6·6	20 14·5	6·8	58·9
	04	240 52·6	05·8	250 57·0	6·5	20 21·3	6·7	58·9
	05	255 52·5	06·3	265 22·5	6·5	20 28·0	6·5	59·0
	06	270 52·5	N20 06·8	279 48·0	6·4	N20 34·5	6·5	59·0
	07	285 52·4	07·3	294 13·4	6·2	20 41·0	6·3	59·0
	08	300 52·4	07·8	308 38·6	6·2	20 47·3	6·1	59·0
TUESDAY	09	315 52·4 ··	08·4	323 03·8	6·1	20 53·4	6·1	59·1
	10	330 52·3	08·9	337 28·9	6·1	20 59·5	5·9	59·1
	11	345 52·3	09·4	351 54·0	5·9	21 05·4	5·7	59·1
	12	0 52·2	N20 09·9	6 18·9	5·8	N21 11·1	5·7	59·1
	13	15 52·2	10·4	20 43·7	5·8	21 16·8	5·5	59·2
	14	30 52·2	10·9	35 08·5	5·7	21 22·3	5·3	59·2
	15	45 52·1 ··	11·4	49 33·2	5·6	21 27·6	5·3	59·2
	16	60 52·1	11·9	63 57·8	5·6	21 32·9	5·1	59·2
	17	75 52·0	12·4	78 22·4	5·5	21 38·0	4·9	59·3
	18	90 52·0	N20 12·9	92 46·9	5·4	N21 42·9	4·8	59·3
	19	105 52·0	13·4	107 11·3	5·3	21 47·7	4·7	59·3
	20	120 51·9	13·9	121 35·6	5·2	21 52·4	4·5	59·3
	21	135 51·9 ··	14·4	135 59·8	5·2	21 56·9	4·4	59·4
	22	150 51·8	14·9	150 24·0	5·1	22 01·3	4·2	59·4
	23	165 51·8	15·4	164 48·1	5·1	22 05·5	4·1	59·4
		S.D. 15·8	d 0·5	S.D. 15·7		15·9		16·1

Lat.	Twilight Naut.	Twilight Civil	Sunrise	Moonrise 19	Moonrise 20	Moonrise 21	Moonrise 22
N 72	--	—	-	[illegible]		--	-
N 70	—	[illegible]	—	00 59	[illegible]	—	-
68			01 20	01 16	01 08	00 56	—
66			02 04	01 29	01 30	01 33	01 44
64		00 23	02 33	01 41	01 47	01 59	02 23
62		01 31	02 55	01 50	02 02	02 19	02 50
60		02 05	03 12	01 59	02 14	02 36	03 11
N 58	00 21	02 29	03 27	02 06	02 25	02 51	03 28
56	01 22	02 47	03 39	02 12	02 34	03 03	03 43
54	01 53	03 03	03 50	02 18	02 42	03 13	03 56
52	02 16	03 16	04 00	02 24	02 50	03 23	04 07
50	02 33	03 28	04 08	02 28	02 56	03 32	04 17
45	03 07	03 51	04 26	02 39	03 11	03 50	04 38
N 40	03 31	04 10	04 41	02 48	03 23	04 05	04 55
35	03 50	04 25	04 53	02 55	03 33	04 17	05 09
30	04 06	04 38	05 04	03 02	03 42	04 28	05 22
20	04 30	04 59	05 22	03 13	03 58	04 48	05 43
N 10	04 49	05 16	05 38	03 23	04 11	05 04	06 02
0	05 05	05 31	05 53	03 33	04 24	05 20	06 19
S 10	05 19	05 45	06 07	03 43	04 37	05 36	06 37
20	05 33	05 59	06 23	03 53	04 51	05 53	06 55
30	05 46	06 15	06 40	04 05	05 07	06 12	07 17
35	05 53	06 23	06 51	04 12	05 17	06 24	07 30
40	06 00	06 33	07 02	04 20	05 28	06 37	07 45
45	06 08	06 44	07 16	04 29	05 40	06 52	08 02
S 50	06 16	06 56	07 33	04 40	05 56	07 12	08 24
52	06 20	07 02	07 40	04 46	06 03	07 21	08 34
54	06 24	07 08	07 49	04 51	06 11	07 31	08 46
56	06 29	07 15	07 59	04 58	06 21	07 43	08 59
~~58~~	~~06 34~~	~~07 23~~	~~08 10~~	~~05 05~~	~~06 31~~	~~07 56~~	~~09 15~~
~~S 60~~	~~06 39~~	~~07 32~~	~~08 23~~	~~05 14~~	~~06 43~~	~~08 12~~	~~09 34~~

N 40	19 12	19 44	20 22	16 52	18 00	19 09	20 15
35	19 00	19 28	20 03	16 43	17 49	18 55	20 00
30	18 49	19 16	19 48	16 35	17 38	18 43	19 47
20	18 31	18 55	19 23	16 21	17 20	18 22	19 25
N 10	18 15	18 37	19 04	16 08	17 05	18 04	19 06
0	18 00	18 22	18 48	15 57	16 50	17 48	18 48
S 10	17 45	18 08	18 33	15 46	16 36	17 31	18 30
20	17 30	17 53	18 20	15 34	16 21	17 13	18 11
30	17 12	17 38	18 07	15 20	16 03	16 53	17 49
35	17 02	17 29	18 00	15 12	15 53	16 41	17 36
40	16 50	17 20	17 53	15 03	15 41	16 27	17 21
45	16 37	17 09	17 45	14 52	15 27	16 10	17 03
S 50	16 20	16 56	17 36	14 40	15 11	15 50	16 41
52	16 12	16 50	17 32	14 34	15 03	15 41	16 31
54	16 03	16 44	17 28	14 27	14 54	15 30	16 19
56	15 53	16 37	17 23	14 20	14 45	15 18	16 06
58	15 42	16 29	17 19	14 12	14 34	15 04	15 50
S 60	15 29	16 20	17 13	14 03	14 21	14 48	15 31

Day	SUN Eqn. of Time 00h (m s)	SUN Eqn. of Time 12h (m s)	SUN Mer. Pass. (h m)	MOON Mer. Pass. Upper (h m)	MOON Mer. Pass. Lower (h m)	MOON Age (d)	Phase
19	03 37	03 36	11 56	09 45	22 11	27	■
20	03 34	03 33	11 56	10 37	23 05	28	
21	03 31	03 29	11 57	11 34	24 03	29	

General Considerations

It helps to know your own EME window as accurately as possible. This can be determined best with the help of the *Nautical Almanac* and *Tables of Computed Altitude and Azimuth* (H.O.-214).[5] The use of these publications is discussed in a later section of the chapter. Most EME operators determine their local window and translate it into GHA (Greenwich hour angle) and declination. This information is a constant, so once it it determined it is usable by other stations just as one would use GMT. Likewise, it helps to know the window of the station to be scheduled. Most EME stations are limited in some way by local obstructions, antenna mounting constraints, geographical considerations, and the like. Therefore, the accuracy of each station's EME window it very important for locating common windows and setting schedule times.

A boresight of some type is practically mandatory in order to align your antenna accurately with the moon. Most antenna systems exhibit some pattern skewing which must be accounted for. A simple calibration method is to peak your antenna

106 DECLINATION SAME NAME AS LATITUDE

Lat. 44°	H.A.	0° 00′	0° 30′	1° 00′	1° 30′	2° 00′	2° 30′	3° 00′	3° 30′	H.A.
		Alt. Az.	Alt. Az.	Alt. Az.	Alt. Az.	Alt. Az.	Alt. Az.	Alt. Az.	Alt. Az.	
	°	° ′ Δd Δt °	° ′ Δd Δt °	° ′ Δd Δt °	° ′ Δd Δt °	° ′ Δd Δt °	° ′ Δd Δt °	° ′ Δd Δt °	° ′ Δd Δt °	°
122	00	46 00.0 1.0 01 180.0	46 30.0 1.0 01 180.0	47 00.0 1.0 01 180.0	47 30.0 1.0 01 180.0	48 00.0 1.0 01 180.0	48 30.0 1.0 01 180.0	49 00.0 1.0 01 180.0	49 30.0 1.0 01 180.0	00
	1	45 59.5 1.0 03 178.6	46 29.5 1.0 03 178.5	46 59.4 1.0 03 178.5	47 29.4 1.0 03 178.5	47 59.4 1.0 03 178.5	48 29.4 1.0 03 178.5	48 59.4 1.0 03 178.5	49 29.4 1.0 03 178.5	1
	2	45 57.8 1.0 05 177.1	46 27.8 1.0 05 177.1	46 57.8 1.0 05 177.1	47 27.8 1.0 05 177.0	47 57.8 1.0 05 177.0	48 27.7 1.0 05 177.0	48 57.7 1.0 05 177.0	49 27.7 1.0 05 176.9	2
	3	45 55.1 1.0 06 175.7	46 25.1 1.0 06 175.6	46 55.0 1.0 06 175.6	47 25.0 1.0 06 175.6	47 54.9 1.0 07 175.5	48 24.9 1.0 07 175.5	48 54.8 1.0 07 175.4	49 24.8 1.0 07 175.4	3
	4	45 51.3 1.0 08 174.3	46 21.3 1.0 08 174.2	46 51.2 1.0 08 174.1	47 21.1 1.0 08 174.1	47 51.0 1.0 08 174.0	48 20.9 1.0 08 174.0	48 50.8 1.0 09 173.9	49 20.8 1.0 09 173.9	4
117	05	45 46.5 1.0 10 172.8	46 16.4 1.0 10 172.8	46 46.2 1.0 10 172.7	47 16.1 1.0 10 172.6	47 46.0 1.0 10 172.6	48 15.8 1.0 10 172.5	48 45.7 1.0 10 172.4	49 15.6 1.0 11 172.3	05
	6	45 40.6 99 12 171.4	46 10.4 99 12 171.3	46 40.2 99 12 171.2	47 10.0 99 12 171.2	47 39.8 99 12 171.1	48 09.6 99 12 171.0	48 39.4 99 12 170.9	49 09.3 99 12 170.8	6
	7	45 33.6 99 13 170.0	46 03.3 99 14 169.9	46 33.1 99 14 169.8	47 02.8 99 14 169.7	47 32.6 99 14 169.6	48 02.3 99 14 169.5	48 32.1 99 14 169.4	49 01.8 99 14 169.3	7
	8	45 25.5 99 15 168.6	45 55.2 99 15 168.5	46 24.9 99 15 168.4	46 54.6 99 16 168.2	47 24.3 99 16 168.1	47 53.9 99 16 168.0	48 23.6 99 16 167.9	48 53.2 99 16 167.8	8
	9	45 16.5 99 17 167.2	45 46.1 99 17 167.0	46 15.7 99 17 166.9	46 45.3 99 17 166.8	47 14.9 99 17 166.7	47 44.4 99 18 166.6	48 14.0 99 18 166.4	48 43.6 99 18 166.3	9
112	10	45 06.4 98 19 165.8	45 35.9 98 19 165.6	46 05.4 98 19 165.5	46 34.9 98 19 165.4	47 04.4 98 19 165.2	47 33.9 98 19 165.1	48 03.3 98 20 165.0	48 32.8 98 20 164.8	10
	1	44 55.2 98 20 164.4	45 24.6 98 20 164.2	45 54.1 98 21 164.1	46 23.5 98 21 163.9	46 52.9 98 21 163.8	47 22.2 98 21 163.7	47 51.6 98 21 163.5	48 21.0 98 22 163.3	1
	2	44 43.1 98 22 163.0	45 12.4 98 22 162.8	45 41.7 98 22 162.7	46 11.0 98 22 162.5	46 40.3 98 23 162.4	47 09.6 98 23 162.2	47 38.8 98 23 162.0	48 08.1 97 23 161.9	2
	3	44 30.0 97 24 161.6	44 59.2 97 24 161.5	45 28.4 97 24 161.3	45 57.6 97 24 161.1	46 26.7 97 24 161.0	46 55.9 97 24 160.8	47 25.0 97 25 160.6	47 54.1 97 25 160.4	3
	4	44 15.9 97 25 160.3	44 45.0 97 25 160.1	45 14.0 97 26 159.9	45 43.1 97 26 159.7	46 12.1 97 26 159.6	46 41.2 97 26 159.4	47 10.2 97 26 159.2	47 39.2 97 27 159.0	4
107	15	44 00.8 97 27 158.9	44 29.8 97 27 158.7	44 58.7 96 27 158.5	45 27.7 96 27 158.4	45 56.6 96 28 158.2	46 25.5 96 28 158.0	46 54.4 96 28 157.8	47 23.2 96 28 157.6	15
	6	43 44.8 96 28 157.6	44 13.7 96 28 157.4	44 42.5 96 29 157.2	45 11.3 96 29 157.0	45 40.0 96 29 156.8	46 08.8 96 29 156.6	46 37.5 96 30 156.4	47 06.2 96 30 156.2	6
	7	43 27.9 96 30 156.2	43 56.6 96 30 156.0	44 25.3 96 30 155.8	44 53.9 95 30 155.6	45 22.6 95 31 155.4	45 51.2 95 31 155.2	46 19.8 95 31 155.0	46 48.3 95 31 154.8	7
	8	43 10.0 95 31 154.9	43 38.6 95 31 154.7	44 07.1 95 32 154.5	44 35.7 95 32 154.3	45 04.1 95 32 154.1	45 32.6 95 32 153.8	46 01.0 95 33 153.6	46 29.5 95 33 153.4	8
	9	42 51.3 95 33 153.6	43 19.7 95 33 153.4	43 48.1 95 33 153.2	44 16.5 94 33 153.0	44 44.8 94 34 152.7	45 13.1 94 34 152.5	45 41.4 94 34 152.3	46 09.7 94 34 152.0	9
	20	42 31.7 94 34 152.3	43 00.0 94 34 152.1	43 28.2 94 35 151.9	43 56.4 94 35 151.7	44 24.6 94 35 151.4	44 52.8 94 35 151.2	45 20.9 94 36 150.9	45 49.0 94 36 150.7	20
	1	42 11.3 94 36 151.1	42 39.4 94 36 150.8	43 07.5 94 36 150.6	43 35.5 93 36 150.4	44 03.5 93 37 150.1	44 31.5 93 37 149.9	44 59.5 93 37 149.6	45 27.4 93 37 149.3	1
	2	41 50.0 93 37 149.8	42 17.9 93 37 149.6	42 45.8 93 37 149.3	43 13.7 93 38 149.1	43 41.6 93 38 148.8	44 09.4 93 38 148.6	44 37.2 93 38 148.3	45 04.9 92 39 148.0	2
	3	41 27.9 93 38 148.6	41 55.7 93 38 148.3	42 23.4 92 39 148.1	42 51.1 92 39 147.8	43 18.8 92 39 147.5	43 46.5 92 40 147.3	44 14.1 92 40 147.0	44 41.7 92 40 146.7	3
	4	41 05.0 92 39 147.3	41 32.6 92 40 147.1	42 00.2 92 40 146.8	42 27.8 92 40 146.0	42 55.3 92 41 146.3	43 22.8 92 41 146.0	43 50.2 91 41 145.7	44 17.6 91 41 145.4	4
97	25	40 41.3 92 41 146.1	41 08.8 91 41 145.9	41 36.2 91 41 145.6	42 03.6 91 42 145.3	42 30.9 91 42 145.0	42 58.2 91 42 144.8	43 25.5 91 42 144.5	43 52.7 91 43 144.2	25
	6	40 16.9 91 42 144.9	40 44.2 91 42 144.7	41 11.4 91 42 144.4	41 38.6 91 43 144.1	42 05.8 91 43 143.8	42 33.0 90 43 143.5	43 00.0 90 44 143.2	43 27.1 90 44 142.9	6
	7	39 51.7 90 43 143.7	40 18.8 90 43 143.5	40 45.9 90 44 143.2	41 13.0 90 44 142.9	41 40.0 90 44 142.6	42 06.9 90 45 142.3	42 33.8 90 45 142.0	43 00.7 89 45 141.7	7
	8	39 25.8 90 44 142.6	39 52.8 90 45 142.3	40 19.7 90 45 142.0	40 46.6 90 45 141.7	41 13.4 89 45 141.4	41 40.2 89 46 141.1	42 06.9 89 46 140.8	42 33.6 89 46 140.5	8
	9	38 59.2 89 45 141.4	39 26.0 89 46 141.1	39 52.8 89 46 140.8	40 19.5 89 46 140.5	40 46.1 89 47 140.2	41 12.7 89 47 139.9	41 39.3 88 47 139.6	42 05.8 88 47 139.3	9
92	30	38 32.0 89 47 140.3	38 58.6 89 47 140.0	39 25.2 88 47 139.7	39 51.7 88 47 139.4	40 18.2 88 48 139.1	40 44.6 88 48 138.8	41 11.0 88 48 138.4	41 37.3 88 49 138.1	30
	1	38 04.1 88 48 139.1	38 30.5 88 48 138.8	38 56.9 88 48 138.5	39 23.3 88 48 138.2	39 49.6 88 49 137.9	40 15.8 87 49 137.6	40 42.0 87 49 137.3	41 08.2 87 50 137.0	1
	2	37 35.5 88 49 138.0	38 01.8 88 49 137.7	38 28.0 87 49 137.4	38 54.2 87 49 137.1	39 20.3 87 50 136.8	39 46.4 87 50 136.5	40 12.4 87 50 136.1	40 38.4 86 51 135.8	2
	3	37 06.4 87 50 136.9	37 32.5 87 50 136.6	37 58.5 87 50 136.3	38 24.5 87 50 136.0	38 50.5 86 51 135.7	39 16.4 86 51 135.3	39 42.2 86 51 135.0	40 08.0 86 52 134.7	3
	4	36 36.6 87 51 135.8	37 02.5 86 51 135.5	37 28.4 86 51 135.2	37 54.2 86 51 134.9	38 20.0 86 52 134.6	38 45.7 86 52 134.2	39 11.4 85 52 133.9	39 37.0 85 53 133.6	4
87	35	36 06.2 86 52 134.8	36 32.0 86 52 134.5	36 57.7 86 52 134.1	37 23.4 85 52 133.8	37 49.0 85 53 133.5	38 14.5 85 53 133.1	38 40.0 85 53 132.8	39 05.5 85 54 132.5	35
	6	35 35.3 85 52 133.7	36 00.9 85 53 133.4	36 26.5 85 53 133.1	36 51.9 85 53 132.7	37 17.4 85 54 132.4	37 42.8 85 54 132.1	38 08.1 84 54 131.7	38 33.4 84 54 131.4	6
	7	35 03.8 85 53 132.7	35 29.3 85 54 132.3	35 54.7 85 54 132.0	36 20.0 84 54 131.7	36 45.3 84 54 131.3	37 10.5 84 55 131.0	37 35.6 84 55 130.7	38 00.7 84 55 130.3	7
	8	34 31.8 84 54 131.6	34 57.1 84 54 131.3	35 22.3 84 55 131.0	35 47.5 84 55 130.6	36 12.6 84 55 130.3	36 37.6 83 56 130.0	37 02.6 83 56 129.6	37 27.6 83 56 129.3	8
	9	33 59.3 84 55 130.6	34 24.4 84 55 130.3	34 49.5 83 56 130.0	35 14.5 83 56 129.6	35 39.4 83 56 129.3	36 04.3 83 56 128.9	36 29.1 83 57 128.6	36 53.9 82 57 128.2	9
82	40	33 26.3 83 56 129.6	33 51.3 83 56 129.3	34 16.2 83 56 128.9	34 41.0 83 57 128.6	35 05.8 82 57 128.3	35 30.5 82 57 127.9	35 55.2 82 57 127.6	36 19.8 82 58 127.2	40
	1	32 52.8 83 57 128.6	33 17.6 83 57 128.3	33 42.4 82 57 128.0	34 07.0 82 57 127.6	34 31.7 82 58 127.3	34 56.2 82 58 126.9	35 20.7 82 58 126.6	35 45.2 81 58 126.2	1
	2	32 18.9 82 57 127.6	32 43.5 82 58 127.3	33 08.1 82 58 127.0	33 32.6 82 58 126.6	33 57.1 81 58 126.3	34 21.5 81 59 125.9	34 45.8 81 59 125.6	35 10.1 81 59 125.2	2
	3	31 44.5 82 58 126.7	32 09.0 81 58 126.3	32 33.4 81 59 126.0	32 57.8 81 59 125.7	33 22.1 81 59 125.3	33 46.3 81 59 124.9	34 10.5 81 60 124.6	34 34.6 80 60 124.2	3
	4	31 09.7 81 59 125.7	31 34.0 81 59 125.4	31 58.3 81 59 125.0	32 22.5 81 59 1[illegible]4.7	32 46.6 80 60 124.3	33 10.7 80 60 124.0	33 34.8 80 60 123.6	33 58.8 80 60 123.3	4
77	45	30 34.4 81 59 124.8	30 58.6 81 60 124.4	31 22.7 80 60 124.1	31 46.8 80 60 12[illegible].7	32 10.8 80 60 123.4	32 34.8 80 61 123.0	32 58.6 80 61 122.7	33 22.5 79 61 122.3	45
	6	29 58.8 80 60 123.9	30 22.8 80 60 123.5	30 46.8 80 61 123.2	31 10.7 80 61 12[illegible].8	31 34.6 79 61 122.5	31 58.4 79 61 122.1	32 22.1 79 62 121.7	32 45.8 79 62 121.4	6
	7	29 22.8 80 61 122.9	29 46.6 80 61 122.6	30 10.5 79 61 122.2	30 34.3 79 61 12[illegible]9	30 58.0 79 62 121.5	31 21.6 79 62 121.2	31 45.2 79 62 120.8	32 08.8 78 62 120.4	7
	8	28 46.3 79 61 122.0	29 10.1 79 62 121.7	29 33.8 79 62 121.3	29 57.4 79 62 12[illegible]	30 21.0 78 62 120.6	30 44.5 78 62 120.3	31 08.0 78 63 119.9	31 31.4 78 63 119.5	8
	9	28 09.6 79 62 121.1	28 33.2 79 62 120.8	28 56.7 78 62 120.4	29 20.2 78 63 12[illegible]	29 43.7 78 63 119.7	30 07.1 78 63 119.3	30 30.4 78 63 119.0	30 53.7 77 63 118.6	9
72	50	27 32.5 78 62 120.2	27 55.9 78 63 119.9	28 19.4 78 63 119.5	28 42.7 78 63 119.[illegible]	[illegible]	29 29.3 77 64 118.6	29 52.5 77 64 118.1	30 15.6 77 64 117.7	50
	1	26 55.0 78 63 119.4	27 18.3 78 63 119.0	27 41.6 78 63 118.7	28 04.9 77 64 118.3	28 28.1 77 64 117.9	28 51.2 77 64 117.6	29 14.2 77 64 117.2	29 37.3 77 64 116.8	1
	2	26 17.2 77 63 118.5	26 40.4 77 64 118.1	27 03.6 77 64 117.8	27 26.7 77 64 117.4	[illegible]	28 12.8 77 64 116.7	28 35.7 76 65 116.3	28 58.6 76 65 116.0	2
	3	25 39.1 77 64 117.6	26 02.2 77 64 117.3	26 25.3 77 64 116.9	26 48.3 77 65 116.6	27 11.2 76 65 116.2	27 34.1 76 65 115.8	27 56.9 76 65 115.5	28 19.6 76 65 115.1	3
	4	25 00.8 77 64 116.8	25 23.7 76 65 116.4	25 46.6 76 65 116.1	26 09.5 76 65 115.7	26 32.3 76 65 115.3	26 55.1 76 65 115.0	27 17.8 76 66 114.6	27 40.4 75 66 114.2	4
67	55	24 22.1 76 65 115.9	24 44.9 76 65 115.6	25 07.7 76 65 115.2	25 30.5 76 65 114.9	25 53.2 76 66 114.5	26 15.8 75 66 114.1	26 38.4 75 66 113.8	27 00.9 75 66 113.4	55
	6	23 43.1 76 65 115.1	24 05.9 76 66 114.7	24 28.6 76 66 114.4	24 51.2 75 66 114.0	25 13.8 75 66 113.7	25 36.3 75 66 113.3	25 58.8 75 66 112.9	26 21.2 75 67 112.6	6
	7	23 03.9 76 66 114.3	23 26.5 75 66 113.9	23 49.1 75 66 113.6	24 11.7 75 66 113.2	24 34.1 75 66 112.8	24 56.5 75 67 112.5	25 18.9 74 67 112.1	25 41.2 74 67 111.7	7

Fig. 3 – An example of use of "Tables of Computed Altitudes," as explained in the text. Note that this page is for use if the declination is of the SAME name as that of the point from which observations are made. (The moon position used for this example is not the one shown in Fig. 2.)

on received sun noise and then align the boresight tube on the sun. The boresight of the antenna is now calibrated and can be used to aim the antenna at the moon. *Readers are cautioned against using a telescope or other device employing lenses as a boresight device!* Even the best of optical filters will not eliminate the hazard from solar radiation when viewed directly. A simple piece of tubing of small diameter and two or three feet long can serve the purpose in this instance. A symmetrical spot of light cast upon a piece of paper near the back end of the tube will indicate alignment.

A remote readout (such as a syncro or selsyn) is a highly recommended convenience. Accuracies of ±2° are usually necessary and can be attained with syncros. A remote readout is particularly important for scheduling when the moon is within 45° of the sun or when the sky is overcast. Very few of us are not bothered by occasional fog, rain, snow, or overcast. Aiming the antenna blindly seldom pays off. Syncros can be calibrated after the antenna has been boresighted on the sun with the help of the *Nautical Almanac* and *Tables of Computed Altitude and Azimuth.* The North Star (Polaris) can also be used for calibration during the nighttime, since its declination and azimuth are essentially fixed at every location in the Northern Hemisphere. Your local latitude is the same as the local elevation of Polaris. Recently, Bob Sutherland, W6PO, and others have proposed a "Universal EME Window." The proposed window is to be located conveniently for USA, African and European stations with the advantage that large fixed arrays could be aimed at a well-defined area of the sky to allow operation during several days of the month. This would be particularly helpful for stations operating on 144 MHz where array size is a problem. (Further details can be obtained by writing to W6PO.)

Finally, the ability to hear one's own EME echos is a big advantage and cannot be overstressed. Once echos can be heard, other parameters can be checked accordingly.

Use of Almanac and Tables

The *Nautical Almanac* is a necessity. It is written for all parts of the earth so it can be used to compare your EME window with the EME window of a station to be scheduled. It lists the position of the moon and sun in GHA and declination for every hour of the year in GMT. The

DECLINATION CONTRARY NAME TO LATITUDE

107

H.A.	0° 00′			0° 30′			1° 00′			1° 30′		
	Alt.		Az.	Alt.		Az.	Alt.		Az.	Alt.		Az.
°	° ′	Δd Δt	°	° ′	Δd Δt	°	° ′	Δd Δt	°	° ′	Δd Δt	°
00	46 00.0	1.0 01	180.0	45 30.0	1.0 01	180.0	45 00.0	1.0 01	180.0	44 30.0	1.0 01	180.0
1	45 59.5	1.0 03	178.6	45 29.5	1.0 03	178.6	44 59.5	1.0 03	178.6	44 29.5	1.0 03	178.6
2	45 57.8	1.0 05	177.1	45 27.9	1.0 04	177.1	44 57.9	1.0 04	177.2	44 27.9	1.0 04	177.2
3	45 55.1	1.0 06	175.7	45 25.2	1.0 06	175.7	44 55.2	1.0 06	175.8	44 25.3	1.0 06	175.8
4	45 51.3	1.0 08	174.3	45 21.4	1.0 08	174.3	44 51.5	1.0 08	174.4	44 21.6	1.0 08	174.4
05	45 46.5	1.0 10	172.8	45 16.6	1.0 10	172.9	44 46.7	1.0 10	172.9	44 16.8	1.0 10	173.0
6	45 40.6	99 12	171.4	45 10.7	99 12	171.5	44 40.9	99 11	171.5	44 11.1	99 11	171.6
7	45 33.6	99 13	170.0	45 03.8	99 13	170.1	44 34.0	99 13	170.2	44 04.3	99 13	170.2
8	45 25.5	99 15	168.6	44 55.8	99 15	168.7	44 26.1	99 15	168.8	43 56.4	99 15	168.9
9	45 16.5	99 17	167.2	44 46.8	99 17	167.3	44 17.2	99 17	167.4	43 47.6	99 16	167.5
10	45 06.4	98 19	165.8	44 36.8	98 18	165.9	44 07.3	98 18	166.0	43 37.7	99 18	166.1
1	44 55.2	98 20	164.4	44 25.8	98 20	164.5	43 56.3	98 20	164.6	43 26.9	98 20	164.8
2	44 43.1	98 22	163.0	44 13.8	98 22	163.1	43 44.4	98 22	163.3	43 15.1	98 21	163.4
3	44 30.0	97 24	161.6	44 00.7	97 23	161.8	43 31.5	97 23	161.9	43 02.3	98 23	162.1
4	44 15.9	97 25	160.3	43 46.8	97 25	160.4	43 17.6	97 25	160.6	42 48.5	97 24	160.8
15	44 00.8	97 27	158.9	43 31.8	97 26	159.1	43 02.8	97 26	159.3	42 33.8	97 26	159.4
6	43 44.8	96 28	157.6	43 16.0	96 28	157.8	42 47.1	96 28	157.9	42 18.2	96 28	158.1
7	43 27.9	96 30	156.2	42 59.2	96 30	156.4	42 30.4	96 29	156.6	42 01.7	96 29	156.8
8	43 10.0	95 31	154.9	42 41.5	95 31	155.1	42 12.9	95 31	155.3	41 44.2	95 30	155.5
9	42 51.3	95 33	153.6	42 22.9	95 32	153.8	41 54.4	95 32	154.1	41 25.9	95 32	154.3
20	42 31.7	94 34	152.3	42 03.4	94 34	152.6	41 35.1	94 34	152.8	41 06.8	95 33	153.0
1	42 11.3	94 36	151.1	41 43.1	94 35	151.3	41 15.0	94 35	151.5	40 46.8	94 35	151.8
2	41 50.0	93 37	149.8	41 22.0	93 37	150.1	40 54.0	93 36	150.3	40 25.9	94 36	150.5
3	41 27.9	93 38	148.6	41 00.0	93 38	148.8	40 32.2	93 38	149.1	40 04.3	93 37	149.3
4	41 05.0	92 39	147.3	40 37.3	92 39	147.6	40 09.6	92 39	147.9	39 41.9	92 39	148.1
25	40 41.3	92 41	146.1	40 13.8	92 40	146.4	39 46.3	92 40	146.6	39 18.7	92 40	146.9
6	40 16.9	91 42	144.9	39 49.5	91 42	145.2	39 22.2	91 41	145.5	38 54.7	91 41	145.7
7	39 51.7	90 43	143.7	39 24.5	91 43	144.0	38 57.3	91 43	144.3	38 30.1	91 42	144.6
8	39 25.8	90 44	142.6	38 58.8	90 44	142.8	38 31.8	90 44	143.1	38 04.7	90 43	143.4
9	38 59.2	89 45	141.4	38 32.4	90 45	141.7	38 05.5	90 45	142.0	37 38.6	90 45	142.3
30	38 32.0	89 47	140.3	38 05.3	89 46	140.6	37 38.6	89 46	140.8	37 11.9	89 46	141.1
1	38 04.1	88 48	139.1	37 37.6	88 47	139.4	37 11.0	89 47	139.7	36 44.5	89 47	140.0
2	37 35.5	88 49	138.0	37 09.2	88 48	138.3	36 42.8	88 48	138.6	36 16.4	88 48	138.9
3	37 06.4	87 50	136.9	36 40.2	87 49	137.2	36 14.0	87 49	137.5	35 47.7	88 49	137.8
4	36 36.6	87 51	135.8	36 10.6	87 50	136.2	35 44.6	87 50	136.5	35 18.5	87 50	136.8
35	36 06.2	86 52	134.8	35 40.4	86 51	135.1	35 14.5	86 51	135.4	34 48.6	86 51	135.7
6	35 35.3	85 52	133.7	35 09.7	86 52	134.0	34 44.0	86 52	134.3	34 18.2	86 52	134.7
7	35 03.8	85 53	132.7	34 38.4	86 53	133.0	34 12.8	85 53	133.3	33 47.2	85 53	133.6
8	34 31.8	84 54	131.6	34 06.5	84 54	132.0	33 41.1	85 54	132.3	33 15.7	85 53	132.6
9	33 59.3	84 55	130.6	33 34.2	84 55	131.0	33 09.0	84 54	131.3	32 43.7	84 54	131.6
40	33 26.3	83 56	129.6	33 01.3	83 56	130.0	32 36.3	84 55	130.3	32 11.2	84 55	130.6
1	32 52.8	83 57	128.6	32 28.0	83 56	129.0	32 03.1	83 56	129.3	31 38.2	83 56	129.6
2	32 18.9	82 57	127.6	31 54.2	82 57	128.0	31 29.5	83 57	128.3	31 04.7	83 57	128.6
3	31 44.5	82 58	126.7	31 20.0	82 58	127.0	30 55.4	82 58	127.4	30 30.8	82 57	127.7
4	31 09.7	81 59	125.7	30 45.3	81 58	126.1	30 20.9	82 58	126.4	29 56.4	82 58	126.7
45	30 34.4	81 59	124.8	30 10.2	81 59	125.1	29 45.9	81 59	125.5	29 21.6	81 59	125.8
6	29 58.8	80 60	123.9	29 34.7	80 60	124.2	29 10.6	81 60	124.5	28 46.4	81 59	124.9
7	29 22.8	80 61	122.9	28 58.8	80 60	123.3	28 34.8	80 60	123.6	28 10.8	80 60	124.0
8	28 46.3	79 61	122.0	28 22.5	79 61	122.4	27 58.7	80 61	122.7	27 34.8	80 61	123.1
9	28 09.6	79 62	121.1	27 45.9	79 62	121.5	27 22.2	79 61	121.8	26 58.4	79 61	122.2
50	27 32.5	78 62	120.2	27 08.9	79 62	120.6	26 45.3	79 62	120.9	26 21.7	79 62	121.3
1	26 55.0	78 63	119.4	26 31.6	78 63	119.7	26 08.2	78 63	120.1	25 44.7	78 62	120.4
2	26 17.2	77 63	118.5	25 54.0	78 63	118.8	25 30.6	78 63	119.2	25 07.3	78 63	119.5
3	25 39.1	77 64	117.6	25 16.0	77 64	118.0	24 52.8	77 64	118.3	24 29.6	78 63	118.7
4	25 00.8	77 64	116.8	24 37.7	77 64	117.1	24 14.7	77 64	117.5	23 51.5	77 64	117.8
55	24 22.1	76 65	115.9	23 59.2	76 65	116.3	23 36.2	77 65	116.6	23 13.2	77 [illegible]	117.0
6	23 43.1	76 65	115.1	23 20.3	76 65	115.5	22 57.5	76 65	115.8	22 34.6	76 [illegible]	[illegible]
7	23 03.9	76 66	114.3	22 41.2	76 66	114.6	22 18.5	76 65	115.0	21 55.8	76 65	[illegible]
8	22 24.5	75 66	113.5	22 01.9	75 66	113.8	21 39.3	75 66	114.2	21 16.6	76 66	[illegible]
9	21 44.7	75 67	112.7	21 22.3	75 66	113.0	20 59.8	75 66	113.4	20 37.2	75 66	[illegible]
60	21 04.8	74 67	111.9	20 42.4	75 67	112.2	20 20.0	75 67	112.6	19 57.6	75 66	[illegible]
1	20 24.6	74 67	111.1	20 02.4	74 67	111.4	19 40.1	74 67	111.8	19 17.7	75 67	[illegible]
2	19 44.2	74 68	110.3	19 22.1	74 68	110.6	18 59.9	74 67	111.0	18 37.6	74 67	111.3
3	19 03.7	73 68	109.5	18 41.6	74 68	109.8	18 19.5	74 68	110.2	17 57.3	74 68	110.6
4	18 22.9	73 68	108.7	18 00.9	73 68	109.1	17 38.9	73 68	109.4	17 16.8	74 68	109.8

2° 00′			2° 30′			3° 00′			3° 30′			H.A.	Lat. 44°
Alt.		Az.	Alt.		Az.	Alt.		Az.	Alt.		Az.		
° ′	Δd Δt	°	° ′	Δd Δt	°	° ′	Δd Δt	°	° ′	Δd Δt	°	°	
44 00.0	1.0 01	180.0	43 30.0	1.0 01	180.0	43 00.0	1.0 01	180.0	42 30.0	1.0 01	180.0	00	122
43 59.5	1.0 03	178.6	43 29.5	1.0 03	178.6	42 59.5	1.0 03	178.6	42 29.5	1.0 03	178.6	1	
43 57.9	1.0 04	177.2	43 27.9	1.0 04	177.2	42 57.9	1.0 04	177.3	42 28.0	1.0 04	177.3	2	
43 55.3	1.0 06	175.8	43 25.3	1.0 06	175.9	42 55.4	1.0 06	175.9	42 25.4	1.0 06	175.9	3	
43 51.6	1.0 08	174.5	43 21.7	1.0 08	174.5	42 51.8	1.0 08	174.5	42 21.9	1.0 08	174.6	4	
43 47.0	1.0 10	173.1	43 17.1	1.0 09	173.1	42 47.2	1.0 09	173.2	42 17.3	1.0 09	173.2	05	127
43 41.2	99 11	171.7	43 11.4	99 11	171.8	42 41.5	99 11	171.8	42 11.7	99 11	171.9	6	
43 34.5	99 13	170.3	43 04.7	99 13	170.4	42 34.9	99 13	170.5	42 05.1	99 13	170.6	7	
43 26.7	99 15	169.0	42 57.0	99 14	169.0	42 27.3	99 14	169.1	41 57.6	99 14	169.2	8	
43 17.9	99 16	167.6	42 48.3	99 16	167.7	42 18.7	99 16	167.8	41 49.8	99 16	167.9	9	
43 08.2	99 18	166.2	42 38.6	99 18	166.4	42 09.1	99 18	166.5	41 39.5	99 18	166.6	10	132
42 57.4	98 20	164.9	42 28.0	98 19	165.0	41 58.5	98 19	165.1	41 29.0	98 19	165.3	1	
42 45.7	98 21	163.6	42 16.3	98 21	163.7	41 46.9	98 21	163.8	41 17.5	98 21	164.0	2	
42 33.0	98 23	162.2	42 03.7	98 23	162.4	41 34.4	98 22	162.5	41 05.1	98 22	162.7	3	
42 19.4	97 24	160.9	41 50.2	97 24	161.1	41 21.0	97 24	161.2	40 51.8	97 24	161.4	4	
42 04.8	97 26	159.6	41 35.7	97 26	159.8	41 06.7	97 25	159.9	40 37.6	97 25	160.1	15	137
41 49.3	96 27	158.3	41 20.4	96 27	158.5	40 51.4	97 27	158.7	40 22.4	97 27	158.8	6	
41 32.9	96 29	157.0	41 04.1	96 29	157.2	40 35.3	96 28	157.4	40 06.4	96 28	157.6	7	
41 15.6	96 30	155.7	40 46.9	96 30	155.9	40 18.2	96 30	156.1	39 49.5	96 30	156.3	8	
40 57.4	95 32	154.5	40 28.9	95 31	154.7	40 00.3	95 31	154.9	39 31.8	95 31	155.1	9	
40 38.4	95 33	153.2	40 10.0	95 33	153.4	39 41.6	95 33	153.6	33 13.2	95 32	153.9	20	142
40 18.5	94 34	152.0	39 50.3	94 34	152.2	39 22.0	94 34	152.4	38 53.7	94 34	152.6	1	
39 57.9	94 36	150.8	39 29.8	94 36	151.0	39 01.6	94 35	151.2	38 33.5	94 35	151.4	2	
39 36.4	93 37	149.5	39 08.4	93 37	149.8	38 40.5	93 37	150.0	38 12.5	93 36	150.2	3	
39 14.1	93 38	148.3	38 46.3	93 38	148.6	38 18.5	93 38	148.8	37 50.6	93 38	149.1	4	
38 51.1	92 40	147.2	38 23.4	92 39	147.4	37 55.8	92 39	147.7	37 28.1	92 39	147.9	25	147
38 27.3	92 41	146.0	37 59.8	92 41	146.2	37 32.3	92 40	146.5	37 04.8	92 40	146.7	6	
38 02.8	91 42	144.8	37 35.5	91 42	145.1	37 08.1	91 42	145.3	36 40.7	91 41	145.6	7	
37 37.6	90 43	143.7	37 10.4	91 43	143.9	36 43.2	91 43	144.2	36 16.0	91 42	144.5	8	
37 11.7	90 44	142.5	36 44.7	90 44	142.8	36 17.6	90 44	143.1	35 50.6	90 44	143.3	9	
36 45.1	89 45	141.4	36 18.3	89 45	141.7	35 51.4	90 45	142.0	35 24.5	90 45	142.2	30	152
36 17.8	89 46	140.3	35 51.2	89 46	140.6	35 24.5	89 46	140.9	34 57.7	89 46	141.1	1	
35 50.0	88 48	139.2	35 23.5	88 47	139.5	34 56.9	89 47	139.8	34 30.3	89 47	140.1	2	
35 21.5	88 49	138.1	34 55.1	88 48	138.4	34 28.8	88 48	138.7	34 02.3	88 48	139.0	3	
34 52.4	87 49	137.1	34 26.2	87 49	137.4	34 00.0	87 49	137.7	33 33.7	88 49	137.9	4	
34 22.7	87 50	136.0	33 56.7	87 50	136.3	33 30.6	87 50	136.6	33 04.5	87 50	136.9	35	157
33 52.4	86 51	135.0	33 26.6	86 51	135.3	33 00.7	86 51	135.6	32 34.8	87 51	135.9	6	
33 21.6	86 52	133.9	32 55.9	86 52	134.2	32 30.2	86 52	134.6	32 04.4	86 51	134.9	7	
32 50.3	85 53	132.9	32 24.7	85 53	133.2	31 59.2	85 53	133.5	31 33.6	85 52	133.8	8	
32 18.4	84 54	131.9	31 53.0	85 54	132.2	31 27.6	85 53	132.5	31 02.2	85 53	132.9	9	
31 46.0	84 55	130.9	31 20.8	84 54	131.2	30 55.6	84 54	131.6	30 30.3	84 54	131.9	40	162
31 13.2	83 56	129.9	30 48.1	84 55	130.3	30 23.0	84 55	130.6	29 57.9	84 55	130.9	1	
30 39.8	83 56	129.0	30 15.0	83 56	129.3	29 50.0	83 56	129.6	29 25.0	83 56	129.9	2	
30 06.1	82 57	128.0	29 41.3	83 57	128.3	29 16.6	83 57	128.7	28 51.7	83 56	129.0	3	
29 31.8	82 58	127.1	29 07.3	82 58	127.4	28 42.6	82 57	127.7	28 18.0	82 57	128.0	4	
28 57.2	81 58	126.1	28 32.8	82 58	126.5	28 08.3	82 58	126.8	27 43.8	82 58	127.1	45	167
28 22.1	81 59	125.2	27 57.9	81 59	125.5	27 33.5	81 59	125.9	27 09.1	81 58	126.2	6	
27 46.7	80 60	124.3	27 22.5	81 60	124.6	26 58.3	81 59	125.0	26 34.1	81 59	125.3	7	
27 10.8	80 60	123.4	26 46.8	80 60	123.7	26 22.8	80 60	124.1	25 58.7	80 60	124.4	8	
26 34.6	79 61	122.5	26 10.8	80 61	122.8	25 46.8	80 60	123.2	25 22.9	80 60	123.5	9	
25 58.0	79 62	121.6	25 34.3	79 61	122.0	25 10.5	79 61	122.3	24 46.7	79 61	122.6	50	172
25 21.1	79 62	120.7	24 57.5	79 62	121.1	24 33.9	79 62	121.4	24 10.2	79 61	121.8	1	
24 43.9	78 63	119.9	24 20.4	78 62	120.2	23 56.9	78 62	120.6	23 33.3	79 62	120.9	2	
24 06.3	78 63	119.0	23 42.9	78 63	119.4	23 19.6	78 63	119.7	22 56.1	78 63	120.1	3	
23 28.4	77 64	118.2	23 05.2	77 63	118.5	22 41.9	78 63	118.9	22 18.6	78 63	119.2	4	
22 50.2	77 64	117.3	22 27.1	77 64	117.7	22 04.0	77 64	118.0	21 40.8	77 64	118.4	55	177
22 11.7	76 65	116.5	21 48.7	77 64	116.9	21 25.7	77 64	117.2	21 02.7	77 64	117.5	6	
21 32.9	76 65	115.7	21 10.1	76 65	116.0	20 47.2	76 65	116.4	20 24.3	77 64	116.7	7	
20 53.9	76 65	114.9	20 31.2	76 65	115.2	20 08.4	76 65	115.6	19 45.6	76 65	115.9	8	
20 14.6	75 66	114.1	19 52.0	76 66	114.4	19 29.3	76 66	114.8	19 06.6	76 65	115.1	9	
[illegible]	[illegible]	[illegible]	19 12.6	75 66	113.6	18 50.0	75 66	114.0	18 27.4	75 66	114.3	60	182
18 55.3	75 67	112.5	18 32.9	75 66	112.8	18 10.5	75 66	113.2	17 48.0	75 66	113.5	1	
[illegible]	[illegible]	[illegible]	17 53.0	74 67	112.0	17 30.7	75 67	112.4	17 08.3	75 67	112.7	2	
17 35.1	74 67	110.9	17 12.9	74 67	111.3	16 50.7	74 67	111.6	16 28.4	74 67	112.0	3	
16 54.7	74 68	110.1	16 32.6	74 68	110.5	16 10.4	74 67	110.8	15 48.2	74 67	111.2	4	

Fig. 4 — An example of the use of a page for declinations that are CONTRARY to the name of observers location. If the observer is at a northern latitude, but the moon is at a south declination, this CONTRARY page is correct. Also, an observer at a southern latitude, but looking for the moon at a north declination should use this page to work out the moon's position.

desired page is the one on the righthand side. A typical page is shown in Fig. 2. The day, dates and times are shown on the left margin. The first column deals with the sun while the second column concerns the moon. The GHA and declinations are listed for every hour of the day. Across the bottom of the page is the S.D. This can be used to determine the distance to the moon as pointed our earlier. The first S.D. listed refers to the first day on the page, the second to the second day, and so on.

If a polar mount is used, the information in the *Nautical Almanac* can be used directly to locate the moon.[6] If not, the next best thing is to use the *Tables of Computed Altitude and Azimuth*. This publication need only be purchased once as long as you do not move to a latitude outside the area for which the publication was purchased. A sample page is shown in Fig. 3.

To use the tables, proceed as follows:

1. Turn to pages containing your local latitude.

a) The tables marked "DECLINATION SAME NAME AS LATITUDE" are for north declinations if your latitude is north.

b) The tables marked "DECLINATION CONTRARY NAME TO LATITUDE" are for south declinations if your latitude is north.

2. HA (Hour Angle) is normalized to your GHA (Greenwich hour angle) east or west of your meridian. Therefore, renumber HA columns as follows:

a) The column on the left hand side of each page is for descending HA.

e.g.: If your LHA (local hour angle) is 122° west longitude, renumber 00° as 122°, 1° as 121°, 2° as 120°, etc.

b) The column on the right hand side of each page is for ascending HA.

e.g.: If your LHA is 122° west longitude, renumber 00° as 122°, 1° as 123°, 2° as 124°, etc.

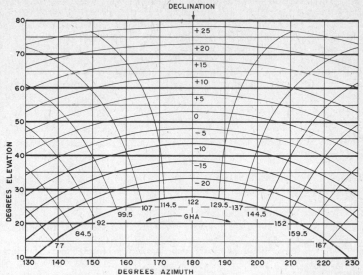

Fig. 5 — A chart like this may be useful to convert GHA and declination figures from the *Nautical Almanac* into degrees of azimuth and elevation. The curved horizontal lines represent declination. The curved vertical lines are for GHA. This chart is drawn for a location at 122° West longitude, 37° N. lat.

3. The numbers across the top of the columns are *declinations*.

e.g.: 2°30| refers to a declination of 2° 30'. Just below the declinations are the local **ALTITUDE** and **AZIMUTH** columns.

Example 1 (refer to Fig. 3)

GHA 71°, N 2° (These moon data from *Nautical Almanac* for year, month, day, time in question). Local coordinates 122° west longitude, 44° north latitude.

Use the **SAME** page, since declination is the same (north) as compared to the local north latitude.

Use the left hand HA column since GHA is east of your meridian or before 122° longitude (GHA 122°). Go to HA 51° (which has been renumbered as 71°) and across to declination equals 2°.

Read *altitude* 28° 28.1' and *azimuth* 117.9°

Example 2 (refer to Fig. 4):

GHA 183°, declination S 2° (from *Nautical Almanac*).

Local coordinates 122° west longitude, 44° north latitude.

Use the **CONTRARY** page, since declination is contrary (south) as compared to local north latitude.

Use the right hand HA column since GHA 183° is west of the 122° local meridian. Go to HA 61° (renumbered 183°) and across to declination of 2°.

Read *altitude* 18° 55.3' and *azimuth* 112.5°. True azimuth equals 360 minus the column reading for a GHA greater than the local hour angle. Therefore, 360° − 112.5° = 247.5°.

Helpful Material

A subscription to *Sky and Telescope* will be helpful to determine apogee, perigee, and location of the galactic plane. A computer printout of the moon's azimuth and elevation from your location is also helpful. Several active EME operators have written appropriate programs and have access to computers to provide this information.

Access to a time-share computer terminal is also helpful. Several individuals have developed programs using various time-share systems which quickly can give local EME coordinates.[7]

A less complicated approach to finding the moon is to generate your own graph based on your location. One can be constructed with the use of the *Tables of Computed Altitude and Azimuth*. A representative chart is shown in Fig. 5.

To generate such a chart you must plot the data from the tables, preferably in 15° increments (since this represents approximately one hour of moon travel). On the southern chart, it may be helpful to also plot intervals of 7-1/2° since the apparent azimuth is changing quite rapidly. One declination can be plotted at a time. Usually data at 5° declination intervals is sufficient. Insert the graph behind a clear plastic holder and mark schedules on the plastic with a china-marking pencil. This gives quick reference during schedules and the marks are easily removable with a cloth afterward.

EME Check-off List

The following questions can be used as a simple guide to determining best schedule times and possibilities. Don't laugh at them; anyone can make a mistake:

1) Do we have a mutual window?

2) Can the other person see the moon at this time?

3) Is the other person available at this time and date?

4) Is the moon at perigee?

5) Is the moon too close to the sun?

6) Is the moon in the galactic plane?

7) Is the declination too low or too high?

The purpose of this section is to sum up many of the aspects of EME scheduling. It is not meant to paint a bleak picture of EME scheduling, but to improve one's chances of success. There is nothing more frustrating than listening for weak signals over a long period of time, only to find out that the other station was not operational at the time.

There will undoubtedly be many exceptions to the guidelines proposed, and possibly other considerations were not mentioned. All too often, computer printouts are relied on too heavily without giving due considerations to other factors. It is also amazing, but true, that many schedules have been attempted when the moon is below the horizon at one of the stations during the entire period! It is hoped that this information will prevent some of these happenings, increase EME contacts, and help acquaint the newcomer to EME with scheduling guidelines.

USING THE HO-229 SIGHT REDUCTION TABLES

In some sections of the country the HO-214 publication (*Tables of Computed Altitude and Azimuth*) may not be available, but is being supplanted by a newer version called *Sight Reduction Tables for Marine Navigations*, Hydrographic Office publication HO-229. This new book may be obtained from the Government Printing Office, although some marine supply houses keep a limited number in stock. However, before ordering one, it might be wise to check with some of the larger public libraries; an evenings work with a pencil and paper will provide enough information to generate a conversion chart for your location.

There are several volumes of the HO-229 publication, as was the case with the HO-214, each volume covering a specific range of latitude. Be sure to use the volume that is correct for your location. As an example, volume 3 covers 30 to 37 degrees North Latitude in the first section, and 38 to 45 degrees in the second part.

The format departs from the older style in several ways, one of which is that each section starts with zero degrees LHA (Local Hour Angle). Zero LHA is located on your local meridian. For instance, the station location of W1AW is approximately 73° west longitude. Thus, when the moon has a GHA (Greenwich Hour Angle) of 73, it is on the local meridian and the LHA is zero. The LHA is always found by subtracting the GHA from the longitude of your location if the moon is east of you, or the longitude from the GHA if the moon is west.

Suppose that the *Nautical Almanac* shows the moon is at GHA 61°. Subtracting 61° from 73° gives an LHA of 12°. Note that the LHA will again be 12° when the moon is at GHA 84°. It is important to remember whether the moon is east or west of the meridian, as will be shown shortly.

To continue with the example, assume that the moon has a declination of North 18°. The pages of HO-229 have the declination information in a column at the edge, starting with 0° declination at the top. Just as in the HO-214, there is a SAME page and a CONTRARY page, and it means exactly the same thing in both books; if the moon has a north declination (above the equator), use the SAME page. If the moon is at a south declination (below the equator) use the CONTRARY page, assuming in both instances that your location is north latitude.

In Fig. 6, a sample of the 12°, 348° LHA page, assuming a station latitude of 42°N, follow the 18°-declination row across to the column of figures under 42°. The first number at that intersection is 63° 54.6 indicating the elevation of the moon above the horizon (horizon = 0°). The second number is the azimuth or beam heading for the antenna (north = 0°, east = 90°, south = 180°, and so on). Assuming that the moon has not passed the local meridian, its position at that moment is 153° azimuth at 63.9° elevation.

Fine, but what happens if the moon has passed the local meridian, and has a GHA of 83°, to stick with a previous example. This is also LHA 12°, but we know that the azimuth must be greater than 180°. To find the true azimuth, subtract the number found in the column from 360°. In this case, 360° −153.3 = 206.7°. Since the declination

Fig. 6 — A sample page from HO-229, Volume 3, covering 42° North, for an LHA of 12°. Note that the title of the page indicates it is for a SAME declination. The book includes a SAME and a CONTRARY page for each LHA.

12°, 348° L.H.A.   LATITUDE SAME NAME AS DECLINATION

N. Lat. { L.H.A. greater than 180°......Zn=Z / L.H.A. less than 180°...........Zn=360°−Z }

Dec.	38° Hc	d	Z	39° Hc	d	Z	40° Hc	d	Z	41° Hc	d	Z	42° Hc	d	Z	43° Hc	d	Z	44° Hc	d	Z	45° Hc	d	Z	Dec.
0	50 25.5	57.9	161.0	49 28.7	58.1	161.3	48 31.8	58.2	161.7	47 34.8	58.3	162.0	46 37.7	58.4	162.4	45 40.4	58.6	162.7	44 43.1	58.6	163.0	43 45.7	58.7	163.3	0
1	51 23.4	57.9	160.5	50 26.8	58.0	160.9	49 30.0	58.1	161.3	48 33.1	58.3	161.7	47 36.1	58.4	162.0	46 39.0	58.4	162.4	45 41.7	58.6	162.7	44 44.4	58.7	163.0	1
2	52 21.3	57.7	160.1	51 24.8	57.9	160.5	50 28.1	58.1	160.9	49 31.4	58.1	161.3	48 34.5	58.3	161.7	47 37.4	58.5	162.0	46 40.3	58.5	162.4	45 43.1	58.6	162.7	2
3	53 19.0	57.7	159.7	52 22.7	57.8	160.1	51 26.2	58.0	160.5	50 29.5	58.2	161.0	49 32.8	58.2	161.3	48 35.9	58.3	161.7	47 38.8	58.5	162.0	46 41.7	58.6	162.4	3
4	54 16.7	57.5	159.2	53 20.5	57.7	159.7	52 24.2	57.8	160.1	51 27.7	58.0	160.6	50 31.0	58.2	161.0	49 34.2	58.3	161.3	48 37.3	58.4	161.7	47 40.3	58.6	162.1	4
5	55 14.2	57.4	158.7	54 18.2	57.6	159.2	53 22.0	57.8	159.7	52 25.7	57.9	160.1	51 29.2	58.1	160.6	50 32.5	58.2	161.0	49 35.7	58.4	161.4	48 38.8	58.5	161.7	5
6	56 11.6	57.3	158.2	55 15.8	57.5	158.7	54 19.8	57.7	159.2	53 23.6	57.8	159.7	52 27.3	57.9	160.2	51 30.7	58.0	160.6	50 34.1	58.2	161.0	49 37.3	58.4	161.4	6
7	57 08.9	57.1	157.6	56 13.3	57.3	158.2	55 17.5	57.5	158.8	54 21.4	57.8	159.3	53 25.2	57.9	159.7	52 28.9	58.0	160.2	51 32.3	58.2	160.6	50 35.7	58.3	161.0	7
8	58 06.0	57.0	157.1	57 10.6	57.2	157.7	56 15.0	57.4	158.2	55 19.2	57.5	158.8	54 23.1	57.8	159.3	53 26.9	58.0	159.8	52 30.5	58.2	160.2	51 34.0	58.3	160.7	8
9	59 03.0	56.8	156.5	58 07.8	57.1	157.1	57 12.4	57.3	157.7	56 16.8	57.5	158.3	55 20.9	57.7	158.8	54 24.9	57.9	159.3	53 28.7	58.0	159.8	52 32.3	58.2	160.3	9
10	59 59.8	56.5	155.8	59 04.9	56.8	156.5	58 09.7	57.0	157.2	57 14.3	57.3	157.8	56 18.6	57.6	158.3	55 22.8	57.7	158.9	54 26.7	57.9	159.4	53 30.5	58.0	159.9	10
11	60 56.3	56.4	155.2	60 01.7	56.7	155.9	59 06.8	57.0	156.6	58 11.6	57.2	157.2	57 16.2	57.4	157.8	56 20.5	57.7	158.4	55 24.6	57.9	158.9	54 28.5	58.0	159.4	11
12	61 52.7	56.1	154.4	60 58.4	56.5	155.2	60 03.8	56.7	156.0	59 08.8	57.1	156.6	58 13.6	57.3	157.3	57 18.2	57.5	157.9	56 22.5	57.7	158.5	55 26.5	57.9	159.0	12
13	62 48.8	55.9	153.7	61 54.9	56.2	154.5	61 00.5	56.6	155.3	60 05.9	56.8	156.0	59 10.9	57.1	156.7	58 15.7	57.3	157.3	57 20.2	57.6	158.0	56 24.4	57.8	158.5	13
14	63 44.7	55.6	152.9	62 51.1	56.0	153.8	61 57.1	56.3	154.6	61 02.7	56.7	155.4	60 08.0	57.0	156.1	59 13.0	57.2	156.8	58 17.8	57.4	157.4	57 22.2	57.7	158.0	14
15	64 40.3	55.3	152.0	63 47.1	55.7	153.0	62 53.4	56.1	153.9	61 59.4	56.4	154.7	61 05.0	56.7	155.5	60 10.2	57.1	156.2	59 15.2	57.3	156.9	58 19.9	57.5	157.5	15
16	65 35.6	54.9	151.1	64 42.8	55.4	152.1	63 49.5	55.8	153.1	62 55.8	56.2	154.0	62 01.7	56.6	154.9	61 07.3	56.8	155.6	60 12.5	57.1	156.3	59 17.4	57.4	157.0	16
17	66 30.5	54.4	150.1	65 38.2	55.0	151.2	64 45.3	55.5	152.2	63 52.0	55.9	153.2	62 58.3	56.4	154.1	62 04.1	56.7	154.9	61 09.6	57.0	155.7	60 14.8	57.2	156.4	17
18	67 24.9	54.1	149.0	66 33.2	54.6	150.2	65 40.8	55.2	151.3	64 47.9	55.7	152.3	63 54.6	56.0	153.3	63 00.8	56.4	154.2	62 06.6	56.7	155.0	61 12.0	57.1	155.8	18
19	68 19.0	53.5	147.9	67 27.8	54.2	149.1	66 36.0	54.7	150.3	65 43.6	55.2	151.4	64 50.4	55.8	152.5	63 57.2	56.1	153.4	63 03.3	56.5	154.3	62 09.1	56.8	155.1	19
20	69 12.5	52.9	146.6	68 22.0	53.6	148.0	67 30.7	54.4	149.3	66 38.8	54.9	150.5	65 46.6	55.6	151.6	64 53.3	55.9	152.6	63 59.8	56.3	153.5	63 05.9	56.7	154.4	20
21	70 05.4	52.2	145.3	69 15.6	53.1	146.8	68 25.1	53.8	148.2	67 33.7	54.5	149.4	66 41.8	55.0	150.6	65 49.2	55.5	151.7	64 56.1	56.0	152.7	64 02.6	56.3	153.7	21
22	70 57.6	51.5	143.8	70 08.7	52.5	145.4	69 18.9	53.3	146.9	68 28.2	54.0	148.3	67 36.8	54.6	149.6	66 44.7	55.2	150.8	65 52.1	55.7	151.9	64 58.9	56.2	152.9	22
23	71 49.1	50.6	142.2	71 01.2	51.6	144.0	70 12.2	52.6	145.6	69 22.2	53.4	147.1	68 31.4	54.2	148.5	67 39.9	54.8	149.8	66 47.8	55.3	150.9	65 55.1	55.9	152.0	23
24	72 39.7	49.6	140.4	71 52.8	50.9	142.4	71 04.8	51.8	144.1	70 15.6	52.8	145.8	69 25.6	53.6	147.3	68 34.7	54.3	148.7	67 43.1	54.9	149.9	66 50.9	55.4	151.1	24

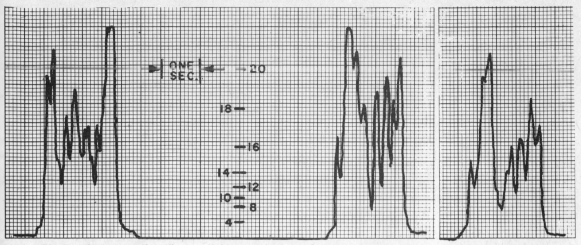

Fig. 7 — Chart recording of moon echoes received at W2NFA on July 26, 1973, at 1630 GMT. Antenna gain 44 dB; transmitting power 400 watts and system temperature 400° K.

did not change (only for convenience in the example — it will change in practice) the moon is now at 206.7° azimuth and 63.9° elevation.

Don't let the foregoing discussion frighten you. It takes much longer to describe the operation than to perform it. If the finding of celestial bodies without a star chart is new to you, bolster your confidence in the numbers by working out a few examples on clear nights (or days — it works for the sun too) and check that the moon (or sun) is really there. Make a simple sighting mechanism by placing a couple of screw eyes in a 2- or 3-foot long board. Calibrate it against a level or plumb-line and a protractor. A sighting of the North Star (Polaris) will indicate your latitude. A line from the North Star through your location, extending south, is your local meridian, or 180°. Calibration of the entire arc from north through east to south will help but is not necessary. Good practice can be obtained by predicting when the moon or sun will cross your meridian, and how many degrees above the horizon it will be when it does so. A check with the simple sighting device will indicate the accuracy of the calculation.

LIBRATION FADING OF EME SIGNALS

The following information on libration fading is taken from a technical report by the Crawford Hill VHF Club. The activities of their station, W2NFA, are well known in EME circles and have been an inspiration to many. We are indebted to the authors of the technical reports, in particular W2IMU, for permission to reprint this information.

One of the most troublesome aspects of receiving a moonbounce signal besides the enormous path loss and Faraday rotation fading, is *libration fading*. This section will deal only with libration (pronounced *lie-bray-shun*) fading, its cause, effects and possible measures to minimize it.

Libration fading of an EME signal is characterized in general as a fluttery, rapid, irregular fading

not unlike that observed in tropospheric scatter propagation. Fading can be very deep, 20 dB or more, and the maximum fading rate will depend on the operating frequency. At 1296 MHz the maximum fading rate is about 10 Hz, and scales directly with frequency.

On a weak cw EME signal, libration fading gives the impression of a randomly keyed signal. In fact on very slow cw telegraphy the effect is as though the keying is being done at a much faster speed. On very weak signals only the peaks of libration fading are heard in the form of occasional short bursts or "pings."

Fig. 7 shows samples of a typical EME echo signal at 1296 MHz. These recordings, made at W2NFA, show the wild fading characteristics with sufficient S/N ratio to record the deep fades. Circular polarization was used to eliminate Faraday fading; thus these recordings are of libration fading only. The recording bandwidth was limited to about 40 Hz to minimize the higher side-band-frequency components of libration fading which persist but are much smaller in amplitude. For those who would like a better statistical description, libration fading is Raleigh distributed. In the recordings shown by Fig. 7, the average signal-return level computed from path loss and mean reflection coefficient of the moon is at about the +15 dB S/N level.

It is clear that enhancement of echoes far in excess of this average level are observed. This point should be kept clearly in mind when attempting to obtain echoes or receive EME signals with marginal equipment. The probability of hearing an occasional peak is quite good since random enhancement as much as 10 dB is possible. Under these conditions however, the amount useful information which can be copied will be near zero. The enthusiastic newcomer to EME communications will be stymied by this effect since he knows that he can hear the signal strong enough on peaks to copy but can't make any sense out of what he tries to copy.

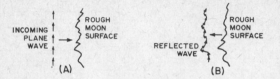

Fig. 8 — Showing how the rough surface of the moon reflects a plane wave as one having many field vectors.

What causes libration fading? Very simply it is due to multipath scattering of the radio waves from the very large (2000-mile diameter) and rough moon surface combined with the relative motion between earth and moon called librations.

To understand these effects, assume first that the earth and moon are stationary (no libration) and that a plane wave front arrives at the moon from your earth-bound station as shown in Fig. 8A.

The reflected wave shown in Fig. 8B consists of many scattered contributions from the rough moon surface. It is perhaps easier to visualize the process as if the scattering were from many small individual flat mirrors on the moon which reflect small portions (amplitudes) of the incident wave energy in different directions (paths) and with different path lengths (phase). Those paths directed toward the earth arrive at your antenna and appear as a collection of small wave fronts (field vectors) of various amplitudes and phases. The vector summation of all these coherent (same frequency) returned waves (and there are a near-infinite array of them) takes place at the feed point of your antenna (the collecting point in the antenna system). The level of the final summation as measured by a receiver can, of course, have any value from zero to some maximum. Remember now that we assumed the earth and moon were stationary, which means that the final summation of these multipath signal returns from the moon will be one *fixed* value. The condition of relative motion between earth and moon being zero is a rare event which will be discussed later in this section.

Consider now that the earth and moon are moving relative to each other (as they are in nature), so that the incident radio wave "sees" a slightly different surface of the moon from moment to moment. Since the moon surface is very irregular, the reflected wave will be equally irregular, changing in amplitude and phase from moment to moment. The resultant continuous summation of the varying multipath signals at your antenna feed point produces the effect called libration fading of the moon-reflected signal.

The term libration is used to describe small perturbations in the movement of astro bodies. Earth libration consists mainly of its diurnal rotation; moon libration consists mainly of its 28-day rotation which appears as a very slight rocking motion with respect to an observer on earth. This rocking motion can be visualized as follows: Place a marker on the surface of the moon at the center of the moon disk, which is the point closest to the observer, as shown in Fig. 9. Then over a period of time we will observe that this marker wanders around within a small area. All this means is that the surface of the moon as seen from the earth is not quite fixed but changes slightly as different areas of the periphery are exposed due to this rocking motion. Moon libration is very slow (of the order of 10^{-7} radians per second) and can be determined with some difficulty from published moon ephemeris tables.

Although the libration motions are very small and slow, the large surface area of the moon, having nearly an infinite number of scattering points (small areas), means that even these slight geometric movements can alter the total summation of the returned multipath echo by a significantly large amount. Since the librations of the earth and moon are calculable, it is only logical to ask if there ever occurs a time when the total libration is zero or near zero? The answer is yes, and it has been observed and experimentally verified on radar echoes that minimum *fading rate* (not depth of fade) is coincident with minimum total libration. Calculation of minimum total libration is at best tedious and can only be done successfully by means of a digital computer. It is a problem in extrapolation of rates of change in coordinate motion and in small differences of large numbers.

At W2NFA several libration fading minima on echoes have been observed, recorded samples of which are shown in Fig. 10. Comparison with Fig. 7 shows the lack of rapid fading, indicating that libration has slowed down considerably. Note that the fades are still quite the same in depth and enhancement. In general, libration fading on echoes will be most severe at moon zenith and will have minimas only in the regions near moon rise or set, elevation angles of roughly 20 to 30 degrees, but not with daily regularity. And most important of all the minima are cusp-like in occurrence and are easily distinguishable for brief periods of approximately one-half hour or less.

Further Considerations of Moon Libration

The simple concept of multipath scattering from the moon must be extended for completeness to include libration spreading. The main component of libration motion is due to the earth's rotation and occurs when the moon is in its zenith position (directly over your station meridian). At this time the observer on earth is moving with considerable tangential velocity which may be

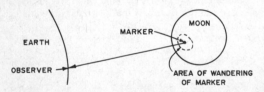

Fig. 9 — The moon appears to "wander" in its orbit about the earth. Thus, a fixed marker on the moon's surface will appear to move about in a circular area.

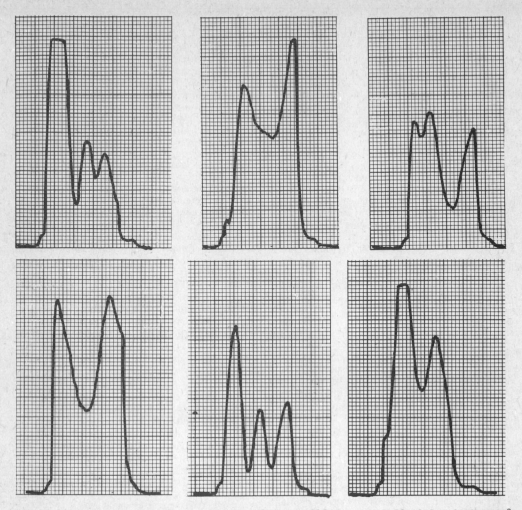

Fig. 10 — Echo samples of low libration taken at W2NFA at 1296 MHz on July 28, 1973, 1130 GMT 30° elevation, 88° azimuth. Note a much lower fading rate than in Fig. 7, but equally deep fades. The time scale and level calibration are the same as for Fig. 7.

translated to simple rotational motion of the moon. Total libration motion of the moon and earth may therefore be considered as simple rotation of the moon over a small interval of time, as depicted in Fig. 11.

Reflections occurring towards the limbs of the moon, designated as points 1 and 2 in Fig. 11, have their radial distance to the earth changing in opposite directions due to the rotation of the moon. Reflections from point 1 are increasing in distance to the earth while reflections from 2 are decreasing. From well-known rules for Doppler frequency shift it is clear that the radio wave reflected from point 1 will be decreasing in carrier frequency while those from point 2 will be increasing in frequency. Reflections from the center of the moon disk, point 3, will not be shifted in frequency because the radial distance to the earth is not changing.

Since reflections are occurring over essentially half the moon surface (the half facing the earth), it is obvious that each reflection point (multipath scattering) will have a Doppler shift of its own according to the change in distance to the earth with libration rotation. The total effect, summed at your antenna terminals, is a spreading or smearing of the incident cw signal into a carrier surrounded by symmetric sidebands which extend out to a maximum of:

$$F = \pm \frac{2\, L_t\, r_m}{\lambda} \quad \text{hertz.}$$

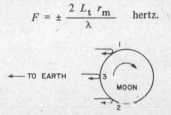

Fig. 11 — Total libration motion of the moon and earth may be considered as simple rotation of the moon, as shown here. Numbered points are discussed in the text.

Here λ is the carrier wavelength, r_m is the moon radius in the same units as λ, ($r_m = 2000$ statute miles or about 10,000,000 feet) and L_t is the total maximum libration rate which is about 12×10^{-7} radians/second. For a carrier frequency of 1296 MHz, the maximum extent of the sidebands will be about ±20 Hz. At 144 MHz, it is about 2 Hz. The total energy in these Doppler spreading sidebands is small in the vhf-uhf range but increases at higher frequencies.

It should be made quite clear at this point that libration spreading caused by Doppler shift of the many reflections over the surface of the moon is a *small* disturbance of the radio signal. The mean or average Doppler shift in carrier frequency caused by the rate of change in average range distance between earth and moon is not considered in this section but can amount to as much as ±4000 Hz near moonrise (+) and moonset (−). This is the more familiar Doppler shift in frequency of an EME signal and sounds like a slowly drifting oscillator.

An overview of moon-reflection distribution with respect to frequency is useful to complete the understanding of libration fading and Doppler spreading effects. When looking at a full moon optically, we see a bright uniformly illuminated disk. At much lower frequencies than light waves the picture is somewhat different. At 25,000 MHz, the disk appears to be brighter at the center, falling off in brightness by 5 or 6 dB at the edge. As we procede lower in frequency the central brightness area becomes smaller and the intensity falls off more rapidly towards the edge. At 1296 MHz the central area of most energy reflection (bright spot) comprises less than 1/3 the total disk area, and the reflected energy falls off by 30 dB or more towards the edge. At 144 MHz the bright central area is even smaller and the edge of the moon disk is all but invisible. Curiously, the average reflection coefficient of the moon remains virtually constant over the entire vhf-uhf range at about 6.5%

This distribution with frequency of the reflection characteristics of the moon has been experimentally verified and is important to keep in mind as we consider further aspects of libration fading and Doppler spreading.

Coherence Bandwidth

The total effect of libration fading and Doppler spreading can be summed up in the following hypothetical experiment. Suppose that we transmit

an a-m signal to the moon. And suppose further that the carrier is modulated by a single tone, the frequency of which can be varied from about 100 Hz to 10,000 Hz. For low modulation frequencies the return signal can be demodulated and, except for the fading, will demodulate normally and be the same as the original signal. As the modulation frequency is increased we notice a curious result. The demodulated signal is becoming distorted and appears to have "selective fading." The fact is that the two sidebands of the returned signal (an a-m signal consists of a carrier with symmetric sidebands, two sidebands for a single modulation tone) have undergone different phase and amplitude changes − they are becoming incoherent.

The coherence bandwidth can then be defined as the frequency separation at which some degree of acceptable coherence still exists. At 1296 MHz the a-m sidebands start becoming incoherent for a modulation frequency of a few kilohertz. This effect essentially scales inversely with frequency so that at 144 MHz the sidebands will be coherent out to about 10 kHz. For these reasons a-m and fm, and other forms of modulation requiring coherent double sidebands are not recommended for voice or wide-band moonbounce communications, especially at frequencies above about 1000 MHz. And for the same reasons, ssb is recommended for all voice communication via the moon.

Space Coherence

One possible method of reducing libration fading is by means of diversity reception where two spaced antennas are used and the receiver outputs are combined on a power basis. To implement such a system the first consideration is how far apart must the antennas be spaced so that the signals are totally uncorrelated. By power combining these incoherent signals a substantial reduction in deep fades will be achieved, resulting in a more constant average signal level.

An estimate of the spacing of the two antennas can be made by a simple geometric analysis of the radio-wave path lengths on a radar basis. The geometry is shown in Fig. 12 for a single pair of reflection points at an arbitrary disk radius of r_0. This geometry permits a simple formula to be derived which gives the distance separation between S_1 and S_2 such that the radio signals are in phase at S_1 and out of phase by 180° at S_2. The formula is:

$$\Delta S = \frac{\lambda \, R_m}{4 \, r_0}$$

where R_m, the distance to the moon, is approximately 250,000 statute miles, λ is the operating wavelength, and r_0 is the disk radius in the same units as R_m − r_0 may be any value from zero to a maximum of 1000 miles. It is obvious then that the space coherence distance, ΔS, can have a value from infinity down to some minimum where $r_0 =$ 1000 miles. Recalling the discussion of energy distribution reflected from the moon it is possible to make a reasonable estimate for r_0 such that a reflection point in a region of high energy reflection is chosen. At 1296 MHz, for example, a

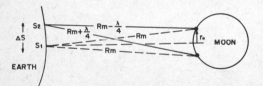

Fig. 12 — Geometry for determining the required spacing, ΔS, between two antennas for diversity reception to minimize the effects of libration fading.

suitable value for r_o would be 100 miles, for which ΔS computes to be about 470 feet!

What about the energy from within the 100 mile radius, which is of large magnitude and indicates that a much greater spacing is demanded? The choice of r_o = 100 miles was made partly in consideration of the following analysis. Inspection of Fig. 7 indicates that fading rates of about 3 Hz are easily observed, along with lower frequency components. At moon zenith the major contribution of libration is the rotation of the earth. A short calculation will reveal that an observer standing at one point near the earth's equator will actually be moving with a tangential velocity of about 1500 feet/second. Since the coherence distance, ΔS, computed above is only half a space cycle it becomes clear that for reflectors at r_o = 100 miles the fading rate as observed on earth will be in the order of 3 Hz! This means that for a diversity antenna spacing of 470 feet, all those fading components above 3 Hz will be uncorrelated. Those below 3 Hz *will* be correlated and hence cannot be reduced at this spacing. Since these quantities are linearly related, a spacing of about 1000 feet will be required to reduce fading rates in the region of 1 Hz by diversity reception at 1296 MHz.

It should be kept in mind that each antenna must be large enough to receive a signal with a reasonable S/N ratio, since the addition of the second antenna will not substantially increase the average power level but will only minimize the deep fading. If one attempts to add the signals coherently from the antennas, the effective gain of the system will double (if both antennas have the same gain) but the fading will be essentially the same as with a single antenna.

Another method of minimizing libration fading is to utilize the coherence bandwidth property in the form of a frequency-diversity system. In its simplest form one would transmit two signals spaced in frequency by greater than the coherence bandwidth, and of nearly equal power, through one antenna.

An appropriate receiving system would be the usual front-end converter down to some i-f where selectivity can be obtained. At this point in the receiving system the signal is split and filtered. The two signals are separately detected and the outputs are combined on a simple rms basis through a resistive network. For cw operation the final beat-note output of the detectors should be adjusted for nearly the same pitch.

Frequency diversity is of course much easier to implement than antenna space diversity. To date, we have no knowedge that either system has been employed in amateur EME work.

EME OPERATING TECHNIQUES

Most EME signals tend to be near the threshold of readability, a condition caused by a combination of path loss, Faraday rotation, and libration fading. This weakness and unpredictability of the signal has led to the development of techniques for

---

TABLE I

Signal Reports Used on 144-MHz EME

T	— Signal just detectable
M	— Portions of calls copied
O	— Complete call set has been received
R	— Both "O" report and call sets have been received
SK	— End of contact

---

exchange of EME information that differs from those used for normal vhf work — the usual RST reporting would be jumbled and meaningless for many EME contacts. Dashes are often chopped into pieces, a string of dots would be incomplete, and complicated words would make no sense at all.

Unfortunately, there is no universal agreement as to procedures for all the bands, although there is similarity. Two-meter operators generally use the "T M O R" system while those on 432 MHz use a similar system, but applied at somewhat different levels of readability. The meanings, and typical use, of each part of the sequence are given in Tables I through IV.

At the moment, there is no widespread system in use for bands other than 144 and 432 MHz. There are so few participants on 50 and 220 MHz that presumably they will have no difficulty in arranging techniques by correspondence, prior to schedules for EME tests. The amount of operation on 1296 MHz is low, but on the increase. Perhaps an operating technique can evolve that will be acceptable to those on any band. The important consideration is that an exchange of information takes place. This information should include three basic parts: calls of both stations, signal reports, and confirmation that previous information was received.

In the schedule sequence for both 144 and 432 MHz, the initial period starts on the hour, but because of the difference in sequence lengths for the two bands, schedules starting on the half hour will not be the same. On two meters, there are 15 sequence periods to the half hour, which would make the period 0030 to 0032 an "even" sequence. This could make a difference, depending on which operator was assigned an "odd" or "even" sequence. Note that *odd* or *even* refers to the sequence number, not the minutes designated within that sequence.

TABLE II

Signal Reports Used on 432-MHz EME

T	— Portions of calls copied
M	— Complete calls copied
O	— Good signal — better than average copy
5	— Excellent signal — solid copy (possibly good enough for ssb work)
R	— Calls and reports copied
SK	— End of contact

TABLE III

144-MHz Procedure – 2-Minute Sequence

Period	1-1/2 minutes	30 seconds
1	Calls (W6XXX de W1XXX)	
2	W1XXX de W6XXX	T T T T
3	W6XXX de W1XXX	O O O O
4	RO RO RO RO	de W1XXX k
5	R R R R R	de W6XXX k
6	QRZ? EME	de W1XXX k

On 432 MHz, there are 12 sequence periods to the half hour. The eastern-most station calls first, and since two 2-1/2-minute periods fill a 5-minute space, it works out conveniently that the eastern (or first) station will call starting with every five minute mark, and start listening 2-1/2 minutes later. Thus a schedule starting at 0030 would be an "odd" period, although operators on 432 MHz seldom label them as such. It is convenient for the operators to simply start with the eastern-most station calling on the hour or half hour, unless arranged otherwise.

Of course there is much room for change in these arrangements, but they do serve as vital guidelines for schedules. As signals become stronger, the rules can be relaxed to a degree, and after many contacts, stations can often ignore them completely, if the signals are strong enough.

Calls are often extremely difficult to hear in their entirety. A vital dot or dash can be missing, which can render a complex call unreadable. To copy both calls completely requires much patience and a good ear. Both calls must be copied, because even though most work is by timed schedules, there can be last-minute substitutions because of equipment trouble at one station, unexpected travel, plan changes or the like, which make it impossible for the scheduled station to appear. Thus, rather than have one station spend the entire period listening, only to find that no one was there, a system of standby stations is becoming more popular. This is good, because nothing will demoralize a newcomer faster than several one-sided schedules.

An exchange of signal reports is a useful and required bit of information: useful because it helps in evaluating your station performance and the prevailing conditions at the time, required because it is a "non-prearranged" exchange, thereby requiring that you copy what was sent as part of the contact. Obviously there are other things that could be included in an "exchange of unknown information," and when conditions permit stronger signals, many operators do include names, elaborate on the signal reports, arrange next schedule times, and so on. Unfortunately, such exchanges are rare.

Confirmation is essential for completion of the exchange. There is no way that you can be sure that the other operator copied what you sent until you hear him say so. That final "R" or "roger" means that he has copied your information, and your two-way contact is complete.

Sending speed is usually in the 5- to 10-wpm range, although it can be adjusted according to conditions and operator skill. Characters sent too slow tend to become chopped up and confusing. High speed cw is hard to copy at marginal signal levels for most amateurs, and the fading that is typical of an EME path can make it well nigh impossible to decipher the content.

Other Modes

Only a few stations have the capability of sending (and receiving) signals of a strength sufficient to allow experimentation with other than cw. There have been some ssb contacts and echoes of RTTY and fm signals have been heard, but no two-way communication by these latter modes have been accomplished to date. In general, only the stations with large parabolic reflectors try these more difficult means of EME work. Such installations are often "borrowed" from some research program for the amateur endeavors.

Frequencies

Most amateur EME work is conducted within a few kHz of some convenient spot frequency. On 144 MHz there is some room to move about, but most operation is very near the low edge, consistent with the ability of the station to stay within the band. The situation is further confused by the requirement that Technician licensees must stay above 145 MHz. There are some EME enthusiasts among the Technician Class licensees, and those amateurs with large enough antennas can work both portions of the band. The antenna problem is mentioned because most high-gain antennas will not maintain their performance over such a wide portion of the band.

Operation on 432 MHz is generally within one to two kilohertz of that frequency, with a few stations going as far afield as 431.997 or 432.003 for general schedules. It is not unknown for a pair of stations to move up 10 or 15 kHz for a contact while others are on the nominal ".000" spot. There has been a movement afoot recently to reach a gentleman's agreement to avoid any short-range, local, or non-DX operation between 432.0 and 432.025 MHz – a concept that most EME enthusiasts heartily approve.

TABLE IV

432-MHz Procedure – 2-1/2-Minute Sequence

Period	2 minutes	30 seconds
1	VE7BBG de K2UYH	
2	K2UYH de VE7BBG	
3	VE7BBG de K2UYH	T T T
4	K2UYH de VE7BBG	M M M
5	RM RM RM RM	de K2UYH k
6	R R R R R	de VE7BBG SK

For operation on 1296 MHz, most stations are within a very few kilohertz of that spot frequency. Many devices, tubes and transistors, would work much better at the low end of the 1215-MHz band, but the 1296.0 spot became popular because it was convenient to triple from an existing 432-MHz exciter.

Of course, it is obvious that as the number of stations on EME increases, the frequency spread must become greater. Since the moon is in convenient locations only a few days out of the month, and only a certain number of stations can be scheduled for EME during a given evening, the answer will be in the use of sumultaneous schedules, spaced a few kilohertz apart. The time may not be too far away — QRM has already been experienced on each of our three most active EME frequencies.

EME Terminology

Altitude — Sometimes used to indicate angular height above the horizon; more properly, elevation.

Apogee — The point of an orbit which is at the greatest distance from the earth.

Az-El — Sometimes El-Az, contraction for azimuth/elevation, describing the motion capabilities of an antenna mounted so that it can rotate freely, to point at any azimuth bearing and at any elevation angle.

Azimuth — The bearing, in degrees, of a point on the horizon where a perpendicular line from a celestial body intersects the horizon. In EME work, numbers procede clockwise from 0° north, with 90° at east, 180° at south, and 270° at west.

Declination — The position of the moon or sun in degrees above or below the celestial equator.

Elevation — Angular height of an object above the horizon. In EME work the horizon is generally designated 0°., and the perpendicular (zenith) is 90°.

EME — Earth-moon-earth, the path taken on a round trip by such communications. *Sometimes called moonbounce.*

Faraday Rotation — The rotation of polarity of an electromagnetic wave as it progresses through the ionosphere.

GHA — Greenwich Hour Angle, the angle of a celestial body with respect to the Zero Meridian (Greenwich).

LHA — Local Hour Angle, the angle of a celestial body with respect to the observers local meridian.

Libration Fading — A fading of signals returning from the moon, caused by uneven surface reflections and minor motions of the moon.

Perigee — The point of an orbit that occurs nearest to earth.

Polar Mount — A mounting for an antenna, the axis of which is aligned with the North Star (Polaris), or is otherwise made to be parallel with the axis of the earth. This system simplifies tracking of the moon (or sun), but limits the usefulness of the antenna to a small portion of the horizon for non-space communications.

S.D. — Semi-diameter of the moon in minutes of arc, listed in almanacs and ephemerides. Useful in determining the position of the moon in its transition from apogee to perigee.

Window — A portion of the sky at which the observer's antenna can be aimed and where the path of the moon will enter the radiation pattern from the antenna. For fully steerable antennas, the window is limited by the horizon or by obstructions in the vicinity; for fixed antennas it is limited by the radiation pattern of the array.

EME References

* Tilton, Michael, "Lunar DX on 144 Mc.," *QST*, March, 1953.

[1] Sky and Telescope magazine is available from Sky Publishing Co., 49-50-51 Bay State Rd., Cambridge, MA 02138.

[2] *Nautical Almanac* is available from Superintendent of Documents, U.S. Government Printing Office, Washington, DC 20402, or U.S. Government Book Stores at $6.50 per copy. A new edition is needed each year and is usually available in the fall of the preceding year.

[3] Ko, "The Distribution of Cosmic Radio Background Radiation," *Proceedings of the IRE*, January, 1958, pages 208-215.

[4] Somerlock, "Sky Temperature Behind the Moon," *QST*, Oct., 1964.

[5] *Tables of Computed Altitude and Azimuth*, publication H.O.-214, by the U.S. Hydrographic Office. This publication is available from the U.S. Government Printing Office for $6. There are several volumes available in 10° increments. Be certain to order the volume which includes your latitude. For example, Volume IV is for latitudes 30-39°, inclusive.

[6] Michael, "Tracking the Moon — In Simple English," *QST*, January, 1965.

[7] Bob Sutherland, W6PO, can furnish computer tapes of suitable EME programs in Basic, Super Basic or Fortran IV for those interested.

Advanced Techniques

Most of the techniques covered in previous chapters of this book have been developed, but the ones to be discussed in this chapter are still in the speculative stage. While many communication techniques and transmission modes exist, relatively few are applicable to amateur use. This fact is sometimes overlooked by critics of amateur radio in arguments that amateurs are not "progressive enough" in adopting new methods. Technically speaking, such criticism lacks validity since most possibilities can be eliminated to begin with.

At the present time, only two areas hold any real promise in future applications for amateur radio – lasers and digital communication. The laser has been widely used in industry and research and in some experimental work in amateur radio. In communications applications, a laser is very similar to uhf and microwave power sources and could replace many of them in point-to-point communication. Its chief drawback is paradoxically enough one of its principal advantages; the intense energy density from high-power devices can perform useful functions but it is also quite hazardous. Unless proper precuations are taken, severe injuries can occur, with eyesight being the most prone to damage.

LASER FUNDAMENTALS

The word *laser* is an acronym for Light Amplification by Stimulated Emission of Radiation.* Lasers take energy at (or near) the visible light spectrum and convert it to a very narrow and intense beam in the same region. A close relative of the laser is the LED (light emitting diode) which takes dc or low-frequency ac power and converts the energy into visible light. The principle of the laser is somewhat similar to that of a very high-Q cavity resonator "shock excited" by a spark transmitter. While the input energy covers a wide band of frequencies, the output of the cavity is on one frequency, or nearly so. Such energy distributions are called incoherent and coherent, respectively.† Turning a transmitter on with no modulation will give coherent radiation. Connecting a diode noise source to an antenna would result in incoherent radiation.

Lasers can either be of the cw or pulsed variety. In this respect, the device is little different from conventional oscillators using solid-state or vacuum-tube components. The basic mechanism by which the energy is converted from one form to another is considerably different, however. In conventional oscillators, dc power from the collector or plate supply is converted to rf energy, with the frequency being more or less independent of the molecular or atomic structure of the generating device. This is not true for the laser. Here, the conversion takes place within the molec-

ular structure of a crystal or gas *directly*. The external "circuits" play a small role in the actual output frequency. Consequently, lasers will only yield output energy on certain frequencies which depend upon the atomic structure of the chemical elements used in the crystal or gas. The fact that the light from an LED is always the same color results from similar considerations. In a laser, incoherent light excites the electrons in the atoms to higher energy levels than they would normally have. The new energy states are unstable and the electrons drop down to lower energy levels. In doing so, energy is released in the form of light. The ends of the crystal or glass tube (gas laser) are such that the light waves reflect back and forth between two mirrored surfaces. One of the ends is only partially reflecting and light energy is transmitted through it to form the light beam. Power sources for lasers include flash tubes or, in the case of diode-type lasers, a dc power supply.

Practical Laser Oscillators

The foregoing discussion outlines some of the basic features of the laser. Since gas lasers are ones of great interest in communications (and are also somewhat easier to understand), the discussion in this section will be limited to this area. However, it should be pointed out that many other laser types exist, including ruby crystal, liquid, and "semiconductor" types.

Any amateur who has experimented with a gas-filled glow lamp (such as the popular NE neon series) near the output of a low-powered transmit-

---

* Lytel, *ABC's of Lasers and Masers*, Howard W. Sams & Co.
† "Cathode Ray," *Wireless World*, Nov. 1964.

Fig. 1 — Energy level diagram. The energy level is usually expressed in ergs or electron volts. Associated with each energy level is a wavelength or frequency. Energy and frequency are related by the equation shown.

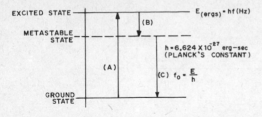

ter is already familiar with the basic physical phenomenon involved in laser operation. Energy from the rf field excites the gas molecules and causes them to emit radiation in the visible part of the electromagnetic spectrum or *light*. The interaction between the rf field and the gas occurs within the outer electron shells of each atom or molecule of the gas in the tube. The mechanism can be explained by the use of an energy-level diagram as shown in Fig. 1. At A, the rf field excites an electron to a higher energy state shown at B. (If a sufficient strong field is applied, the electron is torn away from the molecule and the process is called ionization, although the term is often applied to any electron in an excited state). If the molecule doesn't become ionized, the electron eventually drops back down to some lower energy level which is stable, and electromagnetic radiation is emitted. The frequency of the radiation and the energy level are related by a unique value called Planck's constant which is denoted by **h**. While there are many ways in which the electron can return to the "ground" or stable state, the ones of most interest in laser operation are those involving the so-called metastable states. Instead of immediately returning to the ground state, the electron drops down to some intermediate state for several cycles. As the name implies, this intermediate or metastable state is unstable and can also be triggered into giving up its energy by some external force or field. If an excitation source (sometimes called a pump signal) is applied to the gas in the tube, some of the electrons will be raised into higher energy states. At any one time, a fraction of the molecules will have electrons occupying metastable states since it takes a comparatively long time before a particular electron drops from this to a lower state. This condition is called population inversion, and provides the means by which laser action is possible.

While the radiation emitted by each molecule contains the same amount of energy (or is on the same frequency), the light emitted from the gas as a whole is not. The reason for this is the physical motion of the gas molecules. When viewed from any angle, some molecules are moving toward the observer and some are moving away. Consequently, the frequency of the radiation reaching the observer is shifted slightly because of the Doppler effect. Instead of a pure spectral line (Fig. 2), a band of frequencies centered around the fundmental fre-

quency is observed. Even though the output seems to be on a single frequency, considerable sideband energy or noise is present.

However, if instead of a simple glass tube, the discharge is enclosed within the configuration shown in Fig. 3A, a different phenomenon is possible. Two highly reflecting and optically smooth mirrors are placed at each end of the discharge tube. If the separation of the mirrors is such that some multiple of a half wavelength associated with the frequency of one of the metastable states exists, a standing wave pattern can occur. Light energy traveling in one direction triggers electrons in the particular metastable state of interest which in turn give up their energy to the passing wave. This is somewhat analogous to the ordinary circuit-type oscillators utilizing feedback. In fact, the laser action is nothing more than a special type of feedback. While most of the energy is contained in the resonant cavity or "tank" circuit, some of it is coupled out by means of a partially transmitting mirror on one end. In this case, the power supply is a vhf source which excites the electrons from the ground state (Fig. 1) to some higher state where they then give up energy to sustain the oscillation.

As might be expected, adjustment of the "cavity" would be quite critical and difficult to perform on the simple arrangement shown in Fig. 3A. Flexible bellows would be required on each end of the tube since the discharge can only occur in near vacuum conditions. The configuration in Fig. 3B gets around the latter problem by a unique means. The ends of the tube are still flat but molded at an angle for the following reason. When electromagnetic radiation impinges upon a dielectric surface such as glass, part of the energy is reflected and part is transmitted into the glass. Imagine a plane cutting the tube in Fig. 3B down the middle as shown in Fig. 3C. At a certain angle θ, a wave front with its electric-field vector in the cutting plane (often referred to as the plane of incidence) will be completely transmitted through the glass and no reflections will occur. For wave fronts with electric field vectors not in the plane of incidence, part of the energy is transmitted and part of it is reflected from the glass. Such a vector is denoted by E2 in Fig. 3C. The angle at which all the energy is transmitted is called the Brewster angle, and the tangent of this angle is equal to the

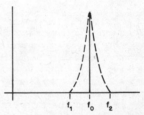

Fig. 2 — Effect of Doppler shift on spectral line. Because of the molecular motion of the gas, the radiated light as seen by a distant observer appears as a band of frequencies (between f1 and f2) rather than a discrete line.

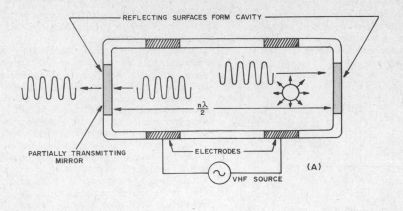

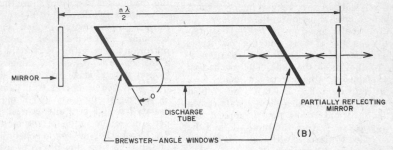

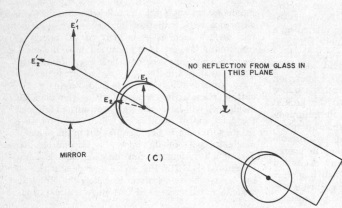

Fig. 3 — Simplified drawing of some typical laser configurations. The effect of the Brewster windows is shown at C. For plane waves incident at the Brewster angle, little attenuation takes place and the transmitted field at the mirror (E1) is nearly the same as the field in the glass tube (E1). At other angles, reflection takes place for fields outside of the plane of incidence (E2), and the transmitted field is attenuated (E2).

index of refraction of the glass.* The angle is sometimes called the polarizing angle since polarized radiation in the plane of incidence will be transmitted with the greatest efficiency. Therefore, oscillations will tend to take place with E vectors in this plane. The reflecting mirrors can now be placed outside of the tube, which simplifies construction and alignment considerably. This latter configuration is one of the more classic laser forms. Some of the gases used are combinations of helium and neon, with output in the red part of the visible spectrum.

* Harris, "Lasers," *Wireless World*, August, 1963.

Laser Communications

As pointed out earlier, lasers offer some promising possibilities in many fields of industry and research. Therefore, it is not suprising that a prodigious amount of theoretical and experimental work has been done with them. At the very least, it is one of the greatest achievements of 20th century science. From a communication standpoint, it does have some drawbacks, however. While laser energy is capable of being formed in a very narrow beam, it is still subject to the same difficulties as any other form of light transmission. Fog and other adverse weather conditions can absorb the light. In addition, even very minute variations in atmospheric temperature can cause deflection and scattering of the laser beam. This severely limits the range of laser communications through free space, and other means have been sought to get around the problem.

An optical waveguide consisting of a very thin dielectric fiber surrounded or clad by another dielectric coating several wavelengths thick has been successfully used to convey the beam over considerable distances and around bends. A number of fibers can be paralleled to reduce the attenuation through the waveguide. One goal is an inexpensive telephone system with a bandwidth greater than that of existing methods.

The terrestrial propagation difficulties do not exist in outer space and the very narrow beamwidth of the laser permits communication over the extremely large distances involved. One fundamental limitation still has to be taken into consideration, however, and that is the particle nature of light. As the wavelength of electromagnetic radiation decreases, the waves begin to behave more like a stream of particles (or quanta) rather than a continuous flow of energy. This causes additional noise sidebands and adversely affects the signal-to-noise ratio achievable. Fortunately, this drawback is offset somewhat by the improved "antenna" efficency for a given aperture as the frequency increases.

While it would seem that amateur radio is not on the verge of multicolored QRM, there are other communications techniques involving lasers which are quite interesting. A very remarkable type of photography called holography is possible using the illumination from a laser. If an object and a photographic plate are illuminated simultaneously by a laser, the combination of the two with light scattered from the object forms a complicated interference pattern on the plate. If the developed plate is then illuminated by another laser, a three-dimensional image is formed. The reason for this is that unlike regular photography, both amplitude and *phase* information of the light scattered from the object is contained in the photographic plate. In essence, all the information contained in the three-dimensional coordinate system is reduced to two dimensions.

Such techniques simplify data storage and transmission and could increase memory readout capability and speeds by a large factor. Instead of a photographic plate, a light-sensitive matrix could be substituted. Used with an appropriate scanning system, this technique could form the basis for an optical memory.*

Lasers and the Future

Opinions concerning the usefulness of lasers range from laboratory curiosities to science-fiction type super tools. While progress has been hard to evaluate, developments have tended to support the latter view. Just what role lasers will play in the future of amateur communications is hard to predict. Statements about "those useless waves" above the microwave spectrum are apt to cause old timers and historians in the amateur ranks to become somewhat restive. After all, the same was said about the short-wave radio spectrum. At the time, it was true since tha state of the art hadn't advanced far enough. Devices were crude, but the same thing applies to the present state of laser technology. Few amateurs around at the time when radio was in its infancy could predict the advances that were to be made. However, one statement is relatively safe to make; future applications of lasers in amateur radio will depend upon how willing amateurs will be in experimenting and learning about the new technique.

* Gambling and Smith, "Laser Applications in Electronics," *Wireless World,* August, 1969.

DIGITAL COMMUNICATIONS

At the present time, there are no specific provisions in the U.S. regulations for amateur use of digital communications. However, special temporary authorization should be requested from the FCC for serious experimentation. The above restrictions do not apply to one-way digitally encoded transmissions to model vehicles or craft under section 97.99 of the U.S. regulations. Also, pulse modulation is limited to frequencies in the 2300 and 5600 MHz bands and frequencies above 40 GHz.

However, there are possibilities for the use of digital modulation in future amateur applications. The following sections outline the techniques involved and some typical applications. The first section appeared as an article in *QST* for March, 1974 and the second in *QST* for October, 1972. Both articles were authored by Vincent Biancomano, WB2EZG.

Very often, innovations in technology appear to materialize miraculously when, in reality, theories postulating their mysteries have existed for years. Add the fact that many of us behave somewhat like inductors — we resist changing ideas. What results can also be attributed to electrical law — the change comes eventually but there is a time lag. There is no reason for this to happen when discussing digital modulation, because amateurs are aware of the subject, though perhaps unknowingly.

The idea of digital signal transmission is as old as the invention of the telegraph, and the art of combining many telegraph signals over a common wire is almost as old. Representation of analog or varying signals by digital means was first tried about 1900 and continued through the 1930s. (Incidentally, single sideband enjoyed its beginning around 1930 or so). As regards analog-digital representation, it was found that the methods used yielded little advantage with respect to conventional amplitude modulation; noise, distortion and crosstalk were not noticeably improved. This eventually led to pulse-code modulation where a given analog amplitude would be represented by a given sequence of equal amplitude digits. This will be better understood later. It is most important now to investigate some familiar ideas under a more powerful microscope.

A Closer Look at Modulation

All of us have a good idea of what modulation means; we make use of it daily for radio communication. If a beginner were to ask us for a definition of the term, however, could we answer satisfactorily? We must be careful in stating, "It is a process used to vary the amplitude, frequency or phase of a radio wave for the purpose of transmitting information." Such a definition is incorrect and is acceptable at most social gatherings, but the whole story is not told because the choice of words is too confining. This we wish to avoid.

Initially, we can try to define modulation as the multiplication of any two frequencies. It will be shown that this is a better definition than the previous widely accepted one. Even then, it will be shown that a better explanation is possible, and what conclusions can be drawn.

Modulating an rf signal with an af one serves two purposes: (1) Many signals in the af range can occupy the spectrum by translation of the audio to chosen radio frequencies. (2) Modulation allows radiation (it is very hard to radiate audio frequencies because of the required physical length of the antenna). Mixing and heterodyning is also modulation in the strictest sense; here, both are radio frequencies.

Now, suppose we have a carrier frequency of the form sin ωt or cos ωt (a pure frequency), and we combine (multiply) it with audio frequency $f(t)$. What results is the spectrum as shown in Fig. 1. This is nothing new to us; sum and difference frequencies are generated. Now suppose we were to modulate a rectangular wave with $f(t)$. What would be the spectrum? We can reason the answer intuitively without resorting to mathematical proof. Since in general, the rectangular wave consists of a fundamental frequency plus harmonics of that frequency, then sum and difference frequencies are generated at the fundamental and each harmonic. Thus the modulation theory not only includes trigonometric functions, but any

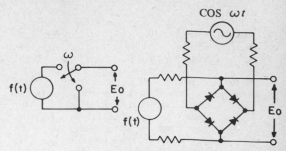

Fig. 2 — Example of the switching type modulator.

periodic function whether it be square, triangular, rectangular or just about any other wave we will encounter. Acutally, the theory is extended to include nonperiodic wave forms too, but there is no need to discuss this. To continue, this immediately gives rise to a discovery. A rectangular wave is a form of dc wave — a switched wave. If $f(t)$ could be switched into the circuit periodically as shown in Fig. 2, modulation would be performed. The audio function $f(t)$, would be multiplied by $R(t)$ the rectangular wave. Thus, there are two ways to modulate: (1) by switching (2) by using nonlinear devices. A good example of (1) is the ring modulator used in ssb, where the diodes serve as switches, not nonlinear elements. We are interested in (1) for obvious reasons.

Sampling of Wave Forms: Modulation

Fig. 3 shows a sine wave of arbitrary frequency. Suppose we desired to represent it by a great number of amplitude-dependent pulses, as shown. This would mean we would have to measure the original signal periodically for its amplitude value. In other words, we would sample this signal. A sample may be defined as a measure of the amplitude of a wave evaluated instantaneously. If we took an infinite number of samples we would reproduce the given wave perfectly. How many samples are required in order to identify the wave? It can be shown that at least two samples per cycle must be taken in order to meet this criteria. If we are observing many frequencies, sampling must be done at least twice per cycle for the highest frequency present. It turns out that even if a perfect wave were to be transmitted, imperfections in the transmission media would make it impossible to recover the signal entirely at the receiver. We would do just as well to approximate the signal at the transmitter by sampling and *quantizing*[1] because then the contents of the *approximated* wave can be completely recovered at a distant point. Not that sampling does not serve the function of approximating the input signal; this is accomplished by the process of quantization. It is important to understand that the samples should have only a finite number of amplitude values, because if there are an infinite number, we cannot properly detect information at the receiving point in the presence of noise. Therefore, when sampling,

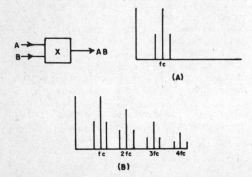

Fig. 1 — The illustration at A shows modulation by means of one frequency. Rectangular-wave modulation is shown at B.

[1] To subdivide into small measurable increments.

Fig. 3 — Some forms of pulse modulation.

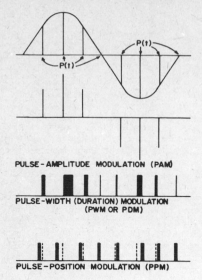

PULSE - AMPLITUDE MODULATION (PAM)

PULSE-WIDTH (DURATION) MODULATION
(PWM OR PDM)

PULSE - POSITION MODULATION (PPM)

we must "round off" amplitude to the nearest preassigned value (quantize), in order to help the S/N ratio. If this is not quite clear, it will be when pulse-code modulation and quantization relations are made. Note that $f(t)$ has been multiplied by the periodic sample $p(t)$. The connection between modulation and sampling is readily seen.

Forms of Pulse Modulation

Fig. 3 shows the different ways in which samples may be used to generate pulses which vary according to a given waveform amplitude. The pulses may vary in amplitude themselves; width or position is another way in which this can be accomplished. These types will be corrupted by noise, distortion, and other types of interference. What would result in each analog sample if PAM (pulse-amplitude modulation) form could be represented by pulses of equal amplitude? This would mean that each amplitude would be differentiated from another by the *number and/or arrangement* of pulses. Thus, we would have pulse-code modulation (PCM). To fix our ideas, let us give a good example of PCM: the Morse Code. Each letter or number is represented by an arrangement of dots and dashes. In Morse, there is not a fixed number of pulses per letter (this method has merit). In commercial PCM, it is usual to find that the number of pulses per amplitude is constant. Now, in theory, we may represent a voltage by however many pulses we choose. For speech, it is found that coding by at least 7 pulses is necessary to cover the dyanmic range encountered. If we have X number of pulses used which may take b values' (b is usually 2: 0 and 1), then the number of analog amplitudes which may be represented is b^X. Note that if the analog amplitudes were not quantized to a maximum number of levels, then we would have to represent an infinite number of analog amplitudes by X pulses, and this cannot be done! Thus, the need for quantization is obvious in PCM.

The Frequency-Time Relationship in Communication

We are all aware of the fact on a given band, for N number of transmissions, N number of transmitters are needed. Ideally, the carriers should be removed from each other to aovid interference. If it were desired to listen to one of these transmissions, our receivers would be brought to the frequency of interest. This is an example of frequency multiplexing of N stations — we detect the desired station on the basis of frequency.

Suppose we had one transmitter on which we desired to place N (separate) transmissions. A way in which we could try this would be to allow a small percentage of the total time for each transmission. In other words, we would sample and transmit each of the N signals periodically. At the receiving end, we would detect the desired signal by locking onto the desired time slot. In other words, detection would be on the basis of time, not frequency. The bandwidth taken by time multiplexing N signals in PAM form would be at least equal to the bandwidth taken by frequency multiplexing N signals, and greater for other forms of pulse modulation, should we desire to again modulate the pulse forms by sin ωt or cos ωt. Normally, PCM is not translated to radio frequency, although there are experimental systems in the microwave range; but if it is done, no bandwidth advantage is gained by time multiplexing.

Time Division Multiplexing (TDM)

It will be noted that the PCM-like code symbol for G (Fig. 4) may be broken into time segments. A human can detect the letter because he knows when the letter begins, that there is one unit per dot, three units per dash, one unit between a dot and a dot/dash, three units between letters of a word, and so on. This is another way of saying that a synchronous type of detection is needed when receiving Morse code. We must also have synchronism (electrical, not human) for a PCM time division system if we are to lock onto the desired time slot.

A block diagram of the system is shown in Fig. 5. It should be stated that transmission by cable is as likely as by means of the ether. The figure is largely self-explanatory in light of our discussion, except perhaps for the filters. It will be recalled that the demultiplexer is actually a switch, but that it also performs modulation on any $G(t)$, creating higher frequency components. The filters, which are identical, remove these unwanted energies from the output, leaving only the original audio.

It should be mentioned, for the sake of completeness, that a process known as *companding*

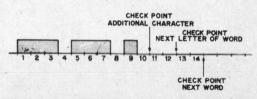

CHECK POINT
ADDITIONAL CHARACTER
CHECK POINT
NEXT LETTER OF WORD

1 2 3 4 5 6 7 8 9 10 11 12 13 14

CHECK POINT
NEXT WORD

Fig. 4 — Illustration of the formation of Morse code letter G.

Fig. 5 — Block diagram of a PCM/TDM system.

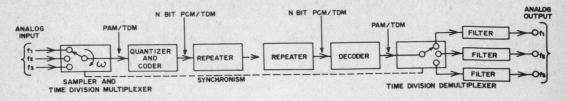

arranges the preassigned values so that the S/N ratio is kept constant. This means that the size of the quantizing steps will depend on the input amplitude values. It will not be discussed further and is mentioned only to alert the reader to the fact that it is an important consideration.

Advantages of TDM-PCM

The following gives advantages and consequently present and future uses for PCM. Please keep in mind that "radio" systems are only one area in which applications appear.

1) Digital signals can be regenerated more effectively by repeaters than can analog signals. This allows virtually undistorted transmission from start to finish.

2) Equipment which handles digital data, including computers, can now effectively process analog data after initial conversion. Communication systems can now have only one type of interface — digital. This cuts cost, because no conversions to analog are needed along the way.

3) A pair of wires can support more than one conversation.

4) Lower costs in producing digital circuits. 5) Waveguides (optical and otherwise) appear to handle digital data with greater efficiency.

6) Advantages in space communications. Signals *below* noise levels can be detected.

Summary and Conclusions

The idea of modulation has been clarified by considering the multiplication of any two frequencies. The relationship of modulation to sampling has been shown. Different forms of pulse modulation were observed and the reason for

coding was explained. A comparison between frequency and time multiplexing was examined. Advantages of PCM were mentioned. There was no attempt to discuss specifics, as the object was to avoid a mathematical treatise. New methods of PCM were not discussed.

One may forecast that PCM will be a byword of future generation communication specialists, and this should include hams. PCM-TDM cannot help but dominate the communications field because it is a good idea, it has been done, and it will be very economical. Now it is up to us to take advantage of the situation and help advance the state of technology.

LIMITED SPEECH RECOGNITION

Voice control of machines has long been under study at many places throughout the country. Unfortunately, success has been obtained only by using sophisticated equipment that the average amateur has no access to. It is difficult enough for circuitry to recognize speech patterns, but in addition, the human factors problem enters. Simply, people pronounce words somewhat the same, but not nearly so alike as to have simple circuits respond to everyone's command.

It would be desirable, however, to utilize the voice as a means for accomplishing certain functions despite the initial drawbacks of the method. Some applications exist for the amateur which will be discussed at length. The following describes a method for achieving a limited speech-recognition scheme for any words desired, using operational amplifiers and integrated-circuit logic, or transistorized circuitry.

Basically, the system consists of a parameter

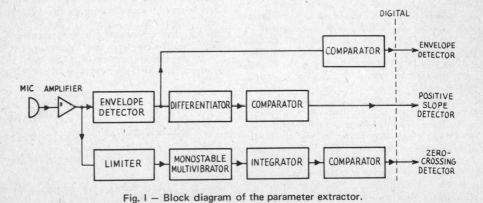

Fig. I — Block diagram of the parameter extractor.

USING
SPEECH-RECOGNITION
CONTROL HERE, OM!

WB2EZG
/2

–JUST ONE
APPLICATION–

extractor, which is essentially an analog-to-digital converter. The logic which follows recognizes the passage of certain speech patterns, called "events." This will be clarified shortly.

The Parameter Extractor

One would desire to use the most reliable characteristics of speech to have the ultimate in a system of this type. By "reliable characteristics," one refers to components of speech that are likely to undergo minimum speaker-to-speaker variation. It is anyone's guess as to what parameters are optimal. The particular extractor constructed had amplitude, zero-crossing (for high frequency content), and positive derivative (rise in energy of spoken word) detectors. A block diagram is shown in Fig. 1, with the schematic in Fig. 2.

Consider the digital-output wave forms. Note that if each output stated is independent of another, at any time, eight events are possible; that is, for a given instant of time, all may be high or low, one of three may be high or low, or two of three may be high or low. Recognition of a word is determined by the occurrence and sequence of events. We are thus faced with the problem of obtaining logic circuits for detecting these sequential events. An example is shown, using two parameters for simplicity.

Logic Design

Observe the two digital outputs for the spoken word "control" which emanates from the parameter extractor (Fig. 3). The word is broken up into four events, designated E1 to E4. The choice is not exactly arbitrary, as one can see. When a change of one or more parameters occurs, an event point can be chosen.† We need logic to detect the four events.

The occurrence of event E1 can set a flip-flop. The amplitude waveform (A) would be taken to an *AND* gate along with the negation output of the zero-crossing wave form, Z, so a flip-flop F1 would be set by $A\bar{Z}$. F1 now acts as a memory, recording the fact that E1 has occurred. This output, "anded" with the next event E2, can now be used to set another flip-flop. F2 is thus set by $F1A\bar{Z}$. Similarly, event three would be recorded by F3, being set by $F1A\bar{Z}$. Event four would need a set input of $F3A\bar{Z}$ to F4. The output of the final flip-flop can

---

† Strictly speaking, five events should be chosen for this word, although four are picked.

be taken to some relay through suitable current drivers to control anything imaginable. The same word can also be used to turn off appliances with some ingenuity in design at the final flip-flop.

Results

One can expect success of the order of better than nine times out of ten if certain precautions are taken and one realizes the system limitations. The circuit is not foolproof. When proper thresholds are set at the comparators in the parameter extractor, the circuit will respond to a wide range of voices. No agc is present at the input circuit, but might be added if needed. One must first be aware that "hollering" the circuit off, or rushing the at which the word is pronounced, only decreases the probability of successful execution. Secondly, words whose binary waveforms approximate closely the chosen word will trip the circuit, even though other events may have occurred in between. The latter may be cured if one is willing to redesign the logic for this effect, using more gates and increasing the cost. Third, one may find that thresholds work adequately for the male population, but not for any but deep-voiced females. Fortunately, such a device would not be used for the whole world, but rather for a few people at most, so there is no problem.

The circuit has the advantage that it is largely invariant to the speed with which the word is pronounced; it is recommended, however, that a timing circuit (monostable) be added in the logic, giving the user a maximum time to pronounce a given word. This is desirable for two reasons. First, it decreases the chances for accidental talk off on two counts. The first is strictly timewise, the second advantage is that a word must be said in isolation of context to effect an output change.

Author shown holding the parameter-extractor circuit board he built.

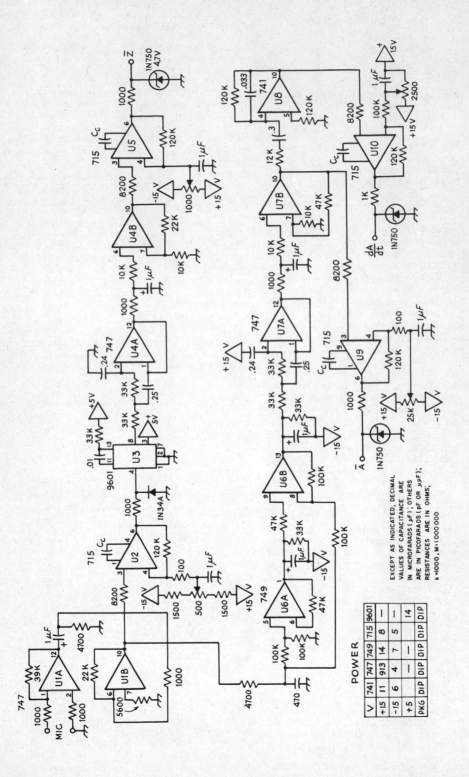

Fig. 2 — Schematic diagram of the WB2EZG parameter extractor.

Fig. 3 — Extractor response for a simple-structured word. Slope detector output is not shown.

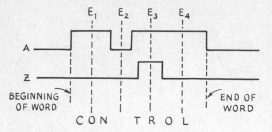

BEGINNING OF WORD

END OF WORD

CONTROL

This means that if one uses the circuit to turn on his rig while using the same microphone he ragchews with, then the word he uses will not accidentally turn off the rig (if the key word is accidentally spoken) unless said in isolation.

To continue, the monostable is also used to reset the flip-flops should a person miss execution with his first try and want to try again. Lastly, one must resign himself to the fact that on some days he will not pronounce the key word or words as he did the day before, and will have to settle for a decrease in the percentage of "hits" versus tries. This is a human error and one cannot expect non thinking logic to decipher a babbling human using simple systems. To conclude, these are the steps that should be followed to obtain a working system:

1) Choose a word or words, meaningful or not, with a reasonable number of events. The longer the word, the more significant the number of events. (Perhaps 8 or 9 events is a reasonable number.)

2) Adjust parameter extractor for near-consistent digital outputs when the phrase is spoken by a small population.

3) Design logic for detection of events.

Applications

Uses for the scheme discussed, as far as amateurs are concerned, may be broken into three categories: entirely practical; semipractical, because present activity in a phase of amateur radio is limited; and future, because of present technology, limited or nonexistent amateur activity, or because it is a disadvantage to have this method of control for other reasons.

A) Practical: Probably this system would be most advantageous to handicapped amateurs. A rig could be turned on, and antenna could be rotated, or a voice command could transmit a standard SSTV or cw message. The second use would be in repeaters, where the control decoder would be designed to respond to a voice command instead of audio tones. The third use would possibly be that of remote band switching in mobile communications. The operator would not have to use his hands to adjust antenna matching networks, etc., an important consideration. Also consider that some day, all *rigs* will probably have instant band switching, which will make it even easier on the mobile operator.

B) Semipractical: A reasonable percentage of amateurs engage in radio control of model airplanes. It has been expressed by the modelers* that their constant goal is realism in model flying. Talking the plane up or down is equivalent to talking to the copilot of the ship. Such commands given to the copilot would be "gear-up" or "ten degree flaps." The last command, incidentally, would appear to be a good choice for a word. Most modelers are not hams, but there is no reason to believe that the aims of both groups differ significantly when it comes to model flying (or model boats).

C) Future: Applications for voice gadgets such

* Interview with Al Lobaito, President, Richmond Model Flying Club, Inc.

Close-up view of the parameter-extractor module.

Fig. 4 — General logic needed for the word "control"

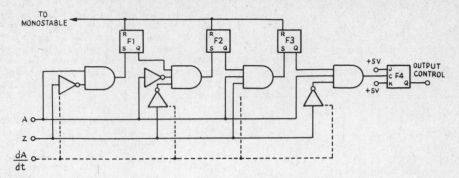

as these might be found in amateur satellite control, or in voice-to-Morse, or voice-to-RTTY converters. Admittedly, these *are* future prospects, but certainly one is not reaching for the moon (!) when the suggestion is made.

Cost

The system described is not a computer, nor could it be if amateurs were to build it. Hence, the system is not nearly as perfect as one would like. This is reflected in the cost, perhaps $25 for the extractor for those with some kind of junk box. The price of the logic circuitry depends on the words chosen and might approach $15 for some words. The price of the power supply is not included. Plus- and minus-voltage supplies are used in the original circuit, but certain low-cost operational amplifiers can be made to work as linear

elements *using olny a single 5-volt supply* Ninety percent or better accuracy is not bad for $40 or so. Perhaps this method of machine control merits consideration by radio amateurs.

APPENDIX

U.S. American Standard Code for Information Interchange

The U.S.A. Standard Code for Information Interchange (USASCII, or, more commonly, ASCII) is an 8-unit code as shown here, used largely with computers. Some Teletype Corp. machines, such as Models 33 and 35, use this code. Because FCC regulations require that U.S. amateurs use a 5-unit code for RTTY operation (see Chapter 5), operation of these machines is presently not permitted for amateur communications.

American Standard Code for Information Interchange (ASCII)

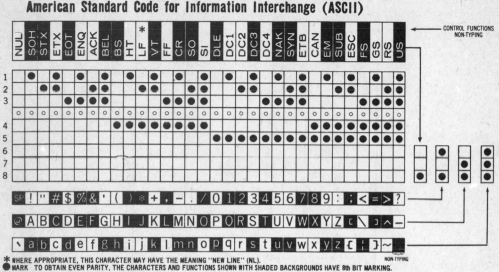

* WHERE APPROPRIATE, THIS CHARACTER MAY HAVE THE MEANING "NEW LINE" (NL).
● MARK TO OBTAIN EVEN PARITY, THE CHARACTERS AND FUNCTIONS SHOWN WITH SHADED BACKGROUNDS HAVE 8th BIT MARKING.

UPON RECEIVING CODE COMBINATIONS FOR ` THROUGH ~, MONOCASE EQUIPMENT SUCH AS MODELS 33 AND 35 PRINT RESPECTIVE CHARACTERS @ THROUGH ^.
(Courtesy of Teletype Corp.)

NUL	Null, or all zeros	DC1	Device control 1
SOH	Start of heading	DC2	Device control 2
STX	Start of text	DC3	Device control 3
ETX	End of text	DC4	Device control 4
EOT	End of transmission	NAK	Negative acknowledge
ENQ	Enquiry	SYN	Synchronous idle
ACK	Acknowledge	ETB	End of transmission block
BEL	Bell, or alarm	CAN	Cancel
BS	Backspace	EM	End of medium
HT	Horizontal tabulation	SUB	Substitute
LF	Line feed	ESC	Escape
VT	Vertical tabulation	FS	File separator
FF	Form feed	GS	Group separator
CR	Carriage return	RS	Record separator
SO	Shift out	US	Unit separator
SI	Shift in	SP	Space
DLE	Data link escape	DEL	Delete

Satellite Orbital Data

The information in Table I originally appeared in *QST* for October, 1969, as part of a discussion of Australis-Oscar 5. The calculations were based on a period of 114 minutes, and an orbital inclination of 101.77 degrees. These data are accurate enough (within reasonable limits) for quick approximations of position of Oscar 6 and 7. By applying the precise information of inclination and period, the formulas will enable the generation of a similar table for satellites having significantly different orbits.

TABLE I

Minutes past ascending node	Actual latitude φ of satellite north	Degrees of Δλ longitude to be added
2	6.2°	1.8°
4	12.4	3.6
6	18.6	5.4
8	24.7	7.4
10	30.9	9.6
12	37.0	11.9
14	43.0	14.5
16	49.1	17.3
18	55.1	21.5
20	60.9	26.6
22	66.6	33.6
24	71.8	44.3
26	76.0	61.9
28	78.3	89.2
30	77.5	119.9
32	74.1	142.3
34	69.3	156.1
36	63.8	164.5
38	58.0	170.4
40	52.1	174.8
42	46.1	178.2
44	40.0	181.1
46	33.9	183.6
48	27.8	185.9
50	21.6	187.9
52	15.4	189.7
54	9.3	191.5
56	3.1	193.4
57	0	194.5

$$\phi = \text{arc sin} \left\{ \left(\sin \iota \right) \left(\sin \frac{360\, \tau}{\rho} \right) \right\}$$

$$\Delta\lambda = \text{arc cos} \left\{ \frac{\cos \left(\frac{360\, \tau}{\rho} \right)}{\cos \phi} \right\} + 0.25\, \tau$$

Where ι = orbit's inclination to equator
 ρ = satellite period (in min.)
 τ = time after ascending node (in min.)

At indicated minutes past ascending node (equatorial crossing south to north) the satellite will be at north latitude indicated, and the number of degrees of longitude in column 3 must be added to the node longitude. The correction factor for the earth's rotation has been included. Amateurs in the southern hemisphere can use the table by subtracting all figures instead of adding them. This will work the satellite backward in time from the ascending node.